ANIMAL AND MAN IN BIBLE LANDS

F. S. Bodenheimer

COLLECTION DE TRAVAUX DE L'ACADÉMIE INTERNATIONALE D'HISTOIRE DES SCIENCES

N° 10

ANIMAL AND MAN IN BIBLE LANDS

BY

Dr F. S. BODENHEIMER

Late Professor of Zoology, Hebrew University, Jerusalem

LEIDEN

E. J. BRILL

1960

Original title

שמעון בודנהיימר, החי בארצות המקרא.
תולדות בעלי החיים בארץ־ישראל ושכנותיה מתקופת האבן ועד לסוף תקופת המקרא.
בלוויית לוחות וציורים.
מוסד ביאליק ירושלים תש״י.

Translation by the author

Copyright 1960 by E. J. Brill, Leiden, Netherlands.

PRINTED IN THE NETHERLANDS

CONTENTS

CONTENTS

I. INTRODUCTORY CHAPTERS

1.1 MULTA, SED NON MULTUM

1. 11. THE SCOPE

Geography and history, archaeology and art of Palestine have found, since long, a well deserved interest and study. Much remains to be done in these fields, but the first exploration is made and a general background has been gained. The exploration of the natural history in our country is much less complete. Solid foundations have been laid in these fields, however, during the last decades. Apart from the faunal exploration of Palestine, animals have made a great impression during all ages on the native inhabitant as well as on the traveller. Domestic animals always were a subject of interest. Other animals were utilised as patterns for textiles, and animal legends and folklore always flowered and circulated among the people of Palestine. Men and animals form part of the landscape of the country. Animals in the landscape and animals in the service and in the thought of man and their changes through the millennia of human occupation of Palestine are to be the topic of this book.

In the dawn of Mt. Carmel man human existence depended almost entirely on the hunt of gazelles and of fallow deer. Ibex-hunt was much later still one of the main sources of existence of the Kilwa men, where religious motives appear to be connected with this hunt. In the dawn of history the bull appears as the incorporation of Baal, the dove is connected with Astarte, the fish with Dagon. Dragons—usually the winged dragons of Babylon—appear in the oldest myths. Animal-headed gods were introduced from Egypt. In a very few cases we were able to interpret the formation of some late legends about such mythic animals. But the origin of their widespread origin in primitive myths still awaits a competent analysis by comparative folklore, in the footsteps of G. FRAZER, before the zoologist can be permitted to add his own remarks. In general the ritual or stylistic significance of each figure in representations of animals must first be studied, before the zoologist can decide which of the often diverging morphological characters are decisive for the zoological identification. In many cases much brain work has been wasted on identifications which remain doubtful, and at best do not add much to the progress of science. A mere name does not always enlarge our knowledge, if no mental connection joins it to a chain of thoughts or facts.

Cultural relations with other countries are of primary importance for many interpretations. Many of our legends have their origin in Mesopotamia (creation, Noah's ark, etc.), others in Egypt, from where cat amulets, scarab seals, pictures of giraffes, etc. penetrated our country. The results of such cultural relations may prevent many wrong identifications of animals, which have come into legends, with the pattern books of artistic schools, under the influence of the Babylonian exile, etc. With regard to the exact zoological identification of ancient texts or art we wish expressly to point out the following: where birds, for instance, can be alternatively be identified as eagle or dove, both on good grounds, the decision is definitely not the task of the zoologists, but of the archaeologist.

It is almost inconceivable why the enormous amount of exact and often easily accessible knowledge of the animal life of Palestine in ancient and in later times has never been collected before. The first attempt, on purely philological grounds, was the stupendous, learned compilation of SAMUEL BOCHART of Caën in his *Hierozoicon* (*about 1650*). Other early attempts were those of RASHI and of LUTHER, who, in addition to philological analysis, tried to interpret the animal life of the Bible in terms of the animal life of S. France or of Germany, in the spirit of their age which still ignored the fact that different faunas belong to different regions. The most comprehensive attempt has been made by Canon H. B. TRISTRAM in his classical *Natural History of the Bible* (1867). His interpretations are based, in addition to philology, on one year's stay in Palestine, which was entirely devoted to the study of the natural history of this country. The important archaeological discoveries of the last fifty years were not yet available to this gifted naturalist, who deserves the title of the father of the natural history of Palestine.

In spite of the varied and extensive material offered in this study we fully realise, that we have merely scraped the surface and that most of the work still remains to be done. Many major problems are left by us in a more complicated state than they were before. This holds good, *e.g.,* for the early history of the camel, for the domestic breeds of cattle and dogs, and for many others. It is hoped, however, that this survey may provoke many corrections, comments and analyses, especially as we have been able to give a more accurate description of the many problems which still await an answer. In this respect we wish to point out especially the taboo with regard to the representation of many animals all over the Middle East or over part of it. The big game, the symbolic animals of religion, the animals of economic interest, the exotic animals on show first roused the interest of the artists. This explains the prevalence of illustrations of animals such as wild bulls, cattle, lions, leopards and cheetah, gazelle and ibex, sheep and goat, ass and onager, hares and dogs. Yet the almost complete absence of illustrations of camels, wolves, foxes, domestic fowl and many others in ancient times is certainly not explained by lack of contact and of familiarity.

We rarely give quotation marks, as we have often condensed, corrected and commented on the reports of the earlier travellers. The reading of the original sources therefore remains indispensable. Our quotations will easily lead to them. Page quotations are often added of books without index.

1. 12. THE ARENA

A difficult problem was the selection of the territorial background of this book. Palestine was never a great centre of creative civilisation. Its position as a border area, the provincial character of its civilisation have always barred such a development. The refractory attitude of Jews and Arabs toward most of the fine arts was another factor.

Civilisations had still a very wide distribution during the older stone age. In the later stone age closer links existed between Palestine and Asia Anterior than with Egypt. It is well known there were strong political and cultural influences of the empires of Egypt, Mesopotamia and S. Anatolia in ancient history. These influences are the more important as the Upper Mesopotamian origin of the Semites, including the Hebrews, at the dawn of history are now beyond doubt. The knowledge of and the myths on animals of that region still form an important background of those of the Bible. Intimate relations of Palestine and of the early Hebrews with Egypt during the 2nd millennium B.C. enlarge the area again. The recent discoveries of even older cultures closely related to that of the Palestine Canaanites bring Syria into close contact with the country. The pages of the Bible are full of foreign influences.

ALEXANDER and the Diadoches brought Palestine well into the realm of the Hellenistic world, a connection strengthened in later centuries by the Roman domination. But even at that period strong Eastern influences continued to influx. Christianity caused as an important revolution in this pagan world. Byzantium contested the country for a not inconsiderable time against the Arab conquest, which brought the animals of the desert and the nomad attitude more to the forefront. But during all these periods Palestine was a distant province of mighty empires with flowering civilisations. The crusaders brought new cultural influxes and mixtures. For many centuries the topographic position of Palestine/Syria at the end of the great routes of the rich Inner-Asiatic trades had made them important natural staple places of international commerce. The Turkish conquest was of fundamental consequence. Palestine rapidly became again a far distant province, far from the flourishing centres of civilisation and losing its economic stability. The breaking down of the old Transasiatic trade, now surpassed by sea-trade, contributed much to this decline from which the country is only just beginning to recover.

J. STRZYGOWSKI (1936) has given good expression to this civilisatory situation of the Middle East for a certain period: "In the course of these last years we have conceived a new idea: We did know the Hellenistic domain of ancient Christian art around the Mediterranean, with its centre first at Rome, later in Anatolia and in the big towns from Alexandria to Antiochia. Today we readily face the existence of a second and third domain of art: the ancient Semitic Orient and Mazdean Persia. These three domains extend in *échelon* from the Mediterranean coast, one after another. The Greek world having overthrown the old Oriental monarchies in the Hellenistic period, could establish contact with the distant civilisations of Iran and India on the soil of Bactria and Gandhara. Later, during the Christian age, the intellectual unity of that region was broken by a school of theology rising in its mid, the school of Nisibis-Edessa, the considerable importance of which for the history of art has not yet been sufficiently recognised. The Syro-Egyptian and Anatolian world does not end with the borders of the Greek language. What is more, it embraces in the first place that Aramaean region which connected almost all Asia to Syria and on which in the Christian era the unity of this large area, first assembled by ALEXANDER and the Diadoches depended. Syria cannot be separated from its hinterland, for which it is the outlet to the sea".

We entirely agree with STRZYGOWSKI and have to extend this statement to almost all periods and to all branches of civilisation. And thus it is obvious impracticable to deal with the history of wild life and its human aspects for Palestine alone. However, it will always remain a matter of personal taste and judgement to what extent the neighbouring areas and civilisations should be drawn into it. Whilst restriction can be applied for periods of relative isolation, this is impossible for times when Palestine formed an integral part of great civilisations such as in the Hellenistic or the Arab eras. No two students will probably agree exactly to the extent of this background. This civilisatory situation very well reflects the biogeographical position. Here again Palestine/Syria is a border zone, in spite of its minute size, where three large regions meet and mix: the extensive Saharo-Sindian deserts of the south and the east, the Irano-Turanian steppes of the interior of Asia, and the narrow Mediterranean zone along the coasts. Ethnographical analysis shows that this biogeographical zonation finds its echo in human history and settlement. Again we feel the impossibility to treat a few isolated border-strips of enormous natural regions as isolated areas.

1. 13. METHODS AND SOURCES

1. 131. GEOLOGICAL SCIENCE

Geological science is the base for the study of Palestine until the dawn of history. The morphological transformations of the country and its neighbours during the Tertiary period reveal themselves in more and more details, as well as contemporaneous land connections. Palaeontology makes us understand the sources of the early animals penetrating Palestine and the analysis of the faunal changes for at least 150.000 years back, since the cave-cultures of the Palaeolithicum. The classical analyses of Miss D. Bate of the well stratified mammal remains from the caves of Galilee and Mt. Carmel have given us a safe lead in this direction.

Very important is the problem of the Tertiary climates and their changes. Today the earlier conceptions about the presence of glaciers on Mt. Lebanon and a corresponding penetration of faunal and floral elements of a boreal character have been abandoned entirely. Periods of heavier and of poorer precipitations occurred during certain periods of the Pleistocene, corresponding to the contemporaneous glacial and interglacial periods. Yet L. PICARD (1936) has shown that "the pluvial period is not only a phenomenon of the Pleistocene but of the whole Post-Miocene epoch". The same author (1937) has shown that a desert climate in the east, a Mediterranean climate in the hills and plains—and, we may add: intercalated zones of steppes—apart from insignificant spatial and temporal fluctuations, had already developed in the Pleistocene, at the beginning of man's appearance in this country. We regard the different opinions of PICARD and Miss BATE in this respect as divergences about the intensity of these rain fluctuations and not as differences in principles, as will be discussed later.

Other discussions concern the correlations of the palaeolithic strata of Palestine to those of Europe. VAUFRAY (1939) puts those, earliest discovered in this country so far, into the Würm glacial, whilst most authorities place them into the Würm-Riss interglacial, a dif-ference of some ten thousands of years!

Great is the progress of prehistorical research within the last decades, mainly due to the work of Miss GARROD, R. NEUVILLE, M. STEKELIS, J. PERROT, and many others. Dating and nomenclature have reached a level of general agreement. This permits the exact dating of the various, rather extensive prehistoric finds in this country, and even their correlation to the contemporaneous cultures of the neighbouring ones.

1. 132. THE ARCHAEOLOGICAL AND HISTORICAL SCIENCES

It is often maintained that there exists no historical *science,* because subjective moments of attitude and knowledge give the events a certain colour, well permitted in art, but not in science. Apart from the questions of the events and the rôle of men at decisive hours of history this doubt is becoming less and less justified. To the solution of all problems of those old cultures an ever increasing material and refined methods of analysis offer reliable keys to the facts. Surprising results on the distribution of textile dyes in antiquity were thus opened up by PFISTER, in consequence of his elaboration of the technological methods for determining the various dyes. Archaeology remains, of course, the main source for antiquity. The excavations of the last two decades have brought so much new light into the earliest history of the Middle East, that all previous textbooks are hopelessly antiquated. This progress of exploration, from the Indus-Valley to Palestine, from Anatolia to Egypt, is by now so advanced that ALBRIGHT and CHILDE could very successfully attempt a synthesis of early cultural development in this part of the world, as it now appears before our eyes. Research and excavations in Palestine itself have well kept pace with this general advance. A reliable classification of the numerous finds is now worked out for pottery, tools, ornaments, scarabs, architecture, etc. The excavations of Jericho, Megiddo, Beisan, Teleilat Ghassul, Lachish, to mention only a few, have opened up the progress of civilization—although in a reversed sequence—step after step, layer after layer before our eyes. Whilst before only large precious or conspicuous objects were collected, now every piece of animal bone, of shell, etc. is carefully collected and studied, sometimes telling interesting tales (cf. the shells from Teleilat Ghassul).

We have explained before that the archaeology of ancient Mesopotamia offers an important background for the Semitic talking peoples settling in Palestine on their westward migrations. We were surprised at the wealth of information offered by Egyptian documents. The old Egyptian novel of Sinuhe plays in the Palestine of Abraham's time. The reports of conquest and of the tributes from Canaan-Retenu tell their tale. And, last but not least, the temple of Thutmose III. at Karnak holds one room, the so-called Botanical Garden, where plants and birds of Palestine are composed into the oldest natural history atlas of Palestine. The inter-relations of ancient art and religion, especially of those of Phoenicia and Syria with Canaan are important in order to understand the animals of cult vessels and of ancient legends. Other important animal documents are the mosaic pavements flourishing in this country during the Roman and Byzantine periods.

Wild animals must have been a terrible menace to the early settlers, until civilisation got rid of them in its holocaust destruction of the natural landscape. Apart from the direct extension of arable land we may mention only the slow but permanent destruction of the forests by man and goat. This early menace found its expression in animal cults and animal totems dominating the life of primitive man in many regions of the world. In the Middle East most of these cults and totems although existent still in many myths and rituals were forgotten with the growth of town cultures and of empires.

Domestic animals have been decisive factors in history. The horses of the Hyksos invaders and their chariots revolutionised warfare, as did elephants in the period of the Diadoches, just as tanks revolutionised modern strategy and decided the first world-war. The asses as beasts of burden opened the road to commerce. Beasts of draught put primitive agriculture on a profitable base. The nomads of the steppe mainly subsisted on the milk and the meat of their flocks. The domestication of the camel enabled the bedawi to pass rapidly with their caravans through deserts, which were closed before. Purple dyes, silkworms, fine-wooled sheep enabled the establishment of important industries. And SOLOMON obtained part of his wealth by a cleverly maintained monopoly in the horse trade of the Middle East.

Other animals of historical importance were the carriers of diseases and famine. JONES has ascribed the breaking down of Greek civilisation to a mighty wave of malaria. Central Africa was closed to husbandry and intensification of agriculture on account of the tsetse-flies bringing the Nagana and other diseases to domestic stock. Outbreaks of the flea-born plague (NAPOLEON), of malaria (RICHARD COEUR-DE-LION) or of famines caused by locusts and voles (early in the 12th century in the Kingdom of Jerusalem) have often influenced the course of history by adding their weight to other circumstances. Manna and quail have to be put on the credit side of the animals.

History of art again, as has been quoted from STRZYGOWSKI, is as a sensitive an indicator for all cultural and commercial interrelations and influences as is any other branch of civilisation.

The early attitude of man towards art has been recently described by W. F. ALBRIGHT (1942, p. 8 ff.). Art begins with an imitative-aesthetic phase. Little active imagination is shown, but an extraordinary development of imitative capacity. It found highly aesthetic expression at about 30.000 to 20.000 B.C. in the European Auragniacian, reaching its peak in the animal cave drawings of Spain and South France. Hunting scenes prevail. The primary stimulation was apparently not the desire for artistical expression, but magical purposes: the animals were represented in order to act as charms, bringing about successful hunts. The artist who could draw the most realistic painting exerted the strongest sympathetic magic, and he was hence the artist most acclaimed for. The older rock-carvings of Kilwa, the neolithic bone and stone sculptures of the Natufians belong to this category. In the Ghassulian chalcolithic age of Palestine we find the masterful wall paintings of Tell Ghassul, a few primitive animal designs on pottery, and an abundance of geometrical patterns. This was the beginning of the imaginative-aesthetic stage of artistic evolution, so highly developed in the early times of the Middle East. Mythology flourished in these settlements and found its artistic expression. In the following periods Mesopotamian, Egyptian, Anatolian and Minoan art all exercised their influence on the subjects as well as on the styles of the Syro-Palestinian art, under the leading influence of Phoenician artists until the iron age.

These stages of artistic development, as has been first pointed out by VERWORN (1917), find their recurrence in the individual development of artistic expression in children. The unconscious mastery and self-confidence results in astonishing expression in the sense of the imaginative-aesthetic line, in earliest youth. It is followed by a break. As soon as the child attempts to draw consciously, this self-confidence disappears and its drawings show a primitive, faulty technique and conception, but an abundance of geometric imagination in ornaments is the result.

1. 133. LITERARY SOURCES, SCIENCE, AND FOLKLORE

The literary sources of the ancients have been surprisingly little used for the study of the natural history of Palestine, whilst they have been well exploited for the history and geography of the country. Those of the oldest periods belong to archaeology. But since ALEXANDER's expeditions Palestine has entered the orbit of the Hellenistic world. Cultural and commercial exchanges were intensive within the empires of the Ptolemaeans and the Seleucids. The important agricultural archives of that period, known as the *Papyri Zenon,* not only disclose the background of agriculture in Lower Egypt in details, but to a high degree also of that of Palestine. ZENON spent one year in Palestine and commercial depots and even farms in this country were under his administration. Many of the writers on Zoology from ARISTOTLE to AELIAN report observations on animals of the Middle East. Outstanding among them are the two Oppians (about 200 A.D.). The *Cynegetica* of OPPIAN of Apamea describes the life and the hunting of the game of the Middle East, as does the Anatolian OPPIAN regarding the marine life of the Levantine coasts in his *Halieutica,* in such a lively way as nobody has done after them.

Many interesting observations are found in the *Mishnah.* The writings of the early fathers of the church are an almost untapped source. Also the commentaries on the *Hexaemeron* and on other books of the Bible contain many valuable observations. Most interesting sources are the early animal books, the *Physiologi.* The oldest Greek versions spread from Alexandria north throughout the Levant, where at an early date they were translated into Syriac. And, in general, Syriac literature contains a wealth of animal fables, of scientific and popular medicine and of other zoological remarks. The early Christian pilgrim texts and the crusader reports are accessible in good editions. But many of the Arab geographers and zoologists are not yet available in translations. Outstanding are the memoirs of a Syrian noble, USAMAH, of the twelfth century A.D., which are full of marvellous and reliable hunting scenes.

Overwhelming is the flood of travel books beginning with the end of the 15th century. FABRI, BREYDENBACH and BELON are some of the early travellers who paid attention to animals. We cannot hope to have exhausted the wealth of information contained in all those books and we will be grateful for any remarks on omissions. A Swedish student, HASSELQUIST, was sent by LINNAEUS to study the animals of the Holy Land and to give a description of them. The unfortunate scholar was only for a few weeks in this country, but spent some years in Egypt and at Smyrna, where he met his untimely death. Fifty years later a group of scientists, such as SAVIGNY, accompanied the expedition of NAPOLEON to Palestine.

Many travellers followed in the 19th century. Many archaeologists from ROBINSON to de SAULCY or CONDER paid attention to animal life or even collected specimens. Most important are the four voyages of Canon TRISTRAM into this country under the auspices of the *Palestine Expedition Fund*. In his *Fauna and Flora of Western Palestine* (1884) he laid the fundament of our faunal knowledge. His much commended *Natural History of the Bible* has been mentioned before. Important results sprang from the travels of LORTET of Lyon in this country. His book *La Syrie d'aujourd'hui* (1884) is still the only general book which does equally justice to the geography, history, archaeology and natural history of the country. Among the later expeditions we only mention those of FESTA of Torino, of BARROIS of Lille, of ANNANDALE of Calcutta. Intensive exploration has begun in this century. Few, however, are the travellers and scientists who give vivid descriptions of animal life. Major C. S. JARVIS is a rare exception. Most observers restrict themselves to technical descriptions. The results and the bibliography of these modern researches were reviewed in two books of the writer (1935, 1937).

Data about folklore have been surprisingly little collected in Palestine. The main sources are treated in the following text. Still more important is the analysis of ancient and recent folklore by comparative methods, so splendidly inaugurated by G. FRAZER. Much judgement and caution, however, is needed in sifting this material. The Biblical laws on clean and unclean food, for instance, can be interpreted in many ways: as relics of ancient totems and taboos, as remainders of animal cults, as aversion to animals connected with pagan gods, or—as FRAZER has convincingly proved in some cases—as wide spread habits of primitive nomads. Another splendid analysis of this master is devoted to the part of the snake in paradise.

We wish to give two more illustrations to show how rich a field of research is still open. The popular conception of the doves as soul birds has led to an abundance of columbaries in pagan tombs in this country. An apotropaic interpretation was given by TORCZYNER in connection with a small tablet of the 7th century A.D. with Hebrew inscriptions from Arslan Tash, where the unique picture of a she-wolf gives protection against the ghosts of the night and the darkness.

Another still inadequately exploited field of research is astronomic symbolism. D'ARCY THOMPSON (1895, here quoted: 1936) has stressed that many of the ancient animal legends have their source not in natural history, but in the constellations and celestial movements of the stars. This was already the opinion of the Greek authors. Father EUSEBIUS (*Pr. Ev.* 3 : 4) expressed this well: "The ancients believed that the legends about Osiris and Isis and all other mythological fables have reference either to the stars, their configuration, their risings and settings, or to the wax and wane of the moon, or to the cycle of the sun, or to the diurnal and nocti-diurnal hemispheres." Whilst many myths have, undoubtedly, such an origin, the process worked in both directions: some observations were suitably transferred to heaven. This is probably true for the sign of the lion, which coincides with the greatest heat of the year when the sun enters it. The common water-spitting lion heads of the ancients have been connected with the beginning of the Nile flood, when the lion of the zodiac is at its peak. The legend of the lion-killing SHIMSHON-HERAKLES is referred to the sun-god killing the lion of the zodiac. And the neighbour of the lion in the zodiac is the virgin, the Ishtar of Mesopotamia, who is closely connected with the lion in many myths. The tale of AELIAN (13 : 11), that the hare detests the voice of the raven, may have its source in the fact that the constellation *Lepus* sets soon after the rising of that of *Corvus*.

The eagle of the legend attacks the swan and is in turn defeated by it. This corresponds with the constellation of *Aquila*, rising in the east immediately after *Cygnus*, but, setting in the west, goes down a little while before *Cygnus* (THOMPSON, p. 107). Other examples are the Halcyonian birds (kingfisher) and the Pleiades (p. 31), the doves and the pleiades (pp. 121, 132), to which the grape-eating doves are referred, the phoenix as the symbol of a cyclic period (p. 183), or the mythical Stymphalean birds (p. 162).

Although one has to be careful in the interpretation of ancient animal and other legends as astronomic myths, there is no doubt that much is still to be learned in this respect. The study of the ancient legends of Mesopotamia and Egypt under this aspect promises interesting results.

1. 134. PHILOLOGY

Comparative etymology was the dominant method, so far, for determining animal names from ancient texts. Today we challenge its dominant position. One example may serve for many: to the philologist the Hebrew *zab* is identical with the Arab *dhab*. *Zab* means tortoise, *dhab* the big *Uromastix*-lizard. The philological argument would give us a valuable hint, if any zoological or other reason would suggest from the context that *zab* may not have been intended for tortoise *). Philology gives little help, as such auxiliary arguments are wanting. Divergent development of words from a common root, usually of a more general meaning originally, is a common occurrence, such as *lechem* (Hebrew = bread) and *lachmi* (Arabic = meat), both obviously derived from a common root for food. *Devash* in ancient Hebrew may mean either, bee-honey or sweet concentrated fruit juices of dates and other fruits (now restricted to bee-honey), whilst in Arabic *dibs* is retained for the latter only and honey is named *assal*. In the same way *deborah* (Hebrew) designates the honey-bee, *dabur* in Arabic the hornet, whilst *nachle,* the Arabic word for honey-bee, corresponds to the Hebrew *nachil* (Swarm of bees).

We entirely agree with the opinion of W. F. ALBRIGHT (1940, p. 17 f.): "Formerly the main special use of linguistic methods was in determining the etymology and hence the primary meaning of a given word. Biblical handbooks are cluttered with false etymologies, as well as with correct ones from which erroneous or undemonstrable deductions have been made. Actually, no competent lexicographer in any language fixes the precise meaning of a word by its etymology, but rather by collecting as many passages where the word occurs as possible or practicable and by listing all meanings and shades of meaning in them. Words change their meaning through use to such an extent that the etymological method of fixing significance is only employed as a last resort, where other evidence is inadequate. Wherever possible the combinatory method (i.e., the collection and comparison of all passages where a word occurs) has replaced the etymological one in decipherment and interpretation, at least among competent scholars."

Many of the animal names of the Old Testament unfortunately remain *nomina nuda*. They are mentioned once or twice only without any zoological connection. We are therefore not astonished that one of the foremost members of the philological school in this country has changed the interpretation of many of these names twice or three times within one generation. One interpretation is just as unsafe as the other. Yet it is regrettable that such

---

*) Actually the *zab* of the Bible is mentioned only in the laws of clean and unclean food. Whereas the big *Uromastyx*-lizard offers a much better food than the tortoise we are probably correct in assuming that the former was referred to in the Bible, and that *zab* took only in a latter period the meaning of tortoise.

changes have a checking effect on the nomenclature of the living Hebrew language, which should have these words at its disposition and use them without any pretence of using them in the exact sense of the Biblical text.

F. HOMMEL (1879) expresses the opinion that the history of animals belongs more to the historical-philological field than to zoology. To a certain extent we can accept this principle. HOMMEL's book 'On the names of mammals in the south-semitic languages' offers a good illustration, what the philological method may achieve when based on comparative studies and serious analysis (not restricted only to the etymology of the roots of names). HOMMEL aims at the reconstruction of the fauna known to the early Semites by careful sifting and comparison. He comes to the historically justified conclusion that the Semitic ancestors —eventually after preliminary migrations—were settled not later than 3000 B.C. (we may assume even before that date) in or around N. Mesopotamia and N. Syria. The common root of all Semitic language certainly was considerably older than that! The faunal character is perhaps best expressed by those animals for which two or more names occurred in ancient Semitic language. Among wild mammals these were: lion, wild ass, gazelles, ibex and probably wild cattle; among domestic stock: cattle, goat, sheep, ass and camel. The following animals are mentioned in the old Arabic poetry (up to 6th cent. A.D.), but not in the old Semitic language: cheetah, jerboa, oryx. Some animals absent in Arabia disappeared from the Arab language of the early period, such as wild cat, mole-rat and deer. Other animals not present any longer still remained in the memory and appeared in poetry: bear, ibex and wild cattle, for instance.

The following list of the old Semitic mammals, retained in almost all historical languages of that group, gives the old Semitic mammalian fauna:

lion: *laitu, labiatu, nahusu*	horse: *parasu, susu.*
leopard: *namiru*	wild ass: *parau, aradu, airu*
wild cat: *dimmu*	domestic ass: *himaru, atanu*
wolf: *dibu*	camel: *gamlu, janaktu, bakru*
jackal: *ahu*	deer: (one of the gazelle names!)
dog: *kalbu*	gazelle: *tabju, azalu, nalu, ?arnu*
fox: *tualu, talabu*	ibex: *wailu, ajjalu, upru*
hyena: *dabuu*	domestic goat: *inzu, taisu, atudu, gadja*
bear: *dubbu*	domestic sheep: *danu, sawahu, kabsu, rahilu, immaru*
hedgehog: *kuppudu*	wild cattle: *rimu, ? arhu*
mole-rat: *huldu*	domestic cattle: *bakaru, alpu, auru, iglu*
mouse: *akbaru, aisu*	? coney: *tapanu*
hare: *arnabu*	wild boar: *hazziru.*

Another chapter of HOMMEL's book, however, clearly shows the limitations of this philological method. The Semitic Geez migrated in the early Christian period from S. Arabia into Ethiopia, close by the sources of the Nile. The study of their mammalian names (from early literature) revealed the following groups:

1. Indigenous Ethiopian animals are called by non-Semitic or newly formed names of Semitic root: elephant, rhinoceros, some monkeys, giraffe, almost all antelopes, the African buffalo, the hyena-dog (and the mule).

2. Old Semitic names for known animals: leopard, bear, hyena, hedgehog, mouse, dog, wild cat, wild boar, horse, camel, cattle, goat, ibex.

3. Not old-, but southern Semitic (Arab) names have: lion, cheetah, fox, hyena, hare, ass, wild ass, domestic pig, domestic cattle, sheep, goat (*ptm.*), whale. "No other Semitic people

has abandoned so many and such common old-Semitic mammal names as the Geez who migrated from S. Arabia into another continent with different climate and fauna. The third group still connects their language with that of other Semitic peoples."

We certainly cannot accept all the results of HOMMEL's analysis. We have no knowledge of domesticated horses with Semitic talking peoples before the early second millennium B.C. With regard to the camel we know positively that the old Sumerians had no name for it, and that *ibilu* was the Assyrian name in the 8th century B.C., a few centuries after its being first mentioned in the Bible. Old as these names are, they certainly were not domesticated by Semites at 3000 B.C. or before that date. They may refer to wild horses and camels, but we lack any evidence in this respect. If really the early Semites came from Central Asia, as some claim, they certainly would have known both these animals in their wild state. Here again we come to the conclusion that even the most careful philological analysis by itself, if not supported by actual or other circumstantial evidence, is unsatisfactory. P. B. MAISLER pointed out (*i.l.*), that *ibilu* originally means the carrier of burden, being derived from the root *'bl*. This clearly illustrates that the Akkadian name *ibilu* was given to an animal, which was a domesticated bearer of burdens at the time of it becoming first known. This purely philological argument abolishes, of course, HOMMEL's theory that the camel had been domesticated by the ancient Semites in C. Asia before they penetrated Mesopotamia. Nothing can however be proven by such simple etymological reasoning: the burden may as well be the hump of the animal, and so refer to the most characteristic feature of the animal's appearance, just as *ushtra,* the bearer or a hump.

A parallel book of H. VAMBÉRY (1879) on the primeval animals of the Turco-Tatars in C. Asia may be mentioned here. The oldest important domestic animals are horse, cattle, sheep, ass and dog. The goat is rare in these wide steppes and restricted to mountain areas. The word for sheep is derived from the word for wild sheep. The camel is regarded as very old. No difference is made between one- and two-humped camel. VAMBÉRY thinks that wild camels were all one-humped, and that the two-humped camel is a domesticated produce of Bactria. With regard to the camel we wish however to point out, that early domestication does not necessary mean old in the sense of the history of the Middle East. We have no exact documentation if and when the early Turks began to domesticate the wild camel. Of wild animals the oldest names concern wild boar, bear, wolf, tiger, leopard, saiga-antelope deer, hyena, wild ass, mouse, hare and wild goat.

1.2. FORMATION OF PALESTINE AND ITS FAUNA IN THE TERTIARY AND IN THE PLEISTOCENE

1. 21. RISE AND MORPHOGENESIS OF PALESTINE

Palestine was never continuously land from the Lower Cambrium onwards. Usually it was completely or almost completely covered by sea, forming part of the great Middle Sea or Thetys. This Thetys sea passed along the northern frontier of the old Gondwana continent. Transjordan emerged definitely from the sea during the Eocene, whilst western Palestine began to emerge as a flat, hilly coat, rich in flat bays and small islands close by the shore only at the very end of the Eocene. This shore remained more or less unchanged during the Oligocene, running somewhat higher than the lower range of the Judaeo-Samarian foot-hills. No great changes took place during the Miocene, except partial and temporary transgressions to Beersheba and through the Emek Yesreel. During the Pliocene the Miocene coastal formations were raised up to 400 m, those of the early Pliocene to 200 m altitude. Limnic-fluviatile freshwater formations are characterized by mollusc shells of *Melanopsis, Hydrobia, Vivipara, Dreissensia, Unio* (*Melanopsis*-stage). The filling sediments of the mainly continental inland-basins from the Miocene to the Quaternary form up to one third of the total thickness of the main formations of Palestine. During the 1.000.000 years since the beginning of the Pleistocene the present features of physical morphology were successively established. No major changes occurred during the Quaternary. The most important one is probably the development of sand-dunes.

The history of Palestine during the Tertiary epoch has been described by Olmstead (1931) in broad lines as follows:

"The waters of the Eocene covered less territory than did the Chalk Sea, for the Lebanon, Upper Galilee and perhaps Judah were islands. With the Oligocene dry land covered much of the Middle East. Denudation began to wear down the uplifted strata, tilting and faulting changed the contours, and perhaps already the strain on earth's crust was producing north and south faulting to eventuate later in the great Rift valley. A rich and varied vertebrate life had made its appearance in Egypt and probably also farther north in the Upper Eocene. Meanwhile the Thetys Sea was slowly contracting into the Mediterranean Sea. Faults produced the mountains of N. Syria. An inland Mesopotamian sea washed the coast of a narrow N. and C. Syria, depositing clays, merls and gypsum bearing salts and oil, the result of a dry desert climate. The Mediterranean Sea broke through into the plain of Esdraelon.

At the early Pliocene the Middle East was above sea-level. The heavy strain of this uplift led to the formation of the present mountain ranges and basins, the Jordan Rift Valley appeared finally as a fissure in its present extent. In the Middle Pliocene the sea rose to about its last level. The level of the waters in the rift valley rose with the heavy rains. For a time the Mediterranean Gulf of Megiddo forced its way into the Jordan Valley. But before the end of the Pliocene the watershed between Jordan and Kishon had been established. A very primitive ape lived in Egypt during the Oligocene and his cousins may have roamed in our area. In the Pliocene apes not far distant from man were living. Yet nothing is known of their existence in ancient Palestine/Syria.

With the transition from Pliocene to Pleistocene our area had assumed essentially its present character. Yet a new Red Sea sent forth its arms east and west of the Sinai peninsula, and through the more westerly its waters united for a time with those of the Mediterranean. The waves reached a hundred feet or more above their present level and laid down sandstone and conglomerates over the Negeb and the Shephelah and along the Syrian coast. Long, narrow, north and south lakes occupied the interior and deposited their sands, gravels, clays and conglomerates. The heavy rains culminated from this transition into the first pluvial period. Lowered temperatures and greater precipitations corresponded to the northern glaciation, and filled the streams to overflowing. Great banks were piled up at their deltas and along their courses. Cut down by the lessened flow of a succeeding period of aridity, they tower 700 feet above the shore line of the present Dead Sea. The Jordan Rift Valley deepened to its present level. Lebanon and Anti-Lebanon rose to their present heights. The present deserts begin to appear. Terrific outpourings of igneous rocks covered the Jolan and Hauran with basalt.

The desert climate of the first interpluvial dried up the brackish interior lakes and left behind great deposits of gysum and rock salt, such as the J. Usdum on the S. E. corner of the Dead Sea. Man certainly had penetrated and settled in the country. Deeper erosion, formation of sand banks along the shores those are the major recent changes since then in the morphology of the country. The oldest invading man was not even a hunter, for he has left no hunting weapons. Wild animals from elephant to ibex roamed over the country, and were probably occasionally trapped. Otherwise the food of these men was what might be caught with his hands or what grew by itself. Fire probably was made use of. The social organisation scarcely surpassed the frame of a (?) monogamic family. Language was still in its embryonal stage. The second wave of settlers, the Neanderthalians were short in stature (up to 165 cm), stocky in build, heavily muscled. The spine was almost straight, yet he could not stand quite erect. His chest was huge and massive. The upper arm was long, the forearm short. Hands and feet were large and much less different than in recent man, especially the big toe still possessing high development and mobility. The big head rested on stooping shoulders, the lower jaw was much more prominent and chinless, the teeth large and the nose flat, the eyes with heavy eyebrow ridges.

This man descended from the still fairly wooded plateaus and hills into the valleys and to the sea coast, and "found the land good". He began to hunt ibex, deer and gazelles. His home was more frequently in caves. Hearths, ashes and charcoal testify to the eating of cooked meats. Mousterian type tools appear.

A renewed pluvial period brought heavier rains and a cooler climate. Along the Mediterranean coast the land sank some 250 feet. Glaciers appeared on the Syrian mountains. We will see however, that the influence of this period has been much exaggerated. Torrential rains brought the great Jordan Valley Lake to its maximum level. Erosion was heavy. In the following drier period the interior lakes fell far below their present level with deep gorge-cutting activity. Fresh outbursts of lava filled the Yarmuk area clear to the Jordan. It is doubtful if a later pluvial still followed. It is also doubtful if the final watershed between the Dead and the Red Seas was created now only, as much evidence points to the assumption, that both these seas never were in contact. The deepening of the Dead Sea and of the Lake of Galilee to the present level followed. The sea level along the shores was slightly raised. Since then the postpluvial period with its Mediterranean climate in Western Palestine/Syria began and offers a favourable environment for the further development of *Homo sapiens*."

1. 22. THE FAUNAL HISTORY OF PALESTINE IN THE TERTIARY EPOCH

Before entering the scene of Palestine's early settlement of animals, we have to glance at the continental connections and the actual fauna of the neighbouring regions at the time of our emergence from the sea. We stress this situation, as no terrestrial or freshwater species has lived in Palestine permanently before the early Tertiary period. For the history of the actual fauna of Palestine only this period is of interest. The habit to discuss jurassic, cretaceous or older historic elements or stocks lacks any real background in this country.

The most important fact is that the old mesozoic Middle Sea or Thetys between the northern and southern continents still existed when the first parts of Transjordan emerged from the sea in Miocene (Fig. 1, 1). The distribution of remains of *Limulus* and of other marine groups of animals, in general as well as in Palestine, offer ample proof. Fig. 1, 2 shows conditions at the transition period from the Upper Oligocene to the Lower Miocene. At that period the Thetys still separates terrestrial connections between the Afro-Arabo-Palestine block and between India completely, between Europe less definitely. The European fauna of the Miocene has been expertly and vividly reconstructed by O. ABEL (1922, p. 203). In character it extremely resembles the present fauna of the Indo-Malayan forest-swamps, even if *genera* and *species* have changed. The swampy forests of Upper Austria, for instance, were then inhabited by elephants and rhinos, by tapirs and wild boars, by Muntjack deer and tiny musk-deer, by civet cats and gibbons. Similar species of the same families of mammals now form the Malayan forest communities.

The fossil and recent distribution of two kinds of sharks again illustrate this point with the addition that at an early date the Arabian block was also separated by sea from the African continent. The tropical shark *Hemipristis sevra* first appeared in the Burdigalian and was characteristic for the Miocene Thetys, of which Palestine was still a part. This shark was regarded as extinct, before it was rediscovered as living in the Red Sea. The giant shark *Carcharodon megalodon* of Miocene origin then lived in the sea separating Arabia/Inner Syria from Africa.

The Thetys had disappeared in the Lower Pliocene and free continental connections permitted infiltration and penetration of Asiatic as well as of European animals. At that period a rather uniform fauna of very different character extended from Attica to Iran. This so-called Pikermi fauna, (Pikermi in Attica, Samos, Maragha in Iran) again showed the type of a present fauna, that of the African savanna. In a savanna-like park landscape there lived, often in huge herds: elephants (*Mastodon* and the giant *Dinotherium*) and some rhinos. *Ceratorhinus* and *Diceros* were closely related to the present Indian, respectively African rhino, with *Aceratherium* from Samos and Maragha. The abundance of cavicornians is of Central-Asiatic origin. Among the groups of the *Aegodontia* only a few gazelles and real antelopes have penetrated into the warmer climate of Africa at a late period. Many *Boodontia* however penetrated Africa probably together with S.E. Europe during the Pliocene (*Pseudotraginae, Bubalininae, Hippotraginae, Tragelaphinae*). Dominant forms at Pikermi were *Gazella brevicornis, Tragoceros amalithae, Oicerus rothi* (as representative of sheep and goats), *Protoryx*, and species of *Palaeoryx, Palaeoreas, Protragelaphus, Helicophora*, a roe deer (*Dicrocerus*) and various giraffes, especially *Helladotherium* as well as a boar (*Sus*). Wild horses were abundant, especially the three-toed *Hipparion mediterraneum* and *H. minus*, of zebra-size and habitus and probably showing also the same pattern. Fig. 2. shows its herds within their natural landscape. This group as well as the zoological names will enforce upon any expert the very close affinity to the present fauna of the African savanna. A representative of a now extinct, burrowing ungulate was the *Chalicotherium*, among rodents only *Hystrix* and *Acomys* were found. A lower ape (*Mesopithecus*) existed there in great herds. The biggest carnivore was the sabre tiger (*Machaerodus*) similar in habitus to the African lion, and the leopard-like *Felisleodon*. The common carnivores were however the hyenas, such as *Hyaenictis graeca* and *Hyaena eximia*. The bear *Hyaenarctos atticus,* which did not follow the rest of the fauna to Africa, the jackal-like *Simocyon* and a badger-like *Mustela* also occurred. The fauna of Samos is richer still. SCHLOSSER (1904) and ABEL regard Iran as the centre of this fauna, from where the species infiltrated and migrated westwards. The greater abundance of the Samos fauna is explained as due to an early interruption of the connection between Samos and the Greek mainland. In general we wish to point out that the great shift of faunas, as that from Iran-Attica to the African savanna area of today, must by no means be conceived to be a real migration, as observed in locusts, lemmings and many ungulates. The slow shift of a climatic area within secular periods for a few kilometres south or north provokes almost imperceptible displacements, certainly not migrations. Yet the accumulation of these secular minor changes and shifts over many thousands of years produces the great shifts, which are often incorrectly called migrations. It was the merit of LYELL and DARWIN to have pointed out this process. And due to this slow process we still find at relatively late periods some, now tropical, savanna animals, as last survivors of the rear guard of this geological southward shift of entire faunas. This slow shift is still more underlined when we recall to our mind the North-American origin of so many mammals in the early Tertiary periods, such as rhinos, camels, horses, and others. It is now doubted that the bulk of the Pikermi fauna originated in the early Tertiary in or round Central Asia. Few groups of the actual recent savanna fauna had entered Africa at that time. We know relatively little about the animals living there at earlier periods, except that they were of a very different character, relics of which have survived in Madagascar and in parts of S. Africa. We recapitulate: the Irano/Greek fauna of the Lower Pliocene showed strong affinities to the actual life-communities inhabiting the Ethiopian savanna. Palestine was on the road of this slow southward trend and most of the savanna animals of the early Palestine history, such as spotted hyena, wart hog, *Megaderma*-bat, hippo, crocodile, rhino and elephants represent the last survivors of a fauna, the bulk of which had since thousands of years withdrawn to much more southern quarters. They were mainly concentrated in the hygrophilous habitats, just as are the palaeotropical relics of our present fauna. Yet not all animals of Ethiopian character belong to this group. There is first a group which has settled in all or most of the southern continents, the old Gondwanaland. A good representative of this Gondwana-fauna are the mouthbreeding fish of the family *Cichlidae* (in the Jordan system represented by a number of species of *Tilapia* and *Paratilapia*), now occurring in C. and S. America, Africa, Palestina/Syria, South Caspia and the Oriental kingdom. L. JOLEAUD (1939) assumes a palaeozoic origin in S. America, followed by migration to Africa and Indonesia. Although they could reach New-Guinea, they arrived too late to penetrate into Australia. In this case the primary origin doubtless was a southern one. But this does not exclude that Palestine actually was invaded by these fishes from the East. The association with the cat-fish (*Clarias lacera*), however, makes this little probable. The second group are animals which have originated from and got form in Africa. Here the conyes (*Procavia*), represented by a *Pliohyrax* in Pikermi and the earthhogs (*Orycteropodidae*) represented by an *Orycteropus* in Samos and Maragha belong.

A special group is formed by the wild cattle (*Bovina*). Species of *Bubalus, Leptobos, Hemibos, Bos* and *Bison* abound in the Siwalik layers of the Upper Pliocene in the Punjab. O. ABEL (1922, p. 98) comes to the conclusion, that these cattle originated from the steppes of Central Asia. At the early Pliocene they penetrated into eastern India and did not spread for quite a time to the west. He assumes that westward migration or penetration of the *Bovinae* occurred during the glacial age only.

Figs. 3 and 4 give some details about a number of animals which are of importance in connection with the early history of their development. Crocodiles are of but little moment, as they are Senonian in origin (JOLEAUD). We do not know when the Nile crocodile entered Africa. Fossils only reach back to the late Tertiary, whilst in Europe crocodile fossils date back to the cretaceous period. They may well have accompanied the hippos, being similarly distributed, although of Miocene origin only. The latter probably got shape in Europe and

India before penetrating into Africa. We have pointed out before that close relatives of both, the recent African and Indian rhinos coexisted at Pikermi. This family appeared in Europe during the Oligocene. The genuine hyenas appeared in S. Europe in the Upper Miocene. The spotted hyena is a close relative of the *Hyaena eximia* living at Pikermi. The Pliocene ancestor of the African lion, *Leo arvernensis,* lived in C. France. The camels originated during the Upper Eocene in N. America, branching into the genuine camels during the Pliocene, covering wide areas of Asia and Europe in the Quaternary, and the lamas of S. America. In the Upper Miocene the giraffes spread from the Mediterranean regions to China. In the early Quaternary still they were common throughout the present Sahara. The present distribution of horses, zebras and asses is the outcome of another development which started in N. America during in the early Eocene. The elephants appear in Africa only since the Pliocene with *Elephas antiquus,* whilst *Elephas meridionalis* and *E. planifrons* inhabited Central and S. E. Asia in the Pleistocene. In the Middle East both these groups overlapped. The African elephant, according to JOLEAUD (p. 101), has reached S. Africa still in the Upper Pliocene. The Indian elephant's area extended to the Upper Euphrates and possibly to Antiochia still in historical times. Another historical distribution of the type, so familiar to us now, is that of the *Tragulidae,* so common in the early Tertiary in Europe, and now restricted to the forests of Africa and Indonesia. Among the birds we find many fossils of ostriches from the Miocene and Pliocene, from Greece to China. Nothing definite is known yet about the time of their penetration into Africa. In the Eocene the dugongs (*Halicoridae*) were common from Egypt to N. Germany. These warm-water mammals are now restricted to some border areas of the Indian Ocean, including the Red Sea, where they occasionally still penetrate as far north as Akaba and Tor.

We felt bound to give these detailed maps and explanations in order to point out the background of the early history of the fauna of Palestine, which cannot be understood without them and which should not be accepted without the study of this documentation. Whilst the opinion about one species or the other may undergo a change by further finds, the following general conclusion will stand: *The early tropical animals of Palestine invaded from the north and east, not from the African territory.* Whilst this is true for the bulk, a few exceptions have been mentioned.

The recent discoveries of Cretaceous and Tertiary fossil beds in Lower and Upper Egypt by STROMER (1904-1926) strongly confirm our thesis. The early fluviomarine beds of Bahariye yielded, amongst others, many Saurians, crocodiles, *Ceratodus,* sharks and rays. The Oligocenous mammals of Lower Egypt were very different from any known contemporaneous European and W. Asiatic fauna. Apart from mammals, many fish (*Pristis, Polypteridae, Protopterus, Siluridae, Pelomedusidae*), reptiles (*Testudo, Crocodiles, Tomistoma*) and a primitive Ratite bird (*Eremopezus*) were discovered. The mammals are represented by:

Halicoridae: *Eosiren, Archaeosiren, Eotherium, Protosiren.*
Proboscidea: *Moeritherium, Palaeomastodon.   Amblypoda:Arsinotherium.*
Hyracoidea: *Sagatherium, Pachyhyrax, Mixohyrax, Megalohyrax, Bunohyrax, Geniohyus.*
Artiodactyla Bunoselenodontia: *Brachyodus, Rhagatherium, ?Ancodus, Mixotherium.*
Primates: *Propliopithecus, Parapithecus, Moeripithecus, ?Apidium .*
Carnivora: *Ptolemaia, Pterodon, Apterodon, Sinopa, Metasinopa, Hyaenodon.*
Rodentia, Insectivora, Chiroptera: *Phiomys, Metaphiomys, Metoldobotes, Provampyrus.*

Only a few mammals are known from the Lower Miocene (*Atelodus, Mastodon*). A representative fauna of the Middle Pliocene from Wadi Natrun shows the Pikermi fauna in full penetration of Lower Egypt in its southward drift to the present savanna area. At that period the Wadi Natrun formed part of the delta of the Nile. In the gallery forests of the river there lived many kinds of monkeys (*Libypithecus, Semnopithecus, Aulaxinuus*) and three species of otters (*Lutra*). A baboon (*Papio*) and probably also some coneys inhabited the rocks, whilst in the steppes we find: many ungulates (*Hipparion, Sus, Hippopotamus, Camelid, ?Libytherium, ?Hippotragus, Tragelaphinae, Mastodon*), carnivores (*Hyaenid, Machaerodus*), a hare and the ostrich. Some of the steppe forms even seem to be specifically identical with Pikermi forms, such as *Hipparion gracile*.

The Quaternary shows, of course, a typical Ethiopic fauna (*Hippopotamus, Giraffa, Bubalus, Elephas*). This important independent evidence of the Egyptian fossil beds confirms the autochthonous development of some groups in Africa, such as coneys and some monkeys, dugongs, *Amblypoda* and *Artiodactyla Bunoselenelenodontia,* crocodiles (*Tomistoma*), and perhaps even the mastodonts, together with many primitive forms of rodents, carnivores, bats and insectivores. Two possibly northern forms appear in the L. Miocene (*Trionyx, Atelodus*). The bulk of the ungulates and carnivores, etc. of the Pliocene fauna was, however, formed by the Pikermi fauna shifting southwards. The fluviatile fauna of the Nile, such as represented for instance by fish or molluscs, was African in character since Cretaceous times and did not change its Ethiopian character since.

1. 23. THE FAUNAL HISTORY OF PALESTINE IN THE PLEISTOCENE

We must ask the general reader to have some patience for a few more pages, to follow into some technical details of the splendid recent researches of the late Miss D. A. BATE, which permit us to draw a picture of the Pleistocenic faunal changes of this country. Her rare achievements are due to much patience and persistence as well as to the careful excavations of Miss GARROD, R. NEUVILLE, a.o. We have to trace the facts in their historical sequence in order to come to the proper understanding of these faunal changes.

In most of the older descriptions of the prehistoric faunal developments of Palestine the presence of a real cold-period is assumed for Palestine, which was based on certain botanical and zoological fossils from the Lebanon and from Palestine. Signs of large glacier-morains in the Lebanon and the existence of a fossil flora of beech, hazel, elm and large-leaved oak were explained by FRAAS (1878) and ZUMOFFEN (1926) as indicators of a northern, boreal invasion during the glacial age. Yet all these plants are still thriving today in N. Syria and S. Anatolia. A similar interpretation was given to the Mousterian station of Adlun near Beirut, where bones of *Rhinoceros tichorhinus, Bison priscus, Dama mesopotamica, Equus caballus, Sus scrofa,* and *Capra primigenia* abounded. DAWKINS (Tristram 1884) assigned some bones of the Lebanon as "probably" belonging to reindeer and elk. These are now recognised as certainly belonging to the fallow deer or to one of the two other deer which certainly lived in Palestine. None of the later, much more extensive discoveries and excavations revealed any indication of the presence of those northern animals here. Accordingly the supposed longhaired Siberian rhino (*Rhinoceros tichorhinus*) is certainly a wrong identification of the heat-loving *Rh. hemitoechus*. In view of our much extended knowledge of prehistoric animal remains from Palestine, Transjordan and the Lebanon, we find no justification for the assumption of a general period of cold with massif intrusion of boreal plants and animals. The extreme scarcity of truly boreal elements (Angara-component) among recent plants and animals of this region decidedly supports this negative palaeontological evidence.

More serious is the claim of BATE (1937) of the occurrence of a typically humid tropical fauna during an adequate clima-period in the middle of the Pleistocene. This opinion is supported by the discovery of bones of the following mammals: *Megaderma watwat,* a now purely palaeotropical genus of bat; *Hyaena crocuta,* the spotted hyena, now inhabiting Africa south of the Sahara, and which spread on the Pleistocene from W. Europe to China; *Phaco-choerus garrodae,* a wart hog. This genus has the same recent and Pleistocene distribution as the spotted hyena. And the hippo, *Hippopotamus amphibius,* which retained a distribution north of the Sahara along the Nile and in Little Africa until historical times. This problem will be discussed later. The oldest animal relics are the bone-bearing beds of Bethlehem, which have not yet been worked out properly (Bate 1941). The bones show relationship with the Pliocene and comprise a *Hipparion* (or *Equus*), a *Stegedon* (or *Elephas*), *Rhinoceros cf. etruscus, Bos sp.* and an antelope. Together with these bones, some of which are suspected of having been split (STEKELIS), a number of flints was discovered, which were supposed to represent very archaic human artifacts of the Lower Palaeolithicum. By most authorities they are regarded, however until further material is available as natural products without human interference (PETTON-THOMPSON).

The dating of *Hemibos palaestinus,* which was discovered by Dr. N. SHALEM 31 m deep in the soil, when a well was bored near Gedera is not yet settled. Only three more species of *Hemibos* are known, all from the Upper Siwalik strata of N.W. India, which may belong either to the late Pliocene or to the early Pleistocene. The Palestine species shows more marks of progression than any of the Indians forms (great breadth of the frontals; well spaced and widely divergent horns), and so it must have belonged to a Pleistocene wave of eastern immigrants, perhaps the same wave which brought the arni-buffalo, the gaur and the wisent to ancient Mesopotamia.

The oldest strata of the Mt. Carmel caves (BATE 1937) which contain bones are associated with an Upper Acheulean industry. To Miss BATE their fauna suggests a hot and damp, even a tropical climate. This stratum (Tabun F) almost exclusively contains extinct, mainly small mammals (Bate 1943 p. 816):

Megaderma watwat (11 individuals)	*Apodemus caesarianus* (16)
Crocidura samaritana (50)	*Apodemus sp.* (large; 2)
Talpa chthonia (7)	*Mesocricetus aramaeus* (67)
Spalax sp. (6)	*Allocricetus jezreelicus* (56)
Philistomys roachi (3)	*Cricetulus sp.* (5)
Microtus sp. (1)	*Gerbillinae* (4)
Arvicanthis ectos (24)	*Dama mesopotamica* (1)
Leggada sp. (3)	*Gazella sp.* (3)

Two genera: (*Philistomys,* a muscardine ancestor of *Eliomys,* and the hamster *Allocricetus*) are extinct today. The other extinct species are all more primitive and generalised in character than the recent forms. Only *Spalax, Microtus, Cricetulus* and *Dama mesopotamica* have possibly survived till our days. Yet the first three may, when more material will be available, well prove to be species of their genera, other than the recent ones. The gazelles certainly were totally different from the present gazelles of the country.

Apart from *Megaderma* relations to the tropics are suggested by *Arvicanthis,* a genus now entirely confined to the Ethiopian kingdom with penetration into Egypt along the Nile, and by *Leggada* which at present shows a palaeotropical distribution. The Palestine form (Bate 1942 p. 484), whilst related to the present Ethiopian group of the genus, shows affinities to a fossil species from India. The species of *Apodemus* are of special interest, as— together with two more species from higher layers—they show specific differences within the range of the same three groups of *Apodemus* (the *sylvaticus-, flavicollis-* and *mystacinus-* group) which still inhabit N. Palestine and Syria now. This is a good example of an autochthonous evolutionary process of Pleistocenous mammals on Palestine soil. The abundance of hamsters suggests a steppe environment, or at most a dry Mediterranean one. The presence of *Talpa chthonia,* a relative of the small mole of S. Italy and Yougoslavia (*T. romana*), suggests Mediterranean conditions. *Leggada* could well have lived in a dry steppe, together with the gazelles. *Dama, Apodemus, Microtus, Spalax,* and gerbilles ask for no climatic changes. *Arvicanthis,* the field rat of Egypt, was certainly bound to hygrophilous habitats, such as swamps or river banks, which even recently were still available.

Thus we cannot agree with Miss BATE that the climate of Tabun F was a tropical one. Possibly it was more humid than today, but even for this assumption we fail to see an urgent need from this faunal assemblage. The small tropical mammals were on the verge of extinction. This fact may eventually justify the conclusion that a more tropical climate existed, for some time at least, during the end of the Pliocene.

The following level (Tabun E) with its Micoquean (Upper Acheulean) civilisation had also a hot and humid climate, growing drier towards the end. The following animals are mentioned from it by BATE (1937, 1942, 1943):

Myotis cf. baranensis	*Apodemus sp. 3.*
Rhinolophus cf. ferrum-equineum	*Apodemus sp. 4.*
Crocidura samaritanus	*Rattus (Mastomys sp.)*
Crocidura katinka	*Mus camini*
Hyaena prisca	*Cricetulus demetros*
Canis cf. lupaster	*Gerbillinae*
Vulpes vinetorum	*Hippopotamus amphibius*
Felis cf. pardus	*Sus gadarensis*
Spalax sp.	*Capreolus capreolus*
Hystrix sp.	*Dama mesopotamica*
Sciurus cf. anomalus	*Capra sp.*
Philistomys roachi	*Alcelaphus sp.*
Ellobius pedorychus	*Bos sp.*
Microtus mc-cowni	*Gazella sp.*
Microtus cf. guentheri	*Equus caballus cf. przewalskii*
Microtus (Chionomys) machintoni	*Equus hemionus*
Apodemus caesareanus	*Procavia cf. syriaca*
Apodemus levantinus	*Rhinoceros cf. hemitoechus*
	Elephas sp.

Megaderma, Talpa, Leggada and the three hamsters of Tabun F have become extinct. *Dama* decreases, whilst gazelles grow more abundant. None of the animals of this list suggest a tropical climate. Most of them fit well into a Mediterranean or a steppe climate. *Hippopotamus* and the large pig *Sus gadarensis* live in hygrophilous habitats, which were present, as above mentioned. The hartebeest (*Alcelaphus*) lived in the steppes with wild horses of the Przewalski-type, widely spread in Europe and Asia in the Upper Palaeolithicum, and with a big and plump wild ass of great size, resembling the kiang of Tibet, and very different from the slender horse-like onager of recent days. The climatically neutral *Rhinoceros hemitoechus* kept them company and the elephant probably was a remnant of the southward drift, unless it was identical with the Indian elephant, which survived at the upper Euphrates and perhaps the Orontes until historical days. The presence of *Chionomys* and of *Ellobius* suggests a mountainous region with fairly cold winters. *Hystrix, Sciurus, Microtus guentheri, Capreolus, Capra,* and *Procavia* (porcupine, squirrel, vole, roe deer, ibex, coney) lead to the recent fauna whilst *Hyaena prisca* is the earlier eco-variant of *H. hyaena*.

The layers of the Lower Levalloiso-Mousterian civilisation (Tabun D and C and Skhul) contain remnants of (Bate 1937, 1942, 1943):

Myotis cf. baranensis   *Apodemus caesareanus*
Crocidura katinka   *Apodemus levantinus*
Crocidura samaritanus   *Apodemus spp. 3 and 4.*
Erinaceus sharonis   *Mus camini*
Hyaena crocuta   *Cricetulus demetros*
Hyaena prisca   *Gerbillinae*
Canis cf. lupaster   *Hippopotamus amphibius*
Vulpes vinetorum   *Sus gadarensis*
Vulpes vulpes   *Phacochoerus garrodae*
Vormela peregusna   *Capreolus capreolus*
Ursus mediterraneus   *Cervus elaphus*
Felis cf. libyca   *Dama mesopotamica*
Felis pardus   *Capra sp.*
Hystrix sp.   *Alcelaphus sp.*
Philistomys roachi   *Bos sp.*
Ellobius pedorychus   *Gazella sp.*
Microtus guentheri   *Equus hemionus*
Microtus (Chionomys) machintoni *Equus cf. hydruntinus*
                                 Rhinoceros hemitoechus
                                 Procavia cf. syriaca.

The climate is drier than with the earlier layers, but hygrophilous habitats for *Hippopotamus* and *Sus gadarensis* are amply available. Gazelles rapidly increase and *Dama* is continuously reduced in numbers. *Crocidura samaritanus, Myotis, Erinaceus sharonis, Philistomys* and *Arvicanthis* are dying out in layer E. *Vulpes vinetorum, Ellobius, Cricetulus demetros,* three species of *Apodemus, Mastomys,* rhinoceros, hippo and *Phacochoerus* towards the end of Tabun D. *Phacochoerus* is now limited to tropical Africa, as is the group of *Rattus (Mastomys)* to which the fossil species from Palestine belonged. This *M. coucha*-group "may be one of the primitive lines that may have given rise to *Mus* on one hand, or part of *Rattus* on the other" (ELLERMAN 1941, p. 169). A fossil representative of this group was found in the earlier Siwalik layers in India. BATE (1942, p. 483) states about *Mus camini* that it represents "a stage of development or specialisation between that of *M. minotaurus* from Crete and recent forms". *Microtus mc-cowni* is possibly a primitive ancestor form of the *M. guentheri*-group. Interesting are the two shrews, each of which possibly was a step towards the two recent species: *Crocidura katinka* towards *C. portali,* and *C. samaritanus* towards *C. russulus* (Bate 1937). The three subsequent forms of hedgehogs, however, (*Erinaceus sharonis, E. carmelitus, E. auritus*) have no relation to each other. We have our doubts about Miss BATE's identification of *Canis lupaster* with the recent jackal (1937, p. 177). This wolf-jackal is regarded as a different species, but it is still an open question. The fox *Vulpes vinetorum* is a very primitive canide, which may eventually be attributed to another genus. From the two bears, the smaller *Ursus mediterraneus* belongs to a group widely spread over Mediterranean islands in the Pleistocene. The rather big representatives of *Ursus arctos,* which appear intermittently since layer E, are probably the ancestors of the recent *Ursus arctos syriacus,* which may have developed during the Aurignacian. We suggest that the bones of the small wild cat may be ascribed to *Felis s. libyca* instead of

F. s. sylvestris. Another interesting addition is *Equus cf. hydruntinus,* a small ass, probably related to the African wild asses. Entirely unidentified is the wild cattle of all layers. *Bos primigenius* and a species of *Bubalus* (aurochs and buffalo) are certainly represented, and other species were probably also present. But the bad state of the bones of these big mammals only leads to an exceptional determination.

The following layer (Tabun B, Wad G; Upper Levalloiso-Mousterian) shows a faunal break. The faunal assemblage more and more shows its modern aspect. Many species have disappeared in the earlier two layers, yet only few new species are added. *Dama* increases again, which points to a heavier rainfall. The tropical assemblage, with the exception of *Hyaena crocuta,* has disappeared for good (Bate 1937):

Hyaena crocuta	*Cervus elaphus*
Canis cf. lupus	*Dama mesopotamica*
Vulpes vulpes	*Capra sp.*
Felis pardus	*Bos sp.*
Spalax sp.	*Gazella sp.*
Hystrix sp.	*Equus hemionus*
Gerbillinae	*Equus cf. hydruntinus*
Sus sp.	*Procavia cf. syriacus*
Capreolus capreolus	

For the Natufian (Wad B) Miss BATE's recent analysis of the antelopes shows that all gazelles were not only specifically different from those of our days, but even belonged to a different group, the *G. granti*-group, now living in East Africa. To the same faunal element belonged the water buck KOBUS. Other, smaller gazelles lived with them in Natufian Palestine, the identification of which was not yet possible. *Dama*-bones are becoming rare, whilst those of gazelles abound. A large, probably domesticated dog (*Canis familiaris matris-optimae*) has made its appearance, together with the long-eared hedgehog (BATE 1937, 1940, 1943):

Erinaceus carmelitus	*Gerbillinae*
Erinaceus cf. auritus	*Sus scrofa var.*
Hyaena crocuta	*Capreolus capreolus*
Canis familiaris cf. matris-optimae	*Cervus elaphus*
Vulpes vulpes	*Dama mesopotamica*
Meles meles	*Capra sp.*
Martes cf. martes	*Alcelaphus sp.*
Vormela peregusna	*Bos sp.*
Ursus cf. mediterraneus	*Gazella decora*
Felis cf. maniculata	*Gazella esdraelonica*
Felis pardus	*Gazella arista*
Spalax sp.	*Kobus cananites*
Lepus sp.	*Equus caballus cf. przewalskii*
Sciurus cf. anomalus	*Equus hemionus*
Microtus guentheri	*Procavia cf. syriaca*
Mesocricetus sp.	

We have omitted a special discussion of the Aurignacian layers (Wad F-C), which are almost identical with the Natufian layers. *Hystrix, Ursus arctos* and *Canis lupus* are the only additions, whilst amongst the antelopes only *Gazella arista* is represented.

Dr. STEKELIS has kindly put at our disposal a list of the faunal assemblage of another Mt. Carmel cave (Abu 'Usba) from an early neolithic station (det. Dr. G. HAAS). This station is highly interesting. Apart from a number of Natufian animals, which survived until our days, a certain number of recent forms has been recorded at Abu 'Usba for the first time (*Gazella arabica, Mus musculus, Apodemus* in its recent species, *Cricetulus migratorius, Acomys cahirinus,* and others). This first record does, of course, not preclude the presence of the species at a much earlier date. Still more important is the survival of some now extinct Natufian species in the Neolithicum of Mt. Carmel. Such forms are *Erinaceus samaritanus,* the spotted hyena, *Gazella decora* and *G. esdraelonica, Capra ?primigenia,* two species of wild cattle, a big ass, and *Sciurus anomalus.* We must however observe, that the dating of STEKELIS is doubted by others.

The discoveries in other caves, such as Zuttiyeh, Umm Qatafah, Shukbah, Kebarah, Emireh, a.o. show that the fauna of the Mt. Carmel caves was not a local one, but was widely spread in every layer over the country. This strengthens the conclusion that real and important faunal changes have occurred. This conclusion is incontestable in view of the latest studies of Miss Bate on the gazelles, hamsters and mice. We may expect that future research will extend the period of existence for a number of species. But the fact that the early Pleistocene, especially among the smaller mammals, showed a high divergence from the present fauna and that almost all the species of those groups which are still represented by various forms in the recent fauna, have more generalised and primitive characters, is well established.

Another group of animals which permits analysis through the cave strata are terrestrial molluscs (BATE 1937 p. 224, Avnimelech 1937 p. 81). No change in the species is observed. The following species were found:

Leucochroa candidissima	*Levantina caesareana* (and var.)
Calaxis saulcyi	*Levantina hierosolyma*
Chondrula septemdentata	*Petraeus fouroussi*
Ericea olivieri	*Petraeus labrosus*
Helicogena cavata	*Petraeus syriacus*
Helicogena figulina	*Theba olivieri*
Euparypha seetzeni	

All these species still occur today. But from the changes in the size of the *Levantina*-species from the excavations of R. NEUVILLE, Avnimelech (1931, p. 91) draws the conclusion that the climate of the Upper Palaeolithicum resembled that of the present day as regards temperature and humidity. He assumes that the early Mesolithicum was characterized by a climate warmer and drier than that of today. This latter conclusion conflicts with the supposition of a more humid climate assumed by Miss BATE.

Bird relics are rare and limited to the caves of Zuttiyeh (BATE 1927, p. 28) and of Umm Qatafah (VAUFREY in NEUVILLE 1931). The list of the determined species, all from the Upper Acheulean and the Levalloiso-Mousterian, is as follows:

Turdus sp.	*Gyps fulvus*
Sturnus vulgaris	*Gallus sp.*
?Pycnonotus sp.	*Columba oenas*
Cypselus melba	*Columba livia*
Apus ?affinis	*Coturnix coturnix*
Athene noctua	*Perdrix sp. (? Alectoris)*
Aquila sp.	*Phasianus hermonis*

All these birds still live in the country, with the exception of the Hermon pheasant, which much resembles some Miocene pheasants from Europe. Pheasants are also known from the Lower Pliocene of Pikermi. At present the pheasant living nearest is *Phasianus colchicus* from the N.E. corner of Anatolia, living in a rather humid climate in dense forests. With regard to *Gallus sp.* judgement must be postponed until more material will be available. Consequently the bird relics give us very little indications with regard to climatic changes.

The same holds good for the reptiles of the Levalloiso-Mousterian. They are represented in the Mt. Carmel caves by a big *Trionyx* and by a *Crocodilus*. *Trionyx nilotica* occurred still recently in the coastal rivers of the country, and *Crocodilus niloticus* has disappeared from the Zerka river only at the beginning of this century. Other caves contained *Emys ?orbicularis, ?Coluber sp.,* frogs and toads, all still surviving in this country.

Freshwater shells are deposited in good series in the gravel of the Lisanstrata of the Upper Jordan Valley from the Upper and Middle Pleistocene. They have been studied by Picard (1934). These Lisan facies are rich in forms and individuals of a few *Melanopsis* (*M. laevigata, M. costata*), which still abound. Giant forms of *Melanopsis laevigata* or of *Theodoxia macrii* are ascribed to hydrological rather than to climatic factors. *Planorbis, Bythinia, Bythinella, Pyrgula, Limnaea* are essentially identical with the present-day occupants. The disappearance of *Ancylus,* occurring in these deposits, was regarded as a proof of the extermination of an earlier cold-loving fauna. Our discovery (BODENHEIMER 1935, p. 32) of *Ancylus fluviatilis* in the Papyrus-thickets of the Upper Jordan refuted this assumption. PICARD (1937, p. 60) also discovered *Vivipara syriaca* and *V. angularis* in Acheulean strata, and their discovery in recent niches is highly probable. Unions from the same provenance showed forms of present occurrence. Whilst PICARD (1934) first believed in the influence of cold and warm periods, he (1937, p. 60) came to the conclusion later that freshwater molluscs do not offer any proof of the theory of the intrusion of a cold-loving fauna; on the contrary they point to the persistence of conditions from the Pliocene, with considerable hydrological changes, of course, in the Jordan Basin, brought about by rain fluctuations.

Marine shells in caves date from the end of the Lower Levalloiso-Mousterian to the bronze age. They served as ornaments and their inhabitants as food. The list of these shells until the end of the Mesolithicum, found in relation to man, runs as follows (BATE, 1937, p. 224):

Arca noe	*Donax trunculus*
Cardium ?deshayesi	*Glycimeris pilosus*
Cardium rusticum	*Glycimeris violacescens*
Cardium edule	*Laevicardium crassum*
Columbella rustica	*Nassarius ?costulatus*
Conus mediterraneus	*Nassarius gibbosulus*
Cypraea moneta	*Osilinus turbinatus*
Dentalium dentalis	*Ostrea crenulifera*
Dentalium vulgare	*Patella caerulea*
Dentalium cf. aratorum	*Pecten jacobaeus*
	Pinna sp.
	Thais haemostoma

Cypraea moneta and *Ostrea crenulifera* are now living in the Gulf of Oman, the latter in the Red Sea as nearest place of occurrence. The other species, apart from *Dentalium cf. aratorum,* are still common Mediterranean forms.

Miss BATE (1932, p. 277) mentions *D. aratorum* together with the foreign *Siphoria luzonica* from Natufian layers in an Athlit cave. The former species (BATE 1937, p. 225) is now regarded as a special, probably extinct species. AVNIMELECH (1937, p. 82) found a number of *Dentalium* in other Natufian deposits excavated by R. NEUVILLE (*D. rectum, D. vitreum, D. vulgare var., D. rubescens, D. entale, D. dentalis*). Most of these species are not Mediterranean today, and are either fossil or came from the Red Sea. Another Red Sea shell is *Nerita maritima,* whilst *Nassa (Arcularia) sp., Glycimeris violacescens* and *Cardium tuberculatum* are still Mediterranean forms. It is more probable that the Red Sea shells were brought here by human traffic than their being contemporaries of ancient Red Sea shells in the Pleistocene Mediterranean Sea.

As prehuman faunal changes depended on and coincided with climatic changes to a high degree, we now must consider the evidence for such changes. Before entering into this discussion, however, we wish to point out again that the remnants of none of the Pleistocene layers justify the assumption that the vegetal aspect of Western Palestine—and to this area alone our discussions are limited—has radically changed since the early Pleistocene: Mediterranean territories and steppes were both represented. The geographical situation easily explains the absence of a pure desert fauna, which nobody would expect to find nowadays on Mt. Carmel, at Zichron Yaakob, in Upper Galilee or on the western slopes of Judaea. The extensive swamps of the coastal plain, behind the dunes or in the Emek Yesreel—drained only recently by Jewish colonists—would have offered favourable conditions to the hygrophilous "tropical" group (hippo, wart-hog, *Sus gadarensis, Arvicanthis*). Fluctuations in the spread of Mediterranean maqui and steppes certainly occurred, but never to the extent that one expelled the other entirely or almost entirely from our area (See Table 1 on pp. 26 and 27).

The careful investigation of Miss BATE suggests some faunal breaks. A greater one is assumed at the end of layer Tabun B, when almost all now tropical hygrophilous animals disappeared together with *Vulpes vinetorum, Eliomys* and *Rhinoceros.* The tropical animals may have died out in consequence of an extended drought. This means that they could stand the normal, but not the extreme climate of the country. They probably could still live in the country where suitable niches were still available, as they are even today in some parts of the Jordan Valley. And *Ellobius,* a typical inhabitant of dry steppes, was certainly not exterminated in consequence of the same causes. Similar faunal breaks occurred at the end of the periods Tabun F, E and D. Also the great difference of the Natufian antelope fauna from that of our days puts us before new embarrassing problems. Further research will teach us if these faunal breaks were really as abrupt as they appear in the light of the excavations of the Mt. Carmel caves. In general the analysis shows that in the early Palaeolithicum many of the present rodents were represented by other, and always by more primitive forms. *Microtus guentheri* and *Spalax ehrenbergi* are almost the only mammals which since then survived unchanged. More remarkable is the fact that the Natufian and even part of the Neolithic gazelles are not our present forms, but others, showing intimate connection with recent forms of the savannas of E. Africa. It should not be assumed, however, that faunal instability was so strong in all or even in most animals. With evertebrates and reptiles the formation of the recent species was essentially ended during the Tertiary. In fishes and birds most changes during the Quaternary concern race formation, but speciation only to a very limited degree.

Miss BATE (1943, p. 815) has made an interesting attempt to correlate the development of the small generalised mammals into the more specialised recent forms to indirect consequences of climatic changes. She comes to the conclusion, for instance, that "the smaller size and less highly modified incisors of *Mesocricetus aramaeus* of Tabun are in great contrast to the very powerful teeth with flattened anterior surfaces of recent species, and suggest that

TABLE 1

The mammals from the Palaeolithicum of the Mt. Carmel caves (from D. M. A. BATE).

I: Tabun G, II: Tabun F, III: Tabun E, IV: Tabun D, V: M. Shkul + Tabun C, VI: Tabun B, VII: M. Wad C-F, VIII: M. Wad B.

Species	I	II	III	IV	V	VI	VII	VIII
CHIROPTERA:								
Megaderma watwat		+						
Myotis cf. baranensis			+	+				
Rhinolophus sp.			+					
INSECTIVORA:								
Crocidura samaritana		+	+	+				
Crocidura katinka			+	+				
Erinaceus sharonis				+				
Erinaceus carmelitus							+	+
Erinaceus cf. auritus								+
Talpa chthonia		+						
CARNIVORA:								
Hyaena crocuta						+	+	+
Hyaena prisca			+	+	+	+		
Canis cf. lupaster			+	+	+			
Canis cf. lupus						+	+	
Canis familiaris matris optimae								+
Vulpes vinetorum			+	+	+			
Vulpes vulpes cf. palaestina				+	+	+	+	+
Meles sp.							+	+
Martes cf. martes							+	+
Vormela cf. peregusna					+	+	+	+
Ursus arctos							+	
Ursus arctos cf. mediterraneus				+	+	+	+	+
Felis libyca							+	+
Panthera pardus			+	+	+	+	+	+
RODENTIA:								
Spalax sp.		+	+	+	+	+	+	+
Hystrix sp.			+	+	+	+	+	
Lepus sp.							+	+
Sciurus cf. anomalus							+	+
Philistomys roachi		+	+	+				
Ellobius pedorychus			+	+	+			
Microtus mc cowni			+					
Microtus guentheri		+	+	+	+	+	+	+
Murinae		+	+	+				
Cricetinae		+	+	+				
Gerbillinae		+	+	+	+			
UNGULATA:								
Hippopotamus amphibius			+	+	+			
Phacochoerus garrodae					+			
Sus gadarensis			+	+	+			

Species	I	II	III	IV	V	VI	VII	VIII
Sus scrofa							+	+
Capreolus capreolus			+	+	+	+	+	+
Cervus elaphus					+	+	+	+
Dama mesopotamica		+	+	+	+	+	+	+
Capra sp.			+	+	+	+	+	+
Alcelaphus sp.			+	+	+		+	+
Gazella sp.		+	+	+	+	+	+	+
Bos sp.			+	+	+	+	+	+
Equus caballus			+	+	+	+	+	+
Equus hemionus			+	+	+	+	+	+
Equus cf. hydruntinus					+	+		
Rhinoceros cf. hemitoechus			+	+	+			
Procavia cf. syriaca			+	+	+	+	+	+
Elephas sp.			+					

this change is due to an alteration of environment from a mild climate with plentiful soft vegetation to one of drier conditions with a harder vegetation." This interpretation, which agrees with the general climatic trend as proposed by this writer, supposes a safer background of knowledge on the modelling effect of the environment than we have today.

That climatic fluctuations have occurred during the Pleistocene is certain. It is equally certain that these fluctuations mainly took place in periods of rainfall and were only of little range in temperature. PICARD (1937, p. 70) points out that "from a palaeo-geographical point of view the Pluvial period is not only a phenomenon of the Pleistocene, but of the whole Post-Miocene epoch."

Perhaps the most lucid comparison of the pleistocenous climatic fluctuations of all belts of the northern hemisphere has been given by the late S. A. Huzayyin (1940). We reproduce here his survey table (see following page).

Whilst we are still uncertain about the extent to which these geological rain fluctuations ranged in the most humid and the extreme dry periods, we must warn the reader to give too liberal an interpretation to the meaning of cool and warm in the three southern belts. The difference was probably not more than a very few centigrades. This is well illustrated by the fact that just the first Pluvial in the Lower Pleistocene (= Diluvium) with its great accumulation of "tropical" animals in Palestine, is classified in Huzayyin's table as predominantly cool.

The following main conclusions are proposed:

1. Since the beginning of the Pleistocene only minor fluctuations of temperature, but more important ones of rains have occurred.

2. Since the beginning of the Pleistocene Mediterranean maqui and steppes areas were prevailing in Western Palestine, whilst the extent of both these territories has mutually fluctuated.

3. The fauna of the Mt. Carmel caves is not a local fauna. All other excavations from Northern and from Western Palestine reveal the distribution of the fauna of every period all over that area.

4. The fauna of Palestine has undergone considerable changes during the Pleistocene. In many small mammals we find generalized and primitive characteristics at the beginning of that period, as compared with the recent species of the same genera or groups. Even the mesolithic and part of the neolithic gazelles show a very different aspect from those of our days. The three present species of Apodemus are represented in the Lower Pleistocene

TABLE 2

Correlation of the major climatic belts in prehistory (after S. A. Huzayyin).

Geological phase	Equatorial belt	Saharo/Arabian belt	Mediterranean belt	Northern belt
Recent	Very recent oscillations	Desiccation with minor oscillations		Cooling
	Makalian wet phase	Neolithic: warm(?), wet	Probably warm, wet phase	Warmest optimum
Late or Post-Diluvium	Dry	Desert conditions	Gradual desiccation	Transition
Upper Diluvium	Two Gamblias with drier interval	Pluvial II (2-3 submaxima), pretty cool	A pluvial phase with wet and dry subphases	Later glacials. Würm I + II.
Middle Diluvium	Interpluvial, with volcanic activity	Interpluvial. Dunes a.o. aeolic formations. Also volcanic activity.	Prob. dry interval with volcanic activity, at least during Monastirian transgression	Riss/Würm interglacial
Lower Diluvium	Kanesian pluvial, first rel. cool, then warm and rel. cool again. Major physiographic phase.	Pluvial I., first rel. cool, then warm and rel. cool again.	Sea regression cool and wet	Riss glacial
			Tyrrhenian transgressian, very warm water, prob. warm, wet	Riss/Mindel interglacial
			Sea regression, cool and wet	Mindel glacial
Prediluvium	Prepluvial	Prepluvial. Gradual oncoming of rel. cool and wet conditions	Milazzian and Sicilian phases, cold and cold waters.	Mindel/Günz interglacial Günz glacial

by vicariant more primitive forms of the same groups. A few 'recent' species, such as *Dama mesopotamica, Cervus capreolus, Microtus guentheri, Procavia syriaca,* lived in the country since the Upper Acheulean. Others, as *Spalax, Capra, Bos,* a.o. lived in this country for the same time, but perhaps in species differing from those of our days.

5. To which extent wolf, badger, marten, hare, and the other new forms of the Upper Levalloiso-Mousterian (Tabun B) are really late immigrants, and exactly at which date and from where they immigrated, or if they were present at an earlier period, must await elucidation by future research.

6. Also a reliable correlation of the climatic fluctuations to the faunal changes is still impossible at the present stage of our knowledge. Whilst the main faunal changes probably coincided with changes of the climate and were caused by them, only suggestions are possible at present.

1.3. EARLY MEN IN PALESTINE

1.31. LIFE AND HUNT OF THE MT. CARMEL MAN

Recent research (NEUVILLE, GARROD, BATE, KÖPPEN, STEKELIS, HUZAYYIN, ALBRIGHT, PERROT, a.o.) has made it possible to establish a fairly reliable chronology of early man in the Middle East.

The Lower Palaeolithic fauna included *Rhinoceros hemitoechus, Hippopotamus,* some wild cattle, camel wild horses and asses, the bear, (cave-) lion, porcupine, spotted hyena and striped hyena (*Hyaena cf. priscus*), leopard, red and fallow deer, gazelle, ibex, coney, vultures, rock partridge, owl, jay and doves (NEUVILLE 1934). Man may have appeared as long as 200.000 years ago in Palestine. The first settlers apparently belonged to the Pre-Neanderthal men, who followed the East-Asiatic *Pithecanthropus* of Java and China, who developed over half a million years ago. These older races have left no anthropological traces in Palestine. During the oldest and longest part of the lower stone age, the Chellean period, surface stations of stone artifacts have been found only, none of them in caves. The oldest cave deposits of human origin appear in Palestine (Mt. Carmel, Galilee) in the later Acheulean, here called Tayacian, about 150.000 years ago. The first of these discoveries was made by NEUVILLE in the cave at Umm Qatafa. ALBRIGHT (1940, p. 90) ascribes the penetration into caves to the harder climate of the Acheulean contemporaneous with the beginnings of the third glacial period of Europe. It is, of course, equally possible that at that date cave-dwelling Neanderthalians first settled in Palestine. The Acheulean was followed by the Micoquean and the Levalloiso-Mousterian. The skeletons of Mt. Carmel and of Galilee, estimated to date back at least 100.000 years belong to that period. At this time cave-dwelling had become a habit and so no conclusions may be drawn from this fact as to the climate of the period. The exemplary analysis of Miss D. M. A. BATE permits us to follow the main changes of the fauna on and around Mt. Carmel. The caves were inhabited by men. No big carnivores could have lived there together with them. Apart from the smallest mammals, such as mice and shrews, and from some bats, which shared the caves with man, most animal remains are of game animals, serving as human food. In some layers the bones are usually broken, as man delighted in their marrow. Gathered fruits and roots completed his diet. Fire was probably known since the oldest cave-dwellers and before.

The very comprehensive analysis of Mt. Carmel man by MCCOWN and KEITH (1939) showed that all mid-Pleistocene men of Palestine were of one type. This type, however, showed a much higher physical variability than is observed in any human population of our days, with many tendencies to and transitions from Palaeanthropic to Neanthropic man. The theory that this variability is due to hybridization is rejected, as no fossil remains of Neanthropic man from these layers have been produced together with true Palaeanthropic Neanderthalians. The tendency of the Mt. Carmel people to diverge into two types is also regarded as being due to an evolutionary divergence of Neanderthalian and modern man from a common human stock. It is therefore assumed that the Mt. Carmel people are not the actual ancestors of the Cromagnons, but Neanderthaloid collaterals or cousins of the ancestors of that type. The fossil remains of the real proto-Cromagnons will probably be discovered still farther to the east. It may be assumed that a progressive and conquering type of humanity evolved in western Asia in the remote times at which the Mt. Carmel peoples lived, and that, as their tribes increased in numbers and in strength, they pushed continually westwards, replacing and exterminating the native Neanderthalians. This is a reasonable explanation of late Pleistocene discoveries in Europe *). It may be pointed out that in the early hunter stage no prisoners were made in wars, as every additional mouth had to be fed. Slaves were made—that means a possibility for mass hybridisation—only since the early stages of agriculture and the existence of nomads with large herds. Before the dawn of history western Asia served as a nursery for Europe, sending out peoples, cultures and languages. This relationship between Asia and Europe goes back to the remote times, in which the Mt. Carmel men lived. Europe was the "Australia" of the ancient world after mid-Pleistocene times, and the people who colonised it, extinguished its Neanderthal inhabitants, just as the whites are now ousting the blacks of Australia. The difficulty of this assumption is the lack of genuine Neanderthal relics in Palestine, so far. The taxonomic position of Neanderthaloid men, as accepted by McCown and Keith, is:

Palaeoanthropus heidelbergensis	(Heidelberg man)
P. ehringsdorfiensis	(Weimar man)
P. neanderthalensis	(man of Düsseldorf and Chapelle aux Saints)
P. krapinensis	(Croatia man)
P. palestinensis	(Mt. Carmel man).

R. galilaeensis from Galilee is identical with the Mt. Carmel man. Among 111 characters of the bone skeleton of *P. palestinensis* we find the following evolutionary distribution:

Neanderthalian	16	14.4 %
Neanthropic	32	28.8
Intermediate	46	41.4
Indeterminate	13	11.7
Peculiar	4	3.6

This table shows a preponderance of Neanthropic Cromagnon characters. Yet, not all characters have the same value. The many Neanthropic characters of the limbs of the Carmel man, for instance, are to a great extent only functionally based, and thus taxonomically of little importance. Characters which are independent of functional variation have a much higher taxonomic value, such as certain dental characters (cusp arrangement of incisors, premolars, molars, etc.) Also characteristic is the very great number of intermediate characters. All this makes the inclusion of the Mt. Carmel man into either Neanderthal or Cromagnon man inadvisable.

Interesting are some conclusions with regard to the morbidity and mortality of Mt. Carmel man (Keith). No traces of caries of the teeth were found, and rheumatoid changes in the joints are almost wanting. The high mortality rate of Mt. Carmel man seems to be characteristic for all Palaeolithic men. Old age and physiological death was probably extremely rare. Among 12 Mt. Carmel individuals the age at death was:

in 4 individuals	between	4—10 years,
1	below	30
5	between	30—40
1	between	40—50
1	above	50.

---

*) This agrees with Weidenreich's analysis (1945) of the Peking Man where he expressed his astonishment to have found types of three different races in one family group, i.e. that variation was higher in early man than in recent man.

The fauna of the Mt. Carmel caves has already been discussed. A few remarks about game animals must be added. Fish apparently did not yet form part of the diet of our palaeolithic man. Fish hooks, harpoons, etc. and ample remainders of fish appear in the Aurignacian (SOERCEL 1922). Molluscs were apparently eaten (AVNIMELECH 1937). Birds have been hunted at least since the Levalloiso-Mousterian, as has been shown by Miss BATE (1927, p. 28) for the Mugharet el-Zuttiyeh in Galilee. Yet bird hunting to extensive degree may have begun much later. The absence of giants among the mammals may have two causes: either hunting them was too difficult or they were too heavy for transporting them into the caves. This concerns elephants, rhinos and wild cattle. That they were hunted, probably all in pits, as described by N. GLUECK, is certain. They were, however, not the usual game. Remainders of big carnivores are also rare or wanting, such as those of lion, leopard, bear, wolf and even wolfjackal. They all must have been living in the area, even if they do not occur in the caves inhabited by man. Only bones of hyenas are found more or less regularly. These animals may have entered the cave when it was temporarily aban-doned or, more probable still, when visiting the carrion of the hunters' game near the cave. The other big carnivores were apparently mainly killed in self-defence. Also wild horses and asses are rare and throughout the layers represented by some teeth only. Gazelles, fallows and red deer and, less common, wild pigs were the main game of Mt. Carmel man. The rarity of the roe deer and of the ibex at Mt. Carmel is astonishing, as they both are well represented in the cave bones from the Lebanon. The latter may have not found a suitable environment on the Carmel. Hartebeests are also rare. Still more astonishing is the rarity of bones of small mammals, such as hares. The main weapons for hunting gazelles and deer were spears with a wooden stem and with a stone head, and arrows, and stone axes for the final killing. The hunters must have been well organised and well acquainted with the habits of the game. And, of course, game must have been sufficiently abundant to make his existence possible. It was a hard life the Mt. Carmel hunter led. As with all primitive hunters there was no place to feed superfluous mouths. When the local population expanded, emigration became imperative.

N. GLUECK (1946, p. 3) in his charming book *The River Jordan* gives us a glimpse of a reconstruction of palaeolithic times, when men still lived, apparently all over the country, together with elephants, rhinos, hippos, warthog, spotted hyena, and others: "With mighty trampling down of reeds barring the way to the Jordan, some elephants burst through to the water's edge, waded into the river, and drank and played to their hearts' content. A bull elephant (*Elephas cf. trogontherii*) trumped loudly in lordly glee, and his harem swished about with gargantuan gracefulness. The baby elephants cavorted with all the abandon of the young. After a while, at the leader's signal, the massive beasts, sides glistening wet and tusks gleaming white and wicked, moved ashore. There they browsed contentedly in the almost impenetrable thickets of the Jordan Valley, through which their hulks had hewn recognisable paths. Suddenly one of them crashed through the cunningly concealed cover of a deep pit, and hurtled down to be impaled on sharpened stakes. With shrill cackling and cries of content there slouched from cover a band of hunters, who hacked at their thrashing victim with heavy axes and spears of flint and basalt, until finally it subsided in death. The entire scene could have taken place and probably often did occur in prehistoric Palestine. Elephants roamed about, not only in the Jordan Valley, but also in the highlands and plains above and beyond them as far as the shores of the Mediterranean Sea," from Bethlehem to Jisr Banat Yakub, and from Mt. Carmel to Nahariya.

BREUIL (1938, p. 67) and MENGHIN have suggested that there may have existed an early Palaeolithic age where bones and wood were more important than stones. They assume that these implements have been destroyed by wind and weather, except those preserved in the great loess deposits of China and those of the lower cave strata of the latter Palaeolithicum. Possibly this phase of 'animal stone' implements (BREUIL) was more pronounced in regions poor in good working stone. In Palestine, bone implements are found only from the Upper Palaeolithicum onward and far into the Bronze age. Proof of any such earlier "bone and wood" period is wanting for this country, which fact does not disprove its existence yet.

Almost all worked bones were fresh bones. Only teeth of boars and bears, etc. of fossilized or heavily decomposed animals were still worked up into pendants for ornament or for amulets. The following animal activities on fresh bones may be mistaken for human work: bones broken by hyenas, bones the end of which is gnawed at by wolves, or bones incised but not broken, by the nibbling of rodents. BREUIL (1938) describes the following early use of bone implements: Whilst very little is known about the use of the horns of the great ruminants, probably due to the quick destruction of cups from horns etc., when exposed to weathering, those of smaller ruminants were amply used in all periods. In the same way as some Mongols still use gazelle horns as daggers, after having been cut off from the skull, they were used over widely distant regions (from China to Palestine and on to Spain) during the Palaeolithicum. With small deer-antlers the pedicle was cut by stone implements, or the skull part still attaching was knocked off. More bulky antlers were cut up after being burnt or broken after being worked with the chisel. Some middle parts with the spongy parts scooped were apparently used as hafts. Cups from skull are known from various localities. Jaw-bones were sometimes made into tools or weapons (cf. SAMSON and the Philisteans, and MACALISTER's reconstruction of a flint-sickle arranged in a jaw at Gezer). The use of split long bones made into various tools, as well as of small bones, such as the ankle, tarsal, feet bones, the heel, etc. for all sort of purposes has survived far into history (cf. Gezer). In all historical periods all bone implements, ornaments and amulets are well polished. BREUIL also mentions a number of possible ways of using the big bones of the big game animals, such as for seats, working benches, etc.

1. 32. LIFE OF THE NATUFIANS IN PALESTINE

Whilst hitherto Egypt, Palestine and France showed a rather uniform cultural development, the civilisations of the upper Palaeolithicum show a cleavage between those of N. Africa and those of W. Asia and Europe. During this period the so-called tropical fauna definitely disappears, such as hippos and rhinos, elephants and warthog. The fauna includes bear, wild cattle, horse, red and fallow deer, gazelles, spotted hyena, wolf and leopard. The weather may have been slightly colder, but certainly drier. No human skeletons are preserved from this Aurignac culture (20.000 to 10.000 B.C.) anywhere in the Middle East. But a remarkable improvement of the arts and crafts took place during this period, from the production of much diversified flint artifacts to specialisation in hunting and fishing methods and tools, to the weaving of nets and mats, and even to early carving and painting. "In the Aurignacian age regular burials became customary and corpses were often buried with ornaments of shells, teeth and bone, as well as with flint tools and weapons and with red ochre for painting the body." (ALBRIGHT 1940, p. 92). But these people had not yet learned to sew leather, if we may judge so from the absence of awls and needles, and possibly they went naked when the weather was warm. We come to this highly probable conclusion from the contemporaneous experience in Europe. From then also date the first primitive female statues, of the steatopygous bushmen type, such as the Venus of Willendorf, obviously serving as amulets.

With the Mesolithicum, which lasted here from about 10.000 B.C. to about 5.000 B.C.

certainly no important climate or fauna changes took place. The Neanderthal man had definitely been replaced, still in the Aurignacian, by the Cromagnon and other races of *Homo sapiens*. We are now in the beginning of the Natufian culture, divided by NEUVILLE into four definite phases. This period is now usually made the starting point of archaeological research. NEUVILLE sets the early Natufian at about 12.000 years B.C., which is regarded by most prehistorians as slightly too early. ALBRIGHT (1940, pp. 93 ff.) describes the Natufians as a "small, slender, long-headed people, markedly resembling the earliest predynastic Egyptians and the chalcolithic men of Byblus. In other words, they belonged to a historical race, probably to the same race from which the Hamites and Semites in later times descended. The only marked difference is in stature and size of bones", which, as is well-known, depend on nutritional and other environmental factors as well as on genetical factors and the degree of amphimixis. The fine sickles point to a knowledge of how to grow wheat or millet, whilst the dog was apparently domesticated in the Upper Palaeolithicum. To this period some very important steps in the domestication of animal stock seem to belong, in the Indus-Ur area as well as in the northern area of the fertile crescent, even if the actual material about these early steps are still modest. We wish to mention here HEHN's thesis, now generally accepted, that primitive agriculture preceded animal breeding. Among the artistic achievements a fawn carved from bones is prominent, as are simple stone mortars and hollowed stone basins and simple stone constructions.

Most important was the discovery of the rock-drawings at Kilwa by NELSON GLUECK and by the HORSEFIELDS in December 1932 during an archaeological scouting tour. Kilwa is an old oasis, halfway between Akaba and Jof, about 150 km east of the former. Situated at the side of a small dry wadi, in a rough sandy plain covered with basalt pebbles and boulders and surrounded by the gloomy hills of Jebel Tubaik, the expedition found an ancient settlement with the ruins of a number of houses still standing. A cistern, a shallow birkeh and the remains of several wells indicated, how the small population of the site had obtained its water supplies during the year. Here there existed a monastic settlement probably about 1000 A.D. The entire number of inhabitants of this temporarily frequented oasis on important desert roads could never have been more than a hundred, and probably a good many less than that during the greater part of the year (GLUECK 1940). On a small Nubian sandstone hill, several hundred meters from the buildings, every smooth surface was covered with prehistoric rock-drawings, which had been completely overlooked by all previous visitors, Gertrud Bell included. Following the publication of this discovery the anthropological institute of FROBENIUS at Frankfurt, which specializes in rock-drawings, sent an expedition to the spot (RHOTERT 1938). The drawings, or better carvings, as they are carved out about 1 cm deep, 2-3 cm broad into the rock, belong to various periods, which are separable by the size, the style and patina of the figures. The oldest drawings were found on the hill just mentioned which is only about 30 m high and, which was called the "Horsefield Hill". Among this ancient group of drawing the ibex is the most common object. The drawings are 1.0 to 1.2 m long, usually occurring in strict profile only and showing a contour line with one fore- and one hindleg only and with one horn. The drawings show the naive intuition and the self-possession of so many earl, artists of the stone age. Occasional overlapping drawings belong to later periods. Other animals represented are: one giant piece of cattle; a wild cat (according to RHOTERT but, an ox according to HORSEFIELD and GLUECK; the long, raised tail supports the former interpretation, as does the short round head); two dromedaries done, in another manner than the many later camel drawings, a reptile, which is, however, interpreted by BREUIL as a leopard, and a hunting scene with dogs. It is a very poor fauna as compared to that represented on the rock-drawings of Little Africa. In spite of the unquestionable presence of a rich fauna consisting of wild asses, gazelles, probably antelopes, oryx, ostrich, hyenas, foxes, hares, wolves, jackals, etc., the ibex was the only main object of the artists of the older period. Often men, drawn at the same time with ibexes, have their arms raised, just as the adorers in many of the illustrations of Little Africa of this period. In later drawings the style is much deteriorated and has become childish, as in all later primitive art. Fig. 7, 1 shows us a very interesting scene: "Nostrils and neckline, horns rising and sweeping back gracefully from the head, then curving and tapering to sharp points touching the back, the foreleg lifted in movement, all these features bound together in a delicate yet strongly portrayed whole give the rock-drawing a vibrant reality, which seems somewhat strange in view of the thousands of years which have elapsed since it was first executed. The head of the ibex is raised, and from its mouth two lines stream, which may possibly be meant to represent streams of blood. If that is correct, we might have here a picture of a wounded ibex poised in flight" (GLUECK). Rhotert thinks that the scene represents the sacrifice of an ibex. As in most specimens the eyes are not drawn. On the back of the ibex we find a small human figure with the raised arms of the adorers. Yet this figure may possibly belong to a slightly later period. If RHOTERT's interpretation is correct, it is of utmost importance for the understanding of one of the many ways which lead to domestication. That the ibex could be caught alive is certain from the scenes where it is shown hunted by dogs. Such an ibex may have been kept for some time, until the day of the solemn sacrifice approached. Such keeping may have led to domestication in certain animals, whilst the ibex proved to be unsuited for this purpose. Another picture shows a female ibex with weak horns and a young ibex. Arrows in the body of various animals indicate that their being hunted was common, perhaps in addition to their capture for ritual purposes. Fig. 7,5 beautifully shows an ibex herd. In fig. 7,4 and 6 we find the figures of two dromedaries, which are by far the oldest representations of this animal. Their style differs considerably from the later camel figures. There is no direct indication of domestication and utilisation of these animals. The lack of riders or burders in two specimens does not prove, of course, that camels were not domesticated at that time, especially as the well-developed humps suggest domestication. The few unique figures of other animals are rather doubtful in their interpretation: one animal is regarded by RHOTERT as the wild goat (*Capra aegagrus*) without any justification. Behind the horns a weaker snake-line appears. Two smaller animals are determined as mungo and hare. This may be correct or not.

Of outstanding interest again is the giant figure of a piece of cattle (2.4 metres long). Whilst the rump is, as usual, in profile the head turns towards the observer, in order to show both horns. This en-face representation is ascribed by Frobenius to a magic conception. Underneath the animal is a man in squatting position, resembling those on the rock-drawings in Little Africa and in Spain. The arms seem to be crossed. Yet abbé BREUIL thinks that this scene represents a bull hunt and that the man is thrusting a spear into the side of the animal. It is difficult to decide on this point, as in side the animal an ibex in continuation of the arms of the man is drawn. The illustrations do not permit to decide if the man is holding a spear, or if he is in the usual attitude of an adorer. From a zoological point of view the appearance of wild cattle in this region would be quite surprising, whilst wild cattle may, of course, have lived at some distance to the north-west in the steppes and forests of Transjordan. In that case the artists must have been nomads. The presence of domesticated cattle in this desert oasis would also require a more humid climate. It may be that this actually was the case, as in the drawings of the latter period ploughs are represented.

We now come to the problem of dating these rock-drawings of the older period. GLUECK and RHOTERT assume that they began in the late Palaeolithicum, thrived during the Mesolithicum and ended before the bronze age. During all the time from about 10.000 B.C. to about 4500 B.C. these drawings were made. The main period of their origin is the Natufian I. All these determinations regarding their age are not only based on the style of the drawings, but even more on the determination of the coexisting implements, all superficial, as the excavations all remained without result. These implements permit a fairly exact fixation of their age. Yet M. STEKELIS, who had the opportunity of investigating into the flint implements of Kilwa, is definitely of the opinion that the oldest rock-carvings of Kilwa belong to the Lower Kilwian culture, reaching back to the early Neolithicum (6000 to 4500 B.C.). As STEKELIS is one of the best authorities on the stone implements of the Middle East, we have to accept his dating.

Between these old Kilwian rock-drawings and the younger ones there is a rather long interval. Glueck ascribes them to the Thamudic period in the 3rd century A.D. Some of them may be slightly earlier or slightly later. Many of them, however, are obviously associated with the Thamudic inscriptions of that period. As fig. 8 shows, the style has much deteriorated, their patina is distinctly different and the size of the animals rarely surpasses 10 to 25 cm in length. Mainly riders on camels or horses, lion, ibex, oryx are drawn. They are of the type so often found in early Arabic and Nabataean inscriptions in the Sinai mountains, and in those of Southern Palestine and Transjordan. Whilst Rhotert regards the style of the Natufian as definitely representing an impoverished derivation of the important African rock-art prospering from Fezzan to Spain, the later carvings are doubtless influenced by Asiatic sources.

Such relatively recent rock-drawings are mentioned, for instance from Transjordan, by R. Burckhardt. Also A. Alt (1935 p. 73) mentions rock-carvings on sandstone in large numbers from the Wadi et Tuwebe to the west of the Gulf of Akaba with Nabataean, Greek and Latin inscriptions. Men and animals, combatants on foot and on horseback, camels and ibexes are the object of the drawings. They correspond in technique to the later period of Kilwa and belong to the end of antiquity. Still later, of course, there are others which are contemporaneous with Arab inscriptions. The following drawings (Fig. 8, 8 and 9) from wadis in the Sinai mountains copied from drawings of the viscount Arconati and of Major, later Fieldmarshal, Lord KITCHENER represent this later Arabic period.

1. 33. THE DAWN OF AGRICULTURE AND HUSBANDRY IN THE NATUFIAN AGE

R. GRADMANN (1934) stressed the importance of the primeval landscapes of the Middle East for the origin of civilisation. Mediterranean forests, mainly composed of oaks, steppes, extending into Central Asia, and deserts, stretching from the Sahara to Sind (N.W. India), are spread over this area. These primeval landscapes have not changed their character (apart from disforestation in the Mediterranean territory) and distribution since at least the Mesolithicum. Fig. 9 illustrates these zones. This assumption is in agreement with the now generally accepted opinion, that no important climatic changes occurred in the Middle East in historical times. The so-called fertile crescent corresponds with the primeval steppe zone in Upper Mesopotamia, inner Syria and the tongues passing south through Palestine and Trans-Jordan. The steppe girdle is the primary zone for settlement. From here during many thousands of years the forest zone was made arable, beginning with the less dense fringes of the forest area. Cultivation was unable to enlarge the zone of steppes into the desert. Thus in the east the steppe remains the frontier of cultivated land.

F. RATZEL (1898, 1900) was the first to point out the importance of the steppes for the origin of civilisation. Hunters and food gatherers as well as early primitive agriculturists found a very suitable environment there. The ancestors of some important cereals, such as those of wheat (*Triticum dicoccoides, T. aegilopoides*) and of barley (*Hordeum spontaneum*) grow wild in the grass steppes of the Middle East. VAVILOV recently promoted the theory that the hard wheat has its home in Abyssinia, the common wheat in south-western Central Asia, because of the abundance of varieties of the cultivated forms in these regions. Yet wild wheat has, so far, not been found in any of these countries, but only in the steppes of the Middle East. The fertile crescent of the Middle East has thus a very good claim of having "invented" wheat and barley cultivation, whilst Vavilov's centres are secondary centres of cultivation only (GRADMANN p. 53).

In the steppes and along their borders lived gazelles, wild sheep and wild cattle, wild goats in the neighbouring mountain ranges. Wild apples, pears, almonds, a.o. grow wild on the borders of the steppe. And the primeval forest of the Middle East was never as dense and impenetrable as that of many other regions. The steppe permitted the creation of the "plough culture": Whilst man was still collecting and hunting, primitive ploughing and sowing of cereals permitted a first step in human settling down. E. HAHN has promoted the idea, that nomadism is a secondary development of primitive agriculture. The domestication of wild cattle certainly is only understandable in connection with ploughing. Ploughing remained, even until these days the function of the primary function of cattle in the primitive agriculture of this region, with milk production being a rare exception. It is quite acceptable to assume that sheep and goat were first domesticated by settled man. Steppe soil remains fertile without manuring, if it is kept fallow for a prolonged time. In the Anatolian steppe on the best soils crop rotation is applied by alternate years of crop and fallow. More usually two or three years of fallow are intercalated between the crops and on the worst soils one year of cultivation is followed by up to eight years of fallow. The possibility of irrigation from the big rivers of the steppes permitted and stimulated more intensive cultivation as well as the foundation of the first towns. The regulation and protection of the irrigation systems evoked a highly developed social organisation. The latest archaeological discoveries in the northern part of this steppe area show that everywhere these first settlements sprang up after 6000 B.C. Also the lowest layers of Jericho are not much later. Below these layers the spade of the archaeologist meets virgin soil showing no trace of building settlements. The seventh to fifth millennia B.C. were thus apparently a most decisive period in human history. They brought the dawn of history with the beginnings of early agriculture, of animal domestication and of permanent building settlements in their sequence. These early beginnings led in due time to higher developed cultures, which reached their climax in the big river empires of the Indus, the Nile, the Euphrates and the Tigris and the other rivers of Anatolia and Syria. All of them are now often regarded as successful derivates of one of the earlier stages of Upper Mesopotamian civilisation. In the train of these developments commercial interrelations with one another and later with the Far East brought new riches and stimulations, even if the traffic of the caravans was only going through the roding of forests opened possibilities for a more stable agriculture in regions with a better and more regular rainfall. Many fruit trees developed there, which were unfit for the steppe. Olive trees, vineyards and fig-trees were connected with the beginnings of this penetration. J. PARTSCH (1889) has shown that the distribution of the olive tree in the Mediterranean region remained almost unchanged since antiquity, and later evidence supports this view. The steppe had also a dominating importance for the oldest routes of trade. The Great Syrian Desert is real desert in its southern part. One ancient route only leads from Trans-Jordan through the big Wadi Sirhan to the oasis of Jauf. The central part of the Syrian desert is almost impassable as it is a large stone desert or hamada. But the northern zone of steppes, the Palmyrena or the Little Desert, is "liberally criss-crossed by routes which have connected the Mediterranean with Mesopotamia from time immemorial" (GRANT 1937, p. 36). This situation is of the greatest consequence. The oldest caravan routes led from Aleppo, in easy reach of the Mediterranean shores, in two days to Meskana on the Upper Euphrates, after that following the course of this river southwards. Another important route led from Damascus over Palmyra to Der ez Zor, continuing either through the Gezirah to Mosul, or to Hit; another one from Damascus over the Rutba Wells to Ramadi. More usual was another route to the north of this line. Rakka on the Euphrates was also connected with Palmyra. All these roads are within the steppe zone of the Syrian Desert.

Caravans in ancient times were animal caravans. For this steppe the words of HANDEL-MAZZETTI (1914, p. 58) are essentially true: "Even in the most desolated looking steppe always a more or less equally spread vegetation cover of the soil is found in high summer, which enables the bedawi to wander everywhere on their raids, without burdening themselves with food for their horses. In the north of Mesopotamia it is easy to find a water hole every day, even if it be a poor one." This holds also good in the Gezirah for donkeys as well as for sheep. Even today large migrations of nomads occur there in winter and spring. Huge migrations were seen there by us throughout April 1943, tribes migrating in small groups with camels, horses, donkeys and sheep. Some groups of the Abu Sleib, a peculiar ethnological group which performs for the bedawi camps and contains artisans also, travelled on donkeys only. The camel certainly is the superior beast of burden for long migrations. But in the steppe caravan traffic on donkeys is easy, at least for a number of months during every year. The traveller who visits the steppe during one season only gets one-sided impressions about the possibility of such traffic. Arguments that ancient oases like Palmyra (Tadmor) could never have been reached without camels, are erroneous. Traffic by camel is certainly easier. The camel couriers mastered the 900 kilometres from Damascus to Baghdad in nine days. Yet asses are still bred by the bedawi of this region. Miss GRANT (1934, p. 51) writes: „The early Assyrians who did not use camels, always moved around the Euphrates and did not venture into the desert at all; and asses, which were always used in the Cappadocian trade of the third and second millennium B.C., could only be used on desert tracks during exceptionally rainy winters, and then only upon a few of them. So from these facts, and the negative indication of inscriptions, it is inferred that camels were not known in Syria and the desert (read: steppe) before approximately 100 B.C. Then it was the Bactrian, two-humped camel which was first used in the desert (steppe). But the single-humped Arabian camels, which have been throughout the historical periods of transdesert trade, were not imported into Syria before the ninth century, or possibly not before the beginning of the eighth century B.C." We disagree with the opinion that ass caravans could and can pass the Palmyrena in exceptional years only, whilst probably being restricted to part of the year only. For a fuller discussion see Part II (Domestic Animals).

The opening of the sea-routes to India was the death-knoll to the important Eastern caravan trade. The high standard of agriculture was destroyed by repeated invasions. And the Arab settlers in these regions did neither know nor care to rebuild or to maintain the complicated irrigation systems (cf. JARVIS 1931, 1936; WOOLEY and LAWRENCE 1937), and contented themselves with a primitive agriculture.

II. ANCIENT ZOOLOGY IN THE MIDDLE EAST

2.1. ANIMALS IN THE LIFE OF THE ANCIENT MIDDLE EAST

It is unavoidable to give a short concentrated zoological survey of the animal species to which we refer again and again in our discussions. Only by accurate taxonomic determination we can hope to obtain a reliable analysis. For this short survey we gratefully acknowledge the valuable lead given by the monographs of H. O. LENZ (1856), O. KELLER (1909, 1913), D. VAN BUREN (1939), and many others. By dealing not too short with the mammals we had, of course, to be rather cursory in the survey of the rest of the animals restricting ourselves to the fauna of the Middle East and of the eastern Mediterranean countries.

2. 11. MAMMALS

A. Monkeys (Primates). The following monkeys were certainly known to the ancients:
a. The tailless (*Macaca sylvana = Inuus ecaudatus*) (as pithekes, simia) of N. Africa and Gibraltar. It is the monkey which appears in the oldest illustrations of the *Physiologus* and the fables of Aesop.
b. *Erythrocebus pyrrhonotus. E. patas* and *Cercopithecus callitrichus* (*C. sabaeus*) (as kybos, cercopithecus), all of East Africa, are found as mummies and on steles in Egypt.
c. The hamadryas *Papio* (*hamadryas;* as kynokephalos cynocephalus) was rather common in Egypt. It was often used in Greece as the prototype of the satyr. A Phoenician relief from Zimbabwa, the Biblical Ophir, is the only ancient representation of a monkey hunt, with hunter and dog.
d. The Indian hanuman *Presbytis* (*Semnopithecus*) *entellus* is found on reliefs, the long-armed gibbon (*Hylobates*) on figurines of ancient Mesopotamia.
e. The baboon (*Papio cynocephalus*) and the Anubis baboon (*Papio anubis doguerra*) were known in Egypt and Assyria. In Egypt they were the model for the hieroglyph *kafu,* possibly also for the Hebrew letter kof.

Many reports on the Indian and African monkeys became widely known since the Hellenistic period. Gorillas were discovered about 500 B.C. by HANNO of Carthage on his cruise to the western shores of tropical Africa.

KELLER (1909, p. 5) reports the following story from Iran: In the days of BALAS BEN BAHRAM, the Arsacid, some Jews rebelled and were transformed into monkeys, delivering their souls to the angel of death seven days later.

B. Chiroptera. Bats were well-known. Whilst their mammalian nature was well-known to the naturalists, since ARISTOTLE at least, they continued to be treated among the birds in popular natural history for a great many centuries to come. Bats were used as amulets. Thus the *Geoponica* (14 : 2) recommends a bat-head to be nailed on a dovecot in order to prevent the pigeons from leaving it. KELLER represents (1909, p. 13) such a charm in the shape of a bat-head from Egypt, belonging to the long-tailed bat (*Rhinopoma microphyllum*). It is quite impossible to determine the species from the literary references. Only where fruit-eating bats are mentioned, the Egyptian fruit bat (*Rousettus aegyptiacus*) is meant.

C. Insectivora. Shrews were deemed sacred in Egypt, probably because cats would not eat and kill them (cf. HERODOT 2 : 67,155). They belonged to a goddess at Buto. Many sarcophagi of sycamore wood with shrew sculptures above and shrew mummies inside have been found. Most of them belong to the sacred shrew (*Crocidura religiosa*), some to the bigger Olivier's shrew (*C. olivieri = C. gigantea*). Shrews are spared by the cat because of their musk-like odour. NIKANDER of Alexandria declared them to be poisonous. The "sweet scented" mice of ancient writers refer to the bisam shrew (*Pesmana moschata*) of the Irano-Turanian regions. Hedgehogs (*Hemiechinus auritus*, in Asia and S. Europe also *Erinaceus europaeus* in various subspecies, in Irak and Egypt also *Parechinus aethiopicus*) were regarded as a bad omen in ancient Egypt. Figurines of hedgehogs wer common in N. Syria and in Mesopotamia. OPPIAN (*Halieutica* 2 : 359 ff.) sings of its fight with snakes: "Such strife upon the dry land a serpent and a prickly hedgehog wage, when they meet in the woods; for enmity is their lot also. The hedgehog, seeing in front of him the deadly reptile, fences himself with his close-set bristling spines and rolls himself to a ball, protecting his limbs under his fence within which he crawls. The serpent, rushing upon him, first assails him with his venomous jaws, but his labour is all in vain. For despite his eagerness he cannot reach the flesh within his devouring teeth; so rough a pile surrounds the hedgehog who, like a round boulder, wheels his shifty limbs, rolling turn on turn, and falls upon the coils of the serpent and wounds him with the sharp arrows of his bristles; and here and there flows the blood and many wounds torment the serpent. Then the clammy snake girds the hedgehog all about with his circling coil and in the embrace of his grievous bonds holds him and bites and puts therein the strength of anger. Then swiftly all the sharp-bristling spines of the hedgehog glide into him yet, impaled upon the prickles, he abates not his effort, though fettered against his will, but remains fast as if held by strong dowels, until he dies; and often by his pressure he destroys the beast as well, and they become doom and bane to one another. But often, too, the dread hedgehog gets away and escapes, slipping from the reptile and his darksome fetter, bearing still upon his spines the flesh of the dead serpent."

All references to the S. European mole (*Talpa caeca*) are beyond our area. In Asia they almost all refer to the mole-rat (*Spalax spp.*), which fills the mole's niche there.

D. Carnivora. Many references to big carnivores are scattered over the text of this book. Here only a short summary. The long-maned African and the short-maned Persian lion *) (*Panthera leo leo* and *P. l. persica*) meet in the Middle East. The latter still lived during the 19th century in Irak. The black lions of PLINY refer to individual lions with black mane and black tail-tassel, not to a special race. The late Alexandrians invented a small, lion-killing animal, the *leontophonos*, as living in Syria, a fable widely accepted until the Middle Ages. When the hunters catch the leontophonos, they burn him, mix the ashes with meat and lay this bait along the runs of a lion. When the lion eats this bait, he dies immediately. The lion knows his deadly enemy and flees before him. But when meeting him he tries to kill him without biting him. Then the *leontophonos* squirts his deadly urine upon the lion. Famous was the tame lion of Ramses II. (DIODORUS SICULUS 1 : 48), who accompanied the king also to battle. DIODOR (3 : 43) also reports on the fertility of the Nabataean plains near Akaba: the pastures are so fertile, that not only all kinds of domestic stock, but also wild (*sic!*) camels, deer and gazelles live in abundance there. Flocks of lions, wolves and leopards often come from the desert to these pastures. The shepherds have to fight them day and night in defence of their stock. Thus, nature mixes the good and the bad, which it accords to man in this region.

---

*) Yet the African lion remains in Africa, the Asiatic one in Asia. In both there is a great variation. Fairly long-maned lions in Asia belong to *P. persica*, fairly short-maned lions in Africa to the African races. The size, extent and colour of the mane is not such an important character as was believed hitherto.

ALEXANDER'S general LYSIMACHUS once killed an enormous lion in Syria, who figures on all his coins. The same LYSIMACHUS was suspected by ALEXANDER of conspiracy. The king ordered to throw him before the wildest of his lions. The lion jumped upon LYSIMACHUS, who had rolled his toga around one arm. This he thrusted into the lion's mouth, holding his tongue and strangling him to death (JUSTINUS 15 : 3). And OPPIAN, the marvellous Syrian poet, sings (*Cynegetica* 3 : 129 ff.): "So also among wild beasts soaring lionesses and swift leopards and tigers of striped back stand forward to defend their children and fight with hunters, and for their young ones are prepared to die, joining issue with the spearmen face to face. In the battle for their offspring they shudder not at the advancing crowd of javelin-throwers, not at the gleaming bronze and flashing iron, non at the swift cast of shaft and shower of stones, but they are eager to die first or save their children." SILIUS ITALICUS (*Punica,* first century A.D.) gives some beautiful descriptions of the fighting lion or of a lion breaking into a farm, killing men and animals.

The tiger (*Panthera tigris*) has its nearest haunts in the Mazenderan, along the south-eastern shores of the Caspian Sea. It became known only during the 4th century B.C., mainly by Alexander's expedition. The Syrian king SELEUCOS sent one tiger as a gift to Athens (about 300 B.C.). All references from the Middle East concern imported animals. We are unable to decide if tiger hunts, perhaps in arenas, as represented on the beautiful hunting mosaics of Antioch, really took place in N. Syria. OPPIAN, much too little known, (*Cyne-getica* 3 : 340 ff.) sings about him: "Next let us sing the tiger of glorious form, than which the cunning nature has vouchsafed naught more pleasant for the eyes to behold amid the great company of wild beasts, as the peacock excels in beauty before the fowls of the air. Like a lioness of the hills wouldst thou behold it, apart only from the hide, which is variegated, with darkling stripes and brilliant sheen. Like are the eyes that lighten with fiery flash beneath the brows; like the body, strong and fleshy; like the long and bushy tail; like the face about the mouth; like the frowning brows above; like the gleaming teeth. Swifter is it than all wild beasts that are; for it runs with speed like its sire, the west wind himself. That is also an empty tale, that all this tribe is female and mates not with a male; for often mightst thou see its handsome spouse of many colors, but not easily couldst thou capture him; for he leaves his young and flees amain when he descries the hunters; but the female follows her cubs and in the anguish of her heart—to the great joy of the hunters—comes straight to the nets."

The leopard's (*Panthera pardus*) name pardos is supposed to be of Semitic origin (*barod* = spotted). He never occurred in Europe in historical times. FLAVIUS VOPISCUS (*De Probo* 19) describes how Emperor PROBUS (about 275 A.D.) arranged a great animal fight and display in the Circus Maximus at Rome. On the second day of this display first 400 Libyan leopards appeared, then 100 Syrian ones, 100 lionesses and 300 bears. Much earlier, however, leopards were sent from the Middle East to Rome. This is shown by the following interesting correspondence between Cicero (*Epistolarum ad familiares* 2 : 11, 8 : 9), then governor of Cilicia, to his friend CAELIUS at Rome. Letter: "My dear CAELIUS, I have given the strictest orders to catch as many leopards as possible in my province for the displays which you, as aedile, intend to give. Unfortunately only a few are to be found here, many more are found in Caria. Whatever I can get I will send to you". Answer: "My dear CICERO, I have asked you for leopards in almost everyone of my letters, but you have done almost nothing. PATISCUS sent me many more, including ten from Africa. Please, do me the favour and let some be caught in the neighbourhood of Cibyra, and write to Pamphylia, because there are more in that place". And again: "Do me a favour. You are always so kind, and you do not have to take more trouble than to write and to order. When you have caught some, give them immediately to the men, whom I sent you to feed them and transport them to Rome. If necessary, I will send more men."

The Libyan wild cat (*Felis silvestris libyca* = *F. ocreata* = *F. maniculata*) and the jungle cat (*Felis chaus*) were the wild ancestors of the domestic cat in Egypt (mainly the former), where their mummies, especially of the former, are often found on special hypogean cemeteries. They were successfully interbred with their own species as well as with the domestic cat. Also the caracal lynx (*Felis caracal*) is represented on old Egyptian monuments. Its ear-tufts are alluded to in the Egyptian-Arabic vulgar name *umm risha't* (mother of feathers). On the Marissa tombs we find these ear-tufts enormously exaggerated. On the same tombs we find the scene of a leopard hunt. All these cats occur in Mesopotamia. The cheetah (*Acinonyx jubatus*) was known and used as a hunting leopard by the old Assyrians and Egyptians. In Egypt it replaced the hyena-dog (*Lycaon pictus*), which held this place throughout the third millennium B.C. as an animal for hunting antelopes and gazelles. A beautiful sculpture of its head was found at Beisan. It was often used in the steppes and deserts of Syria by emirs and sheikhs for hunting the gazelle. We fail to understand, why OPPIAN does not mention this animal.

It is remarkable how rare ancient illustrations of wolves (*Canis lupus*) are in the Middle East. VAN BUREN (1939, p. 13) knows only one reference from Mesopotamia. Another has just been discovered on a remarkable old Aramaic amulet from the 7th century B.C. from N. Syria. A few wolves appear on the Roman mosaic pavements of Palestine. In Rome, as in Egypt and Greece, wolves were deemed sacred (cf., for instance, DIODORUS SICULUS 1 : 88, LIVIUS 3 : 29, 10 : 27, 21 : 46, 23 : 37, 41 : 9; PAUSANIAS, *Graeciae descriptio* 10 : 14). DIO CASSIUS (*Historia Romae* 69 : 15) tells about the Jewish revolt under HADRIAN: HADRIAN's general *Julius Severus* conquered the Jewish towns and fortresses. 580.000 Jews were killed in battles and in ambushes; many died from hunger, diseases and fire, so that Judaea was almost bare of inhabitants. This end was prophesied to the Jews before the war: the revered monument of SOLOMON burst suddenly and a pack of howling wolves and hyenas entered their towns. And OPPIAN reports (*Cynegetica* 3 : 282 ff.): "And if thou shouldst flay a wolf and from his hide make a sounding tambor, it alone of all sounds its deep note and it alone makes a din, while all tambors that had a goodly sound before are silent and hush all their noises. Sheep even when dead shudder at a dead wolf."

Jackal (*Canis aureus*) and fox (*Vulpes vulpes*), in Egypt also the smull desert foxes (*Vulpes rüppelli* and *Fennecus zerda*), with their enormous ears, are intermixed in the animal fable. Whilst all Greek and Roman fables refer to the fox, most of the animals mentioned in the tales of Palestine or Irak are jackals. The name fox was often retained when Greek fables were translated back into Oriental languages, whilst the oldest Oriental source had meant the jackal. It is difficult to distinguish between them in the few representations we have got of them, because of lack of care in details. The fox is sculptured on the Jewish tombs at Beth Shearim, the jackal on the old Arabic sculptures at Khirbet Mefjar. OPPIAN describes the jackal's catching (*Cynegetica* 4 : 212 ff.): "I have heard that with trenches and like devices men capture also the bold jackals and deceive the tribe of leopards; only with much smaller trenches, and they cut not a pillar of stone, but a beam of oak. And they do not hang aloft a kid, but a puppy, the privy parts of which they bind with thin straps. In its agony it straightway howls and barks, and its cry is heard by the leopards."

The striped hyena (*Hyaena hyaena*) was well-known, of course, but little represented. The spotted hyena (*H. crocuta*) the krokotos of the ancients, was known as an exotic animal only. It was nowhere regarded as sacred, but often as unclean. Certain organs of it played an important part in magic. OPPIAN (*Cynegetica* 3 : 262 ff.) says of it: "Mark also the dread saw-toothed, the weak-sighted hyena, the foe of dogs and mighty hounds, a night-farer and night-wanderer, since for it there is light by night but darkness by day. The hyena has the midst of the back arched and it is shaggy all about, and the dread body is marked on either side with close-set dark stripes. It is narrow and long of back and tail."—A valley of hyenas (*Ge Zeboim*) is mentioned in the history of Saul (cf. also JEREMIAH 12 : 9). And HIERONYMUS, who lived for many years in Palestine, translates the name of the monster in Threni 4 : 3 by *lamiae* (hyenas), following the translation of the Septuaginta. The genet, *Genetta genetta* is found in some Egyptian wall paintings.

The mongoose (*Herpestes ichneumon*) is often mentioned as an Egyptian animal since HERODOT, mainly as the cunny enemy of the crocodile and of its eggs. The marten (*Martes foina*) was called kunebi or stinking animal in Greece on account of its bad smelling, a quality also mentioned in the Babylonian Talmud and by RASHI. Its fur was much appreciated and bartered. It is still sold in large quantities on the fur market at Mosul. The weasel (*Mustela nivalis*) was sacred to the moon in Egypt. In Greece and Rome it was appreciated as a killer of mice, until it was, at a relatively late date, replaced by the domestic cat. In Spain it was used (STRABO 3 : 3) for hunting rabbits, and PALLADIUS (*De re rustica* 4 : 9 : 4) mentions that many people keep tame weasels against moles. The otter (*Lutra lutra*) is rarely mentioned, but a figurine of it is exhibited in the Palestine Museum of Archaeology in Jerusalem. The badger (*Meles meles*) and its southern cousin, the ratel (*Melivora capensis*), are likewise extremely little mentioned.

The bear (*Ursus arctos* and, to the south, *U. a. syriacus*) was well-known, of course. SOSTRATOS wrote a (lost) book about it in the first century B.C. On Egyptian monuments the Syrian as well as the Abyssinian bear appear among the tribute animals. But, in general, ancient bear representations are rather rare.

E. Rodentia. Little attention was paid to the graceful squirrel (*Sciurus anomalus*), described by OPPIAN (*Cynegetica* 2 : 586 ff.): I will also not go into the shaggy race of the feeble squirrel, which in the fiery season of midsummer erects its tail to shelter his self-roofed dwelling.

The beaver (*Castor fiber*) has only recently been finally exterminated in N. Syria and in Anatolia. Its fur and fat were used for medical purposes. The old fable of the self-castration of the pursued beaver, when hunted for its testicles, lead to the word castrate (treat like a castor). It was hunted at night with a torch in the hand. It fears fire and remains motionless, and can thus easily be caught (Anonymus MATTHAEUS, the Byzantine 54). The dormouse *(Glis glis)* was kept for its meat in Rome in special jars, the *gliraria,* just as we keep rabbits today. OPPIAN (*Cynegetica* 2 : 575 ff.) leaves "the tiny, tender, weakling dormice. These indeed remain with eyes closed all the winter season, drunk with sleep. Hopeless creatures! to take no food! not to behold the light! In their lairs, so deep asleep are they, they lie as dead and a wintry lot is theirs. But when the eyes of spring first smile and the flowers in the meadows newly bloom, they stir their sluggish bodies from their secret lair and open their eyes and behold the light of the sun, and with new delight bethink them of sweet food, and once more become alive and dormice once again."

The existence of representations of rats and mice from ancient Egypt is doubtful, whilst paintings of cats and mice form a common topic in late, Coptic art. Remainders of the rat (*Rattus rattus alexandrinus*) and of the porcupine mouse (*Acomys cahirinus*) have been found by LORTET and GAILLARD (p. 38) in Ptolemaean bird mummies *). These rats were

---

*) We still ignore the date of the first appearance of rat and mouse in Palestine. Miss Bate (1937) could none of the bones from our caves refer to them.

possibly responsible for the destruction of all leather on armour and weapons, which forced SENAHERIB to give up the siege of Pelusium (HERODOT, JOSEPHUS, ZONARAS), and in consequence that of Jerusalem. A few old Mesopotamian figurines of mice or rats are recorded by VAN BUREN (1939, p. 26). Housemice were well-known in Rome and Greece. And the same holds almost certainly good also for the Middle East (cf. AESOP, the Mishnah and the Babylonian Talmud). Or listen again to OPPIAN (*Halieutica* 2 : 135): "As a boy sets a guileful doom for greedy mice; and the mouse, not dreaming of the ambush of the trap, is driven within by the desire of the belly; and swiftly the hollow vessel claps to above him and, for all his endeavour, he can no more escape from the strong cover, till the body seizes and kills him, mocking the while his prey..." In the Middle East the wild ancestors of the housemouse are native (*Mus musculus praetextus* (= *genilis*) and *M. m. bactrianus* in the East). KELLER (1909, p. 203) points out that rats are first reliably known from a 12th century quotation of THEODORUS PRODROMUS, a Byzantine monk. Possibly it lived and arrived at an earlier date in S. E. Europe, but again the oldest mention of *Rattus rattus rattus* in Central Europe is from the 12th century, those of the bigger *R. norvegus* even from the 18th century. The home of the rat is Central Asia. Interesting and convincing is the complete absence of bones of mice and rats from the prehistoric mussel- and oyster-beds in N. Europe, and in the pile-houses of the lake-dwellers in Switzerland, both ideal habitats for them. The Latin word *murire* and the Greek *sminthein*, both for whistling, are both either onomatopoeic derivations or descriptions.

Very often however vole-outbreaks and complaints about them are mentioned. GUENTHER's vole (*Microtus guentheri*) in various subspecies, is the common vole of the Middle East it, being replaced towards the north-east by *M. socialis,* and in Egypt by the Nile field-rat (*Arvicanthis niloticus*). ARISTOTLE (*Hist. Anim.* 6 : 30) has given a superb description of vole outbreaks: "The phenomena of generation of the vole are most astonishing, both for the number of the young and for the rapidity of recurrence in the births. The rate of propagation of voles in the fields and the destruction that they cause, are beyond all telling. In many places their number is so incredible that but very little of the cereal crop is left for the farmer; and so rapid is their proceeding that sometimes a small farmer will one day observe that the time for reaping has come, and on the following morning, taking his reapers a-field, he finds his entire crop devoured. Their disappearance is unaccountable: in a few days not a mouse will be there to be seen. And yet in the time before these few days men fail to keep down their numbers by smoking them out and by unearthing them, or by regularly hunting them and turning in swine upon them; for pigs turn up the vole-galleries by rooting with their snouts. Foxes also hunt them, and in particular the ferocious ferrets, but they all together make no way against the prolific qualities of the voles and the rapidity of their breeding. When they are superabundant, nothing succeeds in thinning them down except the rain; but after heavy rains they disappear rapidly."

All over the Greek colonies of Asia we find Apollo Smintheus as god of the voles, since the times of Homer. He sends and takes off the summer heat and the voles. He is also connected with the plague. We find this Apollo Smintheus, for instance, on the coins of Alexandreia Troas, with bow and arrow in his left, with a mouse in his right. We should make it clear that neither ancient artists nor naturalists distinguished voles clearly from mice. Therefore we often find field-mice with long tails. In a few cases, where small mice climb up an ear of wheat or barley, the long tail indicates the tiny harvest mouse (*Micromys minutus*) on Greek coins. In Italy other field-mice (such as *Pitomys* a.o.) also occurred. We know some cases where the artist doubtless intended to represent a vole and figured a long-tailed mouse. The famous sculptor SKOPAS made a remarkable statue of Apollo Smintheus.

Aelian (12 : 5) tells us that the Delphi oracle ordered the Aeolians and the Troians to sacrifice to Apollo Smintheus so that he may liberate them from their vole plagues. The Philistines (I *Samuel* 6. 4 ff.) almost certainly referred to the same god or rather to his local variant, in connection with the return of the Ark of the Covenant. Interesting is a 'statement' of the '*Mirabilia Romae*' (35 : 31 p), that still at that time the golden mice and the golden buttocks were seen in Rome within the Ark of the Covenant, which TITUS brought to the capital.

Among the fables we may mention that in Egypt voles are born from the mud after the flooding of the Nile. This finds its echo in a remark of the Mishnah on mice that are half ment, half soil (Hullin 9 : 6). ANTIGONOS of Karystos and many others maintain, that the liver of the mouse increases and decreases in volume, just as the ovaries of the sea-urchin do, with the phases of the moon (KELLER 1909, p. 200).

Porcupine mice (*Acomys cahirinus*) and jerboas (*Jaculus jaculus,* or in eastern Egypt the bigger *J. orientalis*) from Egypt are mentioned by many Greek writers. Illustrations of the jerboa are known from Egypt as well as from Babylon. The mole-rat (*Spalax spp.*) as the Asiatic variant of the S. European mole (*Talpa caeca*) has been noted before. OPPIAN (*Cynegetica* 2 : 612 ff.) will not sing "a truth of the earthborn tribe of the mole-rats, eaters of grass and blind, albeit a rumour not to be believed has spread among men that the mole-rats boast themselves sprung from the blood of a king... But not even so did PHAETOON lull his wrath to rest, but speedily turned him into the race of mole-rats which were before not; wherefore even now the race remains blind and gluttonous of food."

A special (lost) poem was been devoted by CLAUDIAN to the porcupine (*Hystrix indica* (and *H. cristata* in the European area). Our OPPIAN (*Cynegetica* 3 : 391 ff.) sings of it: "Than the porcupines there is nothing in the shady wood more terrible to behold nor aught more deadly. Their size is like that of the bloody wolves; short, small, and strong is their body, but their hide bristles all about with rough and shaggy quills, such as those with which the cunning tribes of hedgehogs are armed. But when far mightier beasts pursue him, then he uses this device. He erects his shorp quills and backward hurls straight the dire shaft that bristles on his flying back, and both flees again and fights as he seeks to escape. Many a time he slays a saw-toothed dog; even so, one would say, shoots a man well skilled in archery. Therefore when the hunters espy him, they do not slip the dogs but devise a trick." — KALLIMACHOS of Alexandria recommends the Laconian dogs for finding the earths of the porcupine. A porcupine with erected spines is painted on the wall of the Marissa tomb. We also find it on a few Egyptian paintings.

F. Lagomorpha. The long-eared big Egyptian hare (*Lepus capensis aegyptius*) is often painted on Egyptian walls, the Iraqi *L. europaeus connori* is common on Assyrian reliefs and seals. *L. europaeus syriacus* is the most common hare of Syria and Palestine. The damage done by it to vineyards and vegetable fields was known in Greece. And often on the Palestinian mosaic pavements we find the hare feeding on grapes. On some Aegean islands, where hares were introduced, they developed into a terrible plague, just as the rabbits in Spain. Hare hunting by traps (cf. the Beisan mosaics), by nets and by dogs was very popular. OPPIAN talks much about hares (*Cynegetica* 1 : 165, 483, 514; 2 : 11; 3 : 86, 153, 460, 504; 4 : 35, 425).

The best description and biology of the common hare in antiquity has been given by XENOPHON (*Cynegeticus* ch. V.), of which we here give a few selected passages:

"7. From the steps which a hare takes in going to her resting place, there arises a stronger scent than from those which she takes in running away from it; for those which she takes in going thither are made at a slower and more hesitating pace, those which she takes in running from it, at a quicker pace; the ground is accordingly saturated with the scent of the one, but it is not even filled with that of the other. The scent is also stronger on woody than on bare ground, as the hare moving around and resting at intervals touches many objects.

10. As the hare reclines, it draws the inner side of the thighs under its flanks, puts as a rule the stretched out forelegs together, letting rest the chin on the tips of the feet and spreads the ears over the shoulder-blades. Thus it covers the soft parts of the neck which are also protected by the thick and soft hair.

11. When the hare is awake, it winks with the eyelids; but when it is asleep, the eyelids are raised and fixed, and the eyes continue unmoved; also, while asleep, it moves its nostrils frequently, but when not asleep, less often.

13. It is so prolific an animal, that when the female has brought forth, she is ready to bring forth again (*i.e.,* is already pregnant again), and may at the same time conceive a third brood. [Superfoetation of the hare, also known to ARISTOTLE *H. A.* IV: 5 has recently been confirmed by HEDIGER in *Physiol. compar. et Oecol.* 1. 1947]. The young hares give a stronger scent than the fullgrown, as they drag their still weak limbs all along upon the ground.

22. There are two kinds of hares: some are large and blackish with much white in their face, while others are smaller and somewhat yellow with little white.

23. Some have the tail varied with rings of different colours, others have a white streak along its sides. Some have greyish, others bluish eyes. In some the black spot at the tips of the ears is big, in others small.

30. The head is light, small, facing downwards and narrow in the forepart; the neck is slender, round, not stiff and of a proper length; the shoulder-blades are straight, and not contracted at the top; the legs are joined to them, light and well attached; the breast is not heavy with flesh; the sides light and symmetrical; the loins agile; the hams fleshy; the flanks yielding and sufficiently loose; the hips round, full everywhere, and separated above by a proper interval; the thighs long, of due thickness, tense on the outside, and not turgid within; the hind legs long and firm; the fore feet extremely flexible, narrow, and straight; the hind ones firm and broad; all the feet caring nothing for rough ground; the hind legs much thicker than the fore ones, and bending a little outwards; the hair short and light.

31. Accordingly to these parts the hare is strong, agile, and very nimble. For its nimbleness we have many proofs. When it goes along quietly, it proceeds by leaps, and nobody has seen it or will see it walking; but putting the hind feet in advance of the fore feet, and on the outside of them, it jumps forward. This is plainly seen by the marks which it leaves on the snow.

32. It has a tail which is not very helpful for speed, as on account of its shortness it cannot steer the body; yet the hare steers by the alternate action of the ears, continuing it, even when it is on the very point of being caught by the dogs; for, lowering one ear, and turning it obliquely on the side on which it is threatened with annoyance, it first sways itself in that direction, and then turns off suddenly in the other, and leaves its pursuers behind in a moment.

33. The hare is so pleasing an animal, that no one who sees it, whether when it is tracked and discovered, or when it is pursued and caught, would not forget whatever other object he admired."

G. Hyracoidea. The coney (*Procavia syriaca*), the *shafan* of the Bible, was described by HIERONYMUS, an early father of the church, as being as big as a hedgehog, like a mouse or a bear living in rock caves, and being common in Palestine. Also POLEMIUS SILVIUS and BADRIOS mention it.

H. Ungulates. KELLER repeats a common error in stating that wild horses were commonly depicted by the Assyrians. This is definitely incorrect. Our plate VII gives a good illustration of the Syrian onager (*Equus hemionus hemippus*), which easily explains how its horselike exterior led to such misidentification. All ancient authors praise the speedy feet of the onager. They were hunted and caught by lassos, or driven by means of heavy dogs. NICOLAUS of Damascus tells us about a hunt with bow and arrows. XENOPHON describes their meat as more delicate than that of deer. Many writers mention it from Anatolia. And OPPIAN (*Cynegetica* 3 : 179 ff.) writes extensively about it. Egyptian pharaohs hunted a North-African wild ass still late in the 2nd millennium B.C.

The deers of the ancient Middle East are the red deer (*Cervus elaphus*), still common in the Anatolian mountains, the fallow deer (*Dama dama* in Anatolia and *D. mesopotamica*), the latter, of giant form, from Mesopotamia to Palestine and still surviving in the Zagros mountains, the roe deer (*Capreolus capreolus*), still living in the Kurdish mountains, and SCHAEFER's fallow deer (*Dama dama schaeferi*) of Egypt. Most of the illustrations of them come from mountainous regions, such as Anatolia, Kurdistan, N. Syria, Assyria, Phoenicia, even from Samaria and Egypt. Apparently there is a grain of truth in the terrible enmity between deer and snakes, so often described by ancient writers (cf., for instance, OPPIAN, *Cynegetica* 2 : 233 ff.). XENOPHON (*Cynegeticus* 9) splendidly describes the hunt of deer. It is most conspicuous that the roe deer, whilst being the most common deer, is very rarely represented (cf. *e.g.* VAN BUREN 1939, p. 43).

The giraffe (*Giraffa camelopardalis*) was imported into Egypt after 2500 B.C., when king SAHEWRA brought it from Ethiopia or Nubia (BRUGSCH). It appears repeatedly in tribute scenes. HILZHEIMER (1926) assumes, that a number of early representations prove its existence in nature in Egypt in predynastic times. ARISTOTLE did not know the giraffe. A giraffe is found among the animals of the Marissa tomb. OPPIAN (*Cynegetica* 3 : 461 ff.) describes it: "Tell also of wild beasts which are of hybrid nature and mingled of two stocks, even the leopard of spotted back joined and united with the camel . . . . . Long is its neck, its body spotted, the ears small, bare the head above, long the legs, the soles of the feet broad; the limbs are unequal and the legs are not altogether alike, but the forelegs are greater while the hindlegs are much smaller and look as if they were squatting on their haunches. From the middle of the head two horns rise straight up, not horny horns, but feeble projections on the head which alongside the ears rise up between the temples. The tender mouth is sufficiently large, like that of a stag, and within are set on either side thin milk-white teeth. A bright gleam lightens from the eyes. The tail again is short, like that of the swift gazelles, with dark hair at the hinder end." The reader will agree that this, as almost every other description, which we have read and will read from OPPIAN of Apamea, is a very creditable kind of work, of powerful and plastic description and in most cases decidedly based on authentic knowledge. It is perhaps the most lively natural history of the mammals of the Middle East so far written. We stress this point especially, as OPPIAN of Apamea has often found unfavourable criticism by the philologists, who so far seem to have been almost his only readers, because of the Greek being poor.

The graceful gazelles (*Gazella gazella, G. dorcas, G. subgutturosa, G. leptoceras*) are extremely common in hunting scenes on reliefs, seals and paintings of Assyria, Egypt, N. Syria and often occur together with lions. KELLER (1909, p. 288, fig. 93 a, b) recognised the Tibetan goa (*Procapra pictivaudata*) with unhorned females and the sharp terminal curvation of the male horns on an old Assyrian hunting relief. The dama gazelle (*G. dama*) is rare on ancient Egyptian monuments.

The common oryx of the ancients is the sabre-horned oryx (*Oryx leucoryx*) of North Africa, less so the straight horned Arabian oryx (*O. leucoryx*) of the deserts and steppes of Arabia, Syria and Mesopotamia. The addax antelope (*Addax nasomaculata*) has only recently become extinct in Egypt, where it was hunted as well as kept in captivity after having been tamed. Another antelope (*Antilope cervicapra*), now restricted to India, abounds in old Mesopotamian representations, together with oryx and gazelles. The form of the horns suggests that even more than one form may have lived there. The N. African hartebeest or bubal antelope (*Alcelaphus buselaphus*) is often mentioned from Egypt and Libya, where it is extinct today (FLOWER 1932 p. 437). OPPIAN probably refers to this antelope (*Cynegetica* 2 : 300): "The antelope again is less in stature than the fallow deer: less than the fallow deer but far mightier than the gazelle: bright of eye, lovely in colour, cheerful of aspect. Straight from the head spring the long branches of its horns but aloft they bend again toward the back with curved points. Above all others doth this race love its own home and its accustomed lair and its dear dwelling in the glades. Even if hunters bind it with twisted ropes and carry it straightway to other regions and far away in the glens leave it there to its freedom, easily doth it come to the sweet home where it used to dwell and endures not to wander as a stranger amid aliens. Not then to men alone is their native land dear, but even in the hearts of the dappled wild beasts is instilled a desire of home."

The wild goat (*Capra hircus*), the ancestor of the domestic goat and still living in the Taurus, the Kurdish and the Cretan mountains, as well as the ibex (*Capra ibex nubiana*), which still survives in S. Palestine, the Sinai and S. Egypt, are both common on old monuments. Both are characterised by their goat beard. But as their different main characters, the more compact rump of the ibex and the different shape of the horns, are often badly neglected in the representations, it is often difficult to distinguish them. In Egypt as well as in the Kilwa rock-carvings, of course, on account of the zoogeographical absence of the wild goat this point gives no difficulty. They are common animals in ancient art everywhere throughout the Middle East. (OPPIAN, *Cynegetica* 2 : 338 ff.).

On the eastern high-plateau of Anatolia and of Armenia the arkal sheep, still inhabiting the Transcaspian steppes (*Ovis orientalis vignei*) abounded. It is the ancestor of all domestic sheep living now in the Middle East, as is the Asiatic mouflon (*Ovis orientalis*) still living in Persian mountains. A few of the Barbary sheep of N. Africa (*Ammotragus lervia*), still survive in Africa Minor. All of them are not uncommon in old representations.

The wild cattle of the ancient Middle East will be repeatedly discussed in the following chapters. Here we will just give the taxonomic arrangement of the wild and domesticated cattle of this region:

1. The arni buffalo (*Bubalus bubalus*) is well represented in some documents of oldest Mesopotamia and India, perhaps also of predynastic Egypt. Today it is restricted to India and the rest of the Oriental kingdom. The arni is the ancestor of the 'jamus', the domestic buffalo.

2. We may just mention the powerful N. African, now extinct, *Bubalus antiquus,* of whom many rock-carvings in N. Africa are preserved, as connection with the cattle from the Kilwa rock-carvings may be possible.

3. The gaur (*Bos gaurus*), another Indian kind of wild cattle, is mentioned here, because

HILZHEIMER has demonstrated its existence in early monuments from Mesopotamia, from which both the gaur and the wild arni disappear at a very early period.

4. The aurochs (*Bos primigenius*) is the most important kind of wild cattle of ancient days. It is the '*rimu*' of Assyria, the '*rem*' of the Bible, and even from Egypt ancient hunting scenes are preserved, which do not occur after the Old Kingdom. This is doubtless the wild ancestor of all our native cattle and the zebus, with the exception of the buffalo. It is rumoured that a few aurochsen may still be living in some remote valleys of the Kurdish mountains.

5. The wisent (*Bison bonasus*) with its rich wool on the front part of the body is marvellously modelled on a very old Persian sculpture from Susa, and bones have been discovered up to the Lebanon. He died out a long time before the aurochs. He is an inhabitant of forests, still living in the mountains of the Caucasus.

Undoubtedly, this abundance of species of wild cattle in the historical era is surprising, all traces of which have by now disappeared.

Elephants are amply dealt with in the text and will therefore be dismissed here (cf. also OPPIAN, *Cynegetica* 2 : 489 ff.). The Indian elephant (*Elephas maximus*) and the African elephant (*Loxodonta africana*) were introduced in a later period. The former lived in the swamps of the Upper Euphrates and perhaps of Antiochia until the beginning of the first millennium B.C. The Numidian elephant perhaps still lived in very early times in eastern Egypt.

The one-horned Indian rhinoceros (*Rhinoceros unicornis*) is found in old Indian reliefs of the oldest Indus-valley cultures. It appears only on two old Mesopotamian seals from about 2500 B.C., only to reappear on the black obelisk of SALMANASSAR. ALEXANDER's expeditions made it widely known throughout the Hellenistic world. A painting was found in the Marissa tombs. The oldest authentic description of the two-horned African rhinoceros (*Diceros bicornis*) is made by ATHENAIOS (5 : 201c), when describing the pompous animal procession of PTOLEMAEUS PHILADELPHUS in Alexandria. Later some were brought to Rome, where DIO CASSIUS (55 : 27) describes an arena fight between an elephant and an African rhino in 5 A.D. A counterpart of SALMANASSAR's Indian rhino is one of the African species in a relief at Pompeji (KELLER, 1909, p. 388, fig. 135), which competes in impressiveness with the famous drawing of DÜRER. OPPIAN (*Cynegetica* 2 : 551 ff.) describes it: "The (Indian) rhinoceros is not much larger than the bounding oryx. A little above the tip of the nose rises a horn dread and sharp, a cruel sword. Charging therewith he could pierce through bronze and with its stroke could cleave a mighty cliff. He attacks the elephant strong though it be and many a time lays so mighty a beast dead in the dust. On his yellowish, hairy brows and on his back dense spots show darkly. All the breed are males and a female is never seen. Whence they come I know not." We must also mention here the curious fact that the Alexandrine Jews, who translated the Septuaginta, rendered the Hebrew *rem* (wild cattle) into *rhinoceros*, perhaps under the impression of the early fables on the unicorn, through unacquaintance with wild cattle, and the impression left by the first African rhinos shown in Alexandria.

The wild boar (*Sus scrofa*), the wild ancestor of domestic pigs, of course, was common everywhere, except in the desert and the dry steppes. The wild form is apparently not represented by the ancient Egyptians, whilst some lively hunting scenes are preserved from ancient Mesopotamia. Its hunt was often sung by poets (cf. OPPIAN, *Cynegetica* 1 : 76, 309; 2 : 332, 457, 465). Many beautiful sculptures and paintings on mosaic pavements of wild boars exist from the Greek to the Byzantine periods.

The hippopotamus (*Hippopotamus amphibius*) was well-known from and in Egypt, where it was exterminated in Roman times because of its ravages on the field. Howevei, it only disappeared in the 12th cent. A.D. The Biblical word *behemoth* does not refer to the hippopotamus, but is a general expression for beasts (H. TORCZYNER). DE VAUX (1946, p. 109) reports it from the Orontes about 1500 B.C. It was moderately hunted in Egypt by harpoons since old times. DIODORUS SICULUS (37 : 35) describes such a hunt: Many people unite for the hunt of a hippopotamus. They surround it on boats and thrust harpoons with barbed hooks into it. A rope is connected with each harpoon, which they let loose until the hippo has bled profusely and looses its strength. The meat is hard and difficult to digest, the intestines uneatable. The Carthaginian Hanno also discovered the pigmy hippopotamus (*Choeropsis liberiensis*) on his famous cruise to the shores of W. Africa (500 B.C.).

I. Whales and other marine mammals. Among the marine mammals the following are the common ones found in the eastern Mediterranean Sea and on its shores:
1. The monk seal (*Monachus monachus*; *Phocidae, Pinnipedia*).
2. Among the dolphins (*Cetacea, Delphinidae*) the most common are the common dolphin (*Delphinus delphis*), so often figuring on pottery, mosaics and figurines, and less common the bottle-nosed dolphin (*Tursiops truncatus*). To the same family belongs the sword whale (*Orcinus orca == Orca gladiator*), the orca of the ancients.
3. Among the pot whales (*Cetacea, Physeteridae*) the sperm whale (*Physeter catodon*) is apparently by far the most common—if that term can be used for such rarely occurring animals—on the shores of Palestine.
4. Among the finn whales (*Cetacea, Balaenopteridae*) the common *Balaenoptera physalus* is found.
5. Among the sirenes (*Ungulata, Sirenia, Dugongidae*) the Red Sea dugong (*Dugong dugong*) is still found in the Gulf of Akaba, where it has, however, grown rare as compared to 150 years ago, when most of the sandals of the eastern Sinai peninsula were made from its skin. The skin of the dugong with its definite mammae and the posterior body in fish shape, gave repeatedly rise to rumours and tales about mermaids.

K. Some remarks on the unicorn. Since ancient times mention of a strange mammal with one frontal horn has been made and many qualities, such as ferocity are, ascribed to it. Since the end of antiquity this unicorn was invested with more and more fables, its body being composed of that of many animals. Similar, definitely mythical, complex creatures with, for instance, the trunk of a lion, the tail of a scorpion, the wings of an eagle, with a scaly neck and bearing one horn on the middle of its forehead, were depicted in ancient Mesopotamia and Iran.

The oldest figures of unicorns are found on seals of Mohenjo-Dare in India. They refer to an antelope with a single horn, curving forwards and upwards. HUTTON (1946) remarks: „The practice is not unknown in the Himalayas of doctoring the horns of sheep, causing two horns to grow into one. I suggest, that the Mohenjo-Dare antelopes were black-buck treated in this way." Recently a similar operation was successfully done by Dr. DOVE in Maine on a calf (cf. LEY 1938). RIDDLE (1946) adds that not any of the small kinds of Indian antelopes, but possibly the saddle-backed Sudanian antelope *Onotragus megaceros* was intended by the artist of Mohenjo-Dare.

Perhaps the oldest mention of a unicorn in literature is that by CTESIAS in his book on India (early 4th century B.C.), who mentions speedy wild asses with a single white and black horn on the forehead, 60 cm long, from which drinking cups are made. ARISTOTLE mentions unicornous wild asses and oryx, and STRABO a horse-like unicorn with the head of a stag. We will discuss in another place that the unicornous aurochsen of ancient Mesopotamia were not intended as representing the animal as unicornous. The reliefs in soft stone usually show both horns, whilst on hard stones the horn was depicted on one side only, the ear on the opposite side. The recent tendency (SCHRADER, ABEL, ANTHONIUS), based on these monuments, to identify the unicorn as aurochs must be rejected.

The present unicorn tradition begins with the Septuaginta. The Alexandrine Jews translated the *rem* of the Bible with *monoceros,* the rhino, of which at that period the first specimens were shown in Alexandria (cf. *Job* 39 : 9 ff.). SAMUEL BOCHART supposes the *rem* to be the oryx. This determination has also found modern supporters, who claim that the profile of the oryx when seen in nature, does not permit to see the two horns apart. *Daniel* (8 : 8) mentions also a goat with one horn on its forehead. We do not intend to follow here the various fabulous unicorns which extend from the *Physiologus* to the end of Mediaeval times, when the unicorn-horse was brought into the British arms. Many may have been the prototypes of such unicorn tales: from the rhinoceros and its ancestor, the *Elasmotherium* of Siberia, to a one-horned oryx, which RIDDELL (1946) saw in Kenya, or the Nilguru (*Boselaphus tragocamelus*; cf. RIDDELL pl. II, 6) which he proposes as an alternative, the tales of all these unicorns, even if supported by partial evidence, being all fabulous.

2. 12. BIRDS

For the birds of antiquity we can refer, apart from KELLER, to the excellent monograph of THOMPSON (1936): *A glossary of Greek birds.* The Egyptian birds will be treated separately. The unfortunate loss of OPPIAN's *Ixeutika* (On bird catching) has been only partly made good by the preservation of a prose extract by DIONYSIUS (quoted here from LENZ 1856 as OPPIAN, *De aucupio*).

A. Birds of prey. The big and the small rapacious birds, and certainly most of the smaller birds, are usually represented "too conventional to permit of any conjectures as to their species" (LAYARD) and very often even to their family. This is essentially true for the Mesopotamian documents, but MOREAU says even for Egypt, that "nothing is more tantalising than the lack of precision with which the ancient Egyptians depicted the *Accipitres.*"

Since oldest times from Mesopotamia to Egypt, eagles are connected with royalty as royal symbols on sceptres, steles, etc. CTESIAS (fr. II ed. MÜLLER) reports that the Indians hunt hares and foxes with eagles. Two-headed eagles, first found in old Mycenaean pottery, developed in the Byzantine era into the well-known two-headed heraldic eagle. From old Sumerian and Hittite figures of lions with eagle wings still more complex fabulous monsters composed of four or more animals, the griffon or gyps developed. Eagles were considered to be divinatory birds. Thus CICERO (*De divinatione* 1 : 15) tells us about the Galatian king DEJOTERUS, how he asked the advice of birds before everything he undertook. Once he was saved by an eagle, which admonished him to return immediately from a travel. He later heard that the room where he was supposed to pass the night, had fallen-in which would undoubtedly have killed him.

The osprey (*Pandion haliaetus*) excels among the water birds on account of its strength. Thus OPPIAN says (*De aucupio* 2 : 1): He is similar to the land-eagles, but gains his food from the sea, mainly fishes coming to the surface. He is not always successful. A big fish, into whose back the osprey clawed, may eventually take his enemy with him to the depths where he is drowned. They say that the osprey be land-eagles, expelled by its parents and bred by other birds. The fishermen take him to be a good omen.—KELLER (1913, p. 12) also refers to the osprey in the old Egyptian lore. As the bird of the sun-god Ra, he not only with his large and beautiful eyes spies on the fishes in the depth of the waters, but looks straight into the sun, without being blinded.

Falcons were sacred in Egypt. The common kestrel (*Falco tinnunculus*) is the most common among the falcon-mummies. HERODOT (2 : 65 ff.) says that whoever kills, intentionally or by accident, a falcon or an ibis, must die. The dead falcons are mainly brought to the town Butes. DIODORUS SICULUS (1 : 87) explains why they are considered sacred in Egypt: Some say because it is useful for killing scorpions, horned vipers, and such; others because of its importance as a divinatory bird, and again others say, that in old times a falcon brought a book to the priests with all the religious rituals accurately registered. OPPIAN (*De aucupio* 1 : 4, 5) says of them: the falcons are often so lazy that they let themselves be fed by others, or—for want of better—catch frogs. Other falcons hunt larks and swallows. They often suffer from their eyes which they know well how to heal by smearing the milky sap of wild lettuce over the eyes. Kites (*Milvus spp.*) are most impudent, flying almost into the hands of man. The punishment for their impudence is the appearance of gout at a certain age. They are said to have been created by the gods out of sinning men.—HERODOT (2 : 22) reports that the kites do not migrate into Egypt, which happens to be essentially true. Falconry originated in India. It was apparently a royal sport in the 7th century B.C. in Assyria (B. MEISSNER). A number of superb falcon sculptures, mainly from Egypt, are preserved. HORAPOLLO (1 : 7) records this bird, sacred to Ra, also as soul-bird. This statement is supported by drawings on mummy bandages.

As contrasted with the other birds of prey, the vultures on Egyptian monuments are easily to divide into the bearded vulture (*Gypaetus barbatus*), the black vulture (*Aegypius monachus*), the griffon vulture (*Gyps fulvus*) and the Egyptian vulture (*Neophron percnopterus*), the two last ones being most common.

The bearded vulture or the lammergeyer is, according to OPPIAN (*De aucupio* 2), rarely seen, as he inhabits the roughest rocks, building his nest high up within caves, and liking to perch along the brim of precipices. He is deeply devoted to his young, and when these are stolen, he refuses to take food or to leave the nest, crying like a woman and shedding tears. Feathers grow dense on his chin, forming a kind of beard. Thereby he is easy to distinguish from other birds. He devours stones and bones of animals dead since long. He eagerly devours whatever he can swallow; what is too large for him, he takes with his claws high up into the air and lets it drop on a rock, until he has smashed it into devourable pieces.

PIETSCHMANN regards the vulture cult as one of the oldest in Egypt. It should also be pointed out that vultures were by no means despised in antiquity. In ancient Mesopotamia, especially in earlier ages, the vulture, as also in Egypt, often took the place of the royal eagle. The Bible shares this appreciation (EZEKIEL, for instance). The old stories about kindness and compassion of vultures to their young have also be connected with one of the vulture names in Hebrew *(racham, from rachem*: compassion) [1]. The antagonistic coupling with the scarabaeus, so often found in Egyptian art is referred by THOMPSON to the fable that all scarabs are males, all vultures females.

Three groups of owls can be distinguished on ancient coins and in other documents: the eagle owl (*Bubo bubo maximus* and *B. b. ascalaphus*), scops owl and long-eared owl (*Otus scops* and *Asio spp.*) form the second, rarely represented group, but occurring on a few coins of Tyre *e.g.* Most common of all is the little owl (*Athene noctua*), in the south sometimes replaced by the barn owl (*Tyto alba*). In Egypt it was a soul bird (BRUGSCH). This, and

---

[1] Prof. B. MAZAR points out, that *rachem* for vulture and for compassion are different words, as the Assyrian *remu* (compassion) corresponds to the latter only.

its howling, in the night perhaps added to its being considered a bad omen. In Greece it was sacred to the goddess Athene. HORAPOLLO (2 : 51) and others mention their use in catching small birds. The scops owl is apparently the *kos* of the Bible (Psalmi 102 : 6, LXX). To this also most of the report about the *nyktikorax* refer, a small part of which means only the night heron (*Nycticorax*).

B. Paroquets (Psittaci). The early mention of paroquets by *Aristotle* is apparently spurious. The earliest mention is from CTESIAS, a Greek physician at the Persian court in his interesting book on India (about 400 B.C.). ALEXANDER's generals apparently brought the first specimens of the rose-ringed paroquet (*Psittacula krameri = Palaeornis torquatus*) with them. They appear in the famous animal procession of PTOLEMAEUS II at Alexandria (ATHENAEUS 9 : 387d). The rose-ringed paroquet, a beautiful green bird with narrow pink collar, is widely spread in India and in Africa from the Sudan southwards. Recently it has been succesfully acclimatized in the Nile delta (MEINERTZHAGEN I, p. 346). To all appearance, Alexandria was in late antiquity, the main market for these paroquets. Perhaps a few other species of the same genus were known during the Roman empire, when these birds grew increasingly popular. In the later legends of the Middle East, from India to the Arab countries, the paroquet plays an important part. In the Persian Paroquet Book, the Tuti Nameh, a paroquet even plays the leading part. OPPIAN (*De aucupio* 1 : 10) warns against keeping paroquets in wooden cages, as they will destroy these, but advises to keep them in iron ones. And the poet Statius mourns over his dead paroquet, looking at its silver cage, now standing empty.

C. The cuckoo and the wood-pecker group. Woodpeckers (mainly *Dryobates*) have found little references, whilst it was known that they feed on insects, hewn from beneath the bark of trees. The wryneck (*Ynx torquilla*) was held in high esteem. APOLLONIUS (1 : 25) describes how four golden wrynecks were suspended from the ceiling of the hall of justice in the royal palace of Babylon, reminding the king of Nemesis, and warning him against vanity. OPPIAN (*De aucupio* 1 : 20) states that sorceresses have a special preference for the wryneck. This bird seeks his food with its long tongue, extending it towards ants. The ants think it to be food, bite into it, and are swallowed (which observation is right).

The common kingfisher (*Alcedo atthis*) with his shining feathers was much more widely known than its more modestly clothed cousins, the Pied and the Smyrna kingfishers (*Ceryle rudis* and *Halcyon smyrnensis*). OPPIAN (*De aucupio* 7) sings of him: No man can name a bird of more lovely voice than the kingfisher's, and none is more beloved by the gods of the ocean. They take even care, that the sea is quiet whilst he breeds. The sea-gods love the kingfisher, who has been transformed from ALCYONE, whilst she mourned excessively over her drowned husband. The kingfisher loves the sea so much, that he nests on its shores and builds his nest from marine weeds. They are of melancholic disposition and when ending their song, call a few times: *ceyx, ceyx* (CEYX was the name of the drowned husband of ALCYONE). But I would not for myself or for anybody else wish to hear their voice, as it indicates bad luck, disaster and death. Therefore Zeus has taken care that the kingfisher flies at night for his food and far from men.

Quite a number of legends has been built up in the Middle East around the hoopoe (*Upupa epops*). We hear, how king SOLOMON dealt with it. KELLER (1913, p. 62) has tried to trace the hoopoe as the source of the widely spread legend of the Shamir: The stink about his nest arouse early suspicion that in this way he might try to hide valuable riches. For the care of the parents by their children, turned into moral by the *Physiologus* (fourth command!), we find a source in HORAPOLLO (1 : 55): The old hoopoes are taken beneath the wings of their children to warm them; that the young help the old birds during their moulting by extracting the old feathers, etc. Again (*idem,* 2 : 92), loud calling of the hoopoe is regarded when occurring during the critical period, as a good omen for the vine harvest. The same story is told about the cuckoo. Both these birds have often been confused in antiquity, for instance in the legend where the cuckoo, instead of the crested, *i.e.* crowned hoopoe, became king of Egypt and Phoenicia. THOMPSON derives its unclean status in Jewish law (*duchiphath*) from antagonism to its sacredness in Egypt.

The egg-parasitism of the common cuckoo (*Cuculus canorus*) was well-known in antiquity. The beautiful bee-eater (*Merops apiaster*) and its feeding on bees were likewise known. The Anatolian Pseudo-ARISTOTLE describes it as making its nests in soft (*i.e.* non-rocky) slopes, into which it burrows holes up to four ells long, in which six to seven eggs are laid. As soon as the young are old enough, they leave the nest to the parents, which they provide with food.

D. *The singing birds* (*Passeres*). The figures as well as the descriptions of the small birds are usually hopelessly "conventional". Any attempt to accurate identification is hopeless, in most cases because the author never intended to refer to a special species, but to small or singing birds in general, even when applying an apparently specific name. THOMPSON (1936) and KELLER (1913) have sifted and compiled an enormous documentation with relatively poor results. Bird-catching was widely spread over the areas of the Mediterranean and of the Middle East, mainly for procuring birds for the table, to a small degree for keeping singing as pets. Both these aims are farcically combined in the anecdote of some new rich man of Rome, who bought the most expensive singing nightingales (*Luscinia megarhynchos*) to put them on his table as food. And good singing nightingales were very expensive at that time, more expensive than the price of good slaves. The old legend of PHILOMELE and ITHYS with its spring mourning points to the Asiatic Adonis cult. THOMPSON gives a number of further references of the connection between Adonis, the spring mourning and the nightingale (*aëdon*). OPPIAN (*De aucupio* 1 : 117) praises the natural gift of the nightingale for singing. The nightingales take much care of the musically gifted among their children, whilst killing the mute ones. They implant a deep love for liberty into their young, so that these will never sing in captivity. It should be mentioned that in wide parts of the Middle East the *bulbul* (*Pycnonotus capensis, P. leucotis*) replaces the nightingale in popular legend.

Thrushes, such as *Turdus merula, T. philomelos, T. pilaris,* were caught in huge quantities by nets and many other traps. Snares were laid for them usually from December to March (PAUSANIAS 8 : 17; OPPIAN 3 : 13). VARRO (*De re rustica* 3 : 5 : 1 ff.) describes large houses specially built for fattening thrushes. The common sparrow (*Passer domesticus*) was known in ancient Greece and Egypt (KELLER 1913, p. 88) as invading fields in big swarms and picking the seeds from them.

Larks, wagtails, finches, pipits, etc. are barely mentioned in ancient documents.

E. *Starlings and crows.* Starlings (*Sturnus vulgaris*) were likewise known as serious destroyers of seeds. A special fable is devoted to this terrible activity by BADRIOS (fable 33). About the Seleucid or locust birds (*Pastor roseus*) we shall give many references later on (see p. 40). HELDREICH says that in modern Greece they are called *hagiopouli* when migrating in spring on account of their devouring locusts then, but *diabolipouli* on their autumn passage, when they devour grapes.

Ravens (*Corvus corax, C. umbrinus*) and crows (*C. corone, C. cornix*) were both of high divinatory importance. Often both are not well distinguished. CICERO (*De divinatione* 1 : 39 : 85) holds ravens flying to the right, crows flying to the left to be good omina. LIVIUS (7 : 26), VALERIUS MAXIMUS (1 : 4) and others give many crow omina of historical events. AELIAN (6 : 7) mentions a monument for a crow in Egypt, which served king MARRES by speedily transmitting letters to their destination. On Assyrian monuments ravens and crows fall in swarms upon the dead on the battle fields. They are believed to have guided ALEXANDER through the desert to the temple of Amon. And the reference to the raven and the dove in the history of NOAH seems to be an old reference to the use of these birds by sailors, who took them on board their ships and used them as guides to the nearest land, as these birds were supposed to smell land. PLINIUS (*Hist. Nat.* 6 : 83) still reports this usage from Toprabane (Ceylon). BASILY (*Hexaemeron* 8 : 6) takes up the old Greek legend about the excessive love of the crow for its children (in contrast herewith the "raven-mother" of Europe), which well may serve as example to men. When the young fly out, the parents accompany them and provide them with food. Males and females live in strict monogamy. When one partner dies, the other remains in widowhood for the rest of its life. Therefore, says HORAPOLLO (1 : 8, 9), two crows are used in the hieroglyphs to designate matrimony. A few splendid crow sculptures have been preserved. We further mention the black and blue jay (*Garrulus atricapillus*) of the olive-groves and the jackdaw (*Corvus monedula*).

OPPIAN (*De aucupio* 1 : 7, 8, 15; 3 : 18, 19) sings of this group: KORONIS, the mistress of Apollo, once sent her servant KORAX to bring water. As KORAX was much delayed, Apollo transformed him into a black bird with crevices in his beak, from which the water which he wants to bring to his young flows away.—The jay is very apt to imitate other voices. I once heard one bleating like a kid, then as a calf, then as a sheep; finally he whistled like a shepherd who calls his flock to the water.—Olives are put into snares to catch crows and jays. Also jars filled with oil are put in places which the crows visit. When they look into the oil, they—seeing their own image—think they see another crow, and jump into the oil to go to their friend. When they have fallen into the oil, they try to flee from it, but as they are covered with oil, they cannot fly and are easily caught in that way.

F. Swallows and flycatchers. The arrival of the swallows, mainly of *Hirundo rustica*, but also of *Delichon urbica* and of *Riparia riparia*, was supposed to coincide with the arrival of spring. In Rhodos and Samos it was followed or preceded by groups of children passing from house to house, singing songs on the spring and on the swallows. The leader of this boy-choir was dressed in a garb, black on the back, white on the front, and holding a clay swallow in his hand. Fragments of the songs of these 'chelidonistai' have been preserved (cf. SAPPHO fr. (52) 88, ATHENAEUS 8: 360c), such as:

> The swallow comes, comes, good weather
> and good years bringing with it,
> white on the belly, black on the back.
> Won't you give us some figs
> from your rich stores?
> A small cup of vine, small basket of cheese,
> and of wheat?
> The swallow also a cake
> won't refuse.
> Shall we go? Shall we accept?
> When you give, we will go; when not we will insist,
> We will even take with us the door or the upper threshold,

or your good wife from within.
She is small, and easily will we remove her.
When you give us something, don't let it be little.
Open, open the door! Don't send away the swallow!
We are no old men, as you see; by God, we are boys!

Similar songs are still sung by boys in Greece on the first of March and in some parts of Russia. The swallow is seen in Egypt all through the year, but never stays to build its nest at Daulis (PAUSANIAS 10 : 4, 9). At Byblos in Syria, Isis the protectress of domestic happiness and of matrimonial love, was changed into a swallow (PLUTARCH, de Iside et Osiride, 15p). In Greece the swallow was connected with Aphrodite, the protectress of the women departments (harem). How commonly it was for swallows to nest on houses can be seen from the rule of the Pythagorean free-masons to keep their houses free from swallow nests, and in this way make themselves recognisable to foreign visiting brethren. An old *Physiologus* of Smyrna shows us swallows rousing farmers early in the morning to go to their work. Of the swifts (*Apus apus, A. melba, A. affinis*) BASILY (*Hexaemeron* 8 : 2) says: Few birds only are weak on their feet, and unable either to walk upon them or to use them for catching their prey. To them belong the swifts. Of the flycatchers (*Muscicapa striata, M. albicollis*), the delight of the Roman gourmets, we are informed by BECHSTEIN that Cyprus, whilst under Venetian rule, annually exported 1000 to 1200 jars of pickled flycatchers to Venice.

G. Doves, fowls and quails. Much is said about these birds among the domestic animals and on quails and partridges in special chapters. About doves we read in OPPIAN (*De aucupio* 3 : 12): The wood pigeons (*Columba palumbus*) are very shy and difficult to catch. They are taken by the following ruse: when the birdcatcher sees them perching on a tree, he spreads his net on the soil, covering it with loose chaff, puts on it some captive and blinded wood pigeons, ties a thread on their feet, hides in a hut made of branches. Then he pulls on the threads and causes thus his decoy-birds to flutter. The wild wood-pigeons fly close to them and the bird-catcher, pulling his cord, closes his net upon them. Rock doves (*Columba livia*) are caught in the same manner, but easier still by snares. Turtle doves (*Streptopelia turtur*) are caught in spots where they come for drinking. The bird-catcher there puts a tame turtle dove as decoy bird, puts a clapnet beside it, and thus allures and catches them.

The rock partridge (*Alectoris graeca*) is the game bird *par excellence*. In the old Mediterranean calendar illustrations we find July as its main hunting season, expressed by a cage with the decoy partridge. OPPIAN (*De aucupio* 7) reports them to be caught by snares or by a deer hide. The hunter crawls into the deer hide, slowly approaches the partridges. These are much pleased to see their friend, come close up to him, and perceive their error only after they are caught in a snare or in a net. Partridge-fights, today still the Kurdish national sport and still practised in some Aegean islands, were extremely popular. AELIAN (4 : 1, 13) says that the good fighter and the loud calling cock lets himself easily be caught, as he knows that he is taken not for food, but to enjoy men by his call and by his fighting. Females are kept close to the place of the partridge fight in order to stimulate the fighting cocks.

The francolin (*Francolinus francolinus*) is described by ALEXANDER of Myndus (ATHE-NAEUS 9 : 388) as slightly bigger than the partridge, somewhat more reddish brown than the colour of red clay. They are easily caught by the hunters because they are plump and have only short wings. They wallow in the dust, have many chickens and feed on seeds. They are said to have been brought from Lydia to Egypt, where they were turned loose in the groves and thickets. Their voice is similar to that of the quails. In times of flood and famine they do much damage to the fields, until boys are sent out crying: Thrice woe to the malefactor!

The quail (*Coturnix coturnix*) will interest us later as having been the food of the Israelites in the desert. DIODORUS SICULUS (1 : 60) tells us how they are caught on the Egyptian coasts, just as today, in long nets. Under the name of 'xennion' the quail was potted and pickled in large quantities in ancient Egypt. Quail fights were extremely popular as they still are in China and India. An Egyptian governor of AUGUSTUS killed and ate a victorious quail, but was quickly struck by retribution. Whilst the old Greeks and Romans apparently did not eat this bird, quail fights, a game called 'quail striking', and quail pets were rather popular. In Phoenicia the quail was held to be the bird of Herakles-Melkath and burned alive as a sacrifice to him. In Greece the quail was dedicated to Artemis, whose holy town Ephesus was called Ortygia in old times. OPPIAN knows (*De aucupio* 1 : 26; 3 : 9), that the quails leave their country, fly over the sea, but fear the view of the sea so much that they shut their eyes before it. Therefore they fly against the sails of ships and are easily taken by the sailors then. As they do not see during their flight, but want to know how far they have travelled, every quail takes three small stones in his beak, and drops them at certain intervals, listening if they fall into water or upon land. When they hear that they have fallen on land, they come down and rest.—Quails are caught in nets, to which they are either allured by decoy-quails in cages, or by being driven, through the movement of a scarecrow towards the net (cf. chapter 712).

H. The ostrich (*Struthio camelus*) lived until recent times in all deserts of the Middle East, from Upper Egypt to N. W. Mesopotamia. In both these regions it was hunted. Assyrian cups from ostrich eggs have been exported in very ancient times as far as China and Etruria. These artful cups must have represented a high value. This bird still lives in parts of Arabia, and stragglers are still occasionally entering Transjordan. In 1940 we obtained an egg from Kerak (given to Dr. O. TYCHO by a local sheikh, and Dr. N. GLUECK received another one from J. TUBEIK near Kilwa). Apart from the eggs, which were also eaten—we see them offered as a tribute from Libya for the table of the pharaoh—the feathers were highly appreciated ornaments for royalty, priests and for selected riding-animals. In the time of Roman decadence the bird served as food. Thus HELIOGABALUS once had 600 ostrich heads served at one banquet, for their brains were regarded a delicacy LAMPRIDIUS the biographer of HELIOGABALUS, adds the curious remark: The emperor offered roast ostriches not unfrequently at his banquets, pointing out that this food be prescribed in Jewish law (i.e. in contradiction with the truth). As hieroglyph the ostrich indicates justice and truth. HORAPOLLO gives an explanation of this: as all feathers of the ostrich are equally long (without preference). Fans of ostrich feathers were highly appreciated. Ostriches before chariots and ostriches as riding-animals remained curiosities. A lioness killing an ostrich is seen in a relief of the theatre of Hierapolis in Syria. We give OPPIAN's description in another place. XENOPHON (*Anabasis* 1 : 5 : 2, 3) met them in the Syrian desert, west of the Upper Euphrates: there were no trees, but various wild animals. Most abundant were wild asses, there were also many ostriches, bustards and antelopes. The horsemen of our army sometimes hunted them. The wild asses, when any one pursued them, would dash forwards for a considerable distance, and then stand still, and again, when the (slower running) horse approached, they did the same. It was impossible to catch them, unless the horsemen, lining up at intervals, kept up the pursuit with a succession of horses. The flesh of those that were taken resembled venison, but was more tender. No one succeeded in catching an ostrich. Those horsemen who hunted that bird, soon desisted from the pursuit, for it far outstripped them in its flight, using its legs for running, its wings as sails. The bustards may be taken, when they are suddenly startled. For they fly but a short distance, like partridges, and soon tire. Their flesh was very delicious.

The ostrich is not mentioned in *Job* (39 : 13-18): H. TORCZYNER has recently shown that this passage is a distorted version of an old Aramaic animal fable (on the raven). The old Syrian *Physiologus* deals with the ostrich: the ostrich looks to heaven to see whether the time has come to lay her eggs. She never lays them before the rise of the Pleiades, the time of the greatest heat. She lays them into the sand and covers them with sand. Then she goes and forgets about them; the sand latches them. If the ostrich knows its time, how much more can this be expected from man in a spiritual sense: we shall look towards heaven, forget the earthly matters and follow Christ.

OPPIAN (*Cynegetica* 3 : 482 ff.) describes its size as huge, so that it can carry a young boy on its broad back. The legs are long, like those of the sluggish camels, and are arrayed as it were with close-set hard scales up to the double thigh. Small is the head that it rears on high but long the hairy dusky neck. They have abundant feathers; yet they do not sail aloft in the high paths of air, but as they run swiftly, they have equal speed to the flying birds. Nor do they mate like birds by mounting, but, like the Bactrian camel, rear to rear. It lays a huge egg, of size to hold so great a bird, armed about with stony shell.—But OPPIAN (*Halieutica* 4 : 620 ff.) refers to another well-known story about the ostrich: As in the woods the antelope, when the ravenous lion attacks it, turning down its head protects itself with a vain defence and hopes itself unseen, till the deadly beast rushes upon it and rends it, it does not lift the head and still whilst perishing thinks to escape. Such foolish device also does the winged bent-necked ostrich of Libya; but its craft is vain.

1. Grallatores and Limicolae. Common birds of game in the steppes are the houbara (*Chlamydotis macqueeni*) and the small bustard (*Otus tetrax,* rarer *O. tarda*) and in the deserts the stone-curlew (*Burhinus oedicnemus*) and the courser (*Cursorius cursor*). OPPIAN (*De aucupio* 3 : 8) mentions the great preference of houbaras for horses. Nets are placed in suitable places with a narrow path between them, through which a single rider slowly passes. The houbaras, seeing the horse, follow it with spread wings and are all caught.

The crested lapwing (*Vanellus vanellus*) is often represented on old Egyptian monuments as a common soul bird. The Egyptian plover (*Pluvianus aegyptius*), also the little ringed plover (*Charadrius dubius*), belong to the "many crocodile birds which enter the mouth of the gaping reptile and clean its teeth" (MEINERTZHAGEN 1930, p. 528). This is the trochilus of the old writers. Many birds distinctly represented on ancient Egyptian monuments will be mentioned in a special paragraph on the old Egyptian fauna.

The common crane (*Grus grus*), and rarer the demoiselle crane (*Anthropoides virgo*) were kept in flocks in Egyptian farms. In the paintings of the tomb of Ti they are seen to be crammed. They probably scarcely produced in captivity, but were replenished by newly captured ones. MOREAU (1930, p. 68) thinks that they were ousted from popular favour in later times by the guinea fowl. HESIOD praises the crane as the reliable announcer to the farmer, when the time of ploughing has arrived (*Opera et dies* 5 : 446). OPPIAN (*De aucupio* 2 : 17, 3 : 11): When the cranes want to leave Thrace, one of them passes them in review, gives the sign for the departure, but he remains behind, alone. The oldest birds are flying in the foremost ranks of the flight, fearing they would be tired, if the young were in front and were flying too speedily. They also often cry out, that none of the swarm may get lost. When one is tired, he is supported by the wings of two other cranes or carried on the back or on the legs, as these are extended backwards in good weather. Before night they hurry to river islands and come down. There they feel safe, as wild beasts either cannot cross the river, or would wake them by the splashing of the water. All cranes sleep standing on one leg. The guards and leaders are always patrolling, and call out immediately when man or beast approaches them, and all take to flight. Cranes are caught in different ways. For instance, a gourd may be made hollow, smeared on its inside with bird-lime, and a beetle which begins to hum is put within. The crane hears the humming, approaches, puts his head into the gourd, catches the beetle, but the gourd now sticks to his head and smears his eyes. Helpless, he remains standing on the spot and is easily caught. If no beetle is at hand, take the leaf of an onion and put it into the hollowed gourd. Cranes are also easily captured, when suspending a bean behind a snare. He puts his head through the snare when taking the bean, but is caught when trying to retract his head. Whilst he tries to fly away, the bird-catcher takes him.—On Delos a certain annual festival was connected with a crane-dance. Crane-fights (among the males only) were also popular, but less common than those of other fowls.

The white stork (*Ciconia ciconia*) was, from old Egyptian times to those of HORAPOLLO (2 : 58), the early fathers of the church and the *Physiologus,* a symbol filial compassion and gratitude. ARISTOPHANES *(The Birds* v. 1353) even states that an old law orders the storks that, as soon as they can fly, they must provide for their parents. In AESOP's fables it appears as the pious bird. And this agrees with its Hebrew name (*hassidah,* the pious). As a destroyer of snakes it was honoured in Upper Greece. Its occurrence on Egyptian monuments remains doubtful. MOREAU (1930) excludes it from his list. And KELLER's (1913, p. 194) documents actually refer to cranes.

The sacred ibis (*Threskiornis aethiopicus*) is, of course, the ancient Egyptian bird *kat' exochen.* It was common in the times of HERODOT's visit to Egypt (2 : 75 ff.), was still not uncommon during NAPOLEON's expedition, but has since disappeared together with the papyrus swamps. MOREAU (1930, p. 66) and LORTET et GAILLARD (1905, p. 173) point out that the bone measurements of the ibis mummies indicate that the Egyptian ibis was different from the form still living in the Sudan. It was sacred to Thoth (the Hermes of the Greeks) and to Isis, the god and the goddess of the moon. FLAVIUS JOSEPHUS (*Ant. Jud.*) remarks on its tameness. An explanation of its sacredness as to its usefulness is futile, as e.g. DIODORUS SICULUS (1 : 87) does in stressing its destruction of snakes, locusts and caterpillars. The annual fight between the ibis and the flying serpents of the legend is regarded by THOMPSON as a symbol: the annual return of the ibis to Egypt coincided with the flood of the Nile, which puts an end to the hot winds and to the sand-storms. Considerable elucidation of the ibis problem has been given by MOREAU (1930 p. 67). He recognised the Hermit ibis (*Comatibis eremita*) in some hieroglyphs by its red beak and head, as well as by the loose mane of feathers. HERODOT's (2 : 75, 76) description of one of the two species of the ibises which fight the flying serpents, one species being "all over deep black, legs of a crane, its beak is much curver, and it is about as big as the landrail", doubtless refers to this bird. R. LANCASTER (1910 p. 124) even suggests quite unnecessarily—that the flying serpents were really locusts. The cliffs and ravines on the hills to both sides of the Nile are fit for the breeding of these birds from rocky hills and mountains, which feed on insects, snails, lizards and serpents. This bird, hitherto unrecorded from Egypt, was seen by MOREAU in migration near the Giza pyramids in early May 1921. The discovery of the Hermit ibis as a breeder on the cliffs of the northern Syrian desert by J. AHARONI in 1912 helps identification as well as interpretation considerably. This also removes the old misunderstanding that the glossy ibis should be the black ibis of the ancients. This black ibis was *Comatibis.*

The many species of herons and egrets were much hunted in Egypt. A boat with a tame Egyptian goose as decoy bird entered the papyrus thickets. A boomerang-like piece of wood was thrown at the birds. Often a *Genetta genetta* was taken in the boat for retrieving the prey hit. The Hebrew word anaphah seems to be identical with the Greek *anopaia* (THOMP-SON). OPPIAN (*De aucupio* 2 : 8): The herons are loved by man. They announce the weather in summer and winter. Before a storm they lay the head on their breast and turn it toward the side from which the storm approaches. No sailor will ever kill a heron: For what the predatory land birds show to the hunter the herons show that to the fishermen. At the beginning all birds ate the same food, but the herons first invented the art to gather food from the water. They have much boasted about this invention, and even boasted to swim better than Poseidon. The angry god has deprived them in punishment of the power to swim. Therefore the herons must fish for ever, standing along the shores, whilst other birds joyously dive after fishes. But the herons catch fish quite aptly: They always stay in such direction that the approaching fish does not see its shade. There are numberless species of herons. Some are short and white, others bigger and multicoloured, others of medium size. Some have a tuft of feathers on the head, others do not. All seek for food in the sea, but nest on land.

The landrail (*Crex crex*) is as big as a turtle dove, long-legged, small and timid. The Septuaginta interpreted *slav* (= quail) as landrail (ATHENAEUS 9 : 393). The purple gallinule (*Porphyrio poliocephalus*), and in Egypt the violet gallinule (*P. madagascariensis*), belong to the most graceful birds of our regions. They are often represented in mosaic pave-ments in Palestine, in mural paintings in Egypt. It was regarded as of lofty moral and great vigilance. The best source for this ornamental bird of imperial Rome was Syria Comagena (PLINIUS, *Hist. Nat.* 10 : 63). OPPIAN (*De aucupio* 3 : 21) describes its capture: To catch the purple gallinule, no bird-lime, no nets are needed. When it sits alone, the bird-catcher ap-proaches it dancing. The delight of the bird in dancing is so great, that it stays where it is, the dancer coming closer and closer. It even begins to dance itself and is thus caught. The beauty of this ornamental bird is sung by Aelian (3 : 42): The purple gallinule is a very beautiful bird... Men love it and feed it carefully. It fits well into rich, beautiful houses, and in temples it promenades freely. Gourmets slaughter the beautiful peacock, but I know of no man, who has slaughtered the gallinule for food.

A long row of flamingos (*Phoenicopterus ruber*) is exhibited on a predynastic jar from Egypt (KELLER 1913, p. 212, fig. 80). Their tongue was considered a delicacy in decadent Rome. The species has only recently ceased to breed in Egypt, but we have noticed them breeding in the Toz-Gölü in C. Anatolia, and have seen flights of this graceful and beautiful bird near Cyprus. A Carthaginian relief of two flamingos flanking Astarte suggests a relation to this goddess (KELLER 1913, p. 210, fig. 78).

L. Natatores. Two species of swans, the mute swan (*Cygnus olor*) and the whooper swan (*C. musicus*) occur in the Middle East as passing migrants, the former also breeds in Greece. A calendar mosaic at Carthage announces its arrival in November. OPPIAN (*De aucupio* 2 : 19) states that swans look for their food in humid meadows and on shores. The echo of their songs resounds in mountains and valleys. They are the best musicians among the birds, and sacred to Apollo. Their song is not sad, but lovely and sweet as the tunes of flutes and harps. They are strong opposing even eagles, when the latter attack them or their young. But the swans never fight, if not forced. They love peace still more than food. They sing early, before the rise of the sun, believing that their voice sounds farther, whilst everybody still sleeps. They also sing on the shores of the sea, except when storms or the roar of the waves are so loud that they could not hear their own song. Also when old, close to death, they won't forget to sing. But then the song is weaker, as they cannot extend their neck or expand their wings any more. Before death they seek a lovely spot, where no other bird and no other swan can hear it, because they would think that they will also die. ATHENAEUS reports (*Dipnosophistae* 9 : 49) that also roasted swans were served. ALEXANDER MYNDIUS states to have observed some dying swans, but never heard them sing. And THOMPSON (p. 107) remarks: Modern naturalists accept the story of the singing swans, confirming that though the mute swan cannot sing, yet the whooper swan can. It is certain that the whooper sings, for many ornithologists state the fact, but I do not think it can sing very well; at the very best, 'dant sonitum rauci per stagna loquacia cygni'. He thinks that the swan-song still hides some mythological allusion. The famous naturalist P. PALLAS (1811, II, p. 212 ff.) states that many whooper swans are tamed in Russia because of their song, whilst the mute swan is little estimated. "His voice has a lovely sound, like silver bells. He also sings in flight, and is heard at a far distance. Also the tradition of the dying swan is no legend: The deadly wounded swan, expelling the air from his trachea with his last breath, produces song-like sounds". The special anatomy of the trachea of the whooper swan was first described by Ulysse ALDROVANDI (1602 *Ornithologia* III : 19 : 5, 6). Beautiful sculptures of Leda with the swan have found their way all through the Hellenistic world. A very good relief from the 3rd century B.C. was even found in the ancient Jewish cemetery of Beith Shearim. In Phoenicia Astarte is connected with the swan.

The wild geese are winter visitors coming to our regions, mostly in small numbers: the grey goose (*Anser anser*), the bean goose (*A fabalis* = A. Segetum), the white-fronted goose (*A. albifrons*) and three species of barnacle geese (*Branta bernicla, B. leucopsis, B. ruficollis*). They are common in beautiful Egyptian paintings and some are also seen in Palestine mosaics. OPPIAN (*De aucupio* 2 : 18, 3 : 22): The geese, as the cranes, have leaders in their flight, put out guards, and call without interruption. But their voice is detestable. When they want to be silent they take a stone in their mouth. They easily forget the places of ample food, and therefore wander and roam about without interruption. They benefit from it in so far as it is not easy for the bird-catcher to capture them.—Duck and geese are taken by snares and nets, into which they are allured on river shores by barley and other cereals. Also the following ruse is used to catch them. The bird-catcher carves a wooden goose and puts it on the water. The wild geese aggregate around this wooden goose and pick with their beaks at it, as it looks strange to them. The hidden bird-catcher pulls the wooden goose closer and closer to the shore. The wild geese follow until they are under the nets, which suddenly clap above them and pursued as well as pursuers are caught.

The Egyptian goose (*Alopochen aegyptiaca*), the foxgoose or *chenalopex* of the Greeks, breeds all over Africa, and still in Upper Egypt, and a few occasionally visit Palestine in winter. According to HERODOT (2 : 72) they were sacred to the Nile god. Its hunt is often depicted. They are supposed to take good care of their children. Thus HORAPOLLO (1 : 53) explains its significance as a son in the hieroglyphs. When a man approaches the family, the parents show themselves to the hunter and lure him away, until the young have had time to hide, and then they fly away.

Many species of ducks, most of them very common winter visitors, are represented in Egyptian wall paintings and in Palestine mosaic pavements. From early Sumerian times to late Assyria, and widely spread in Syria, duck weights, in series from tiny to very heavy ones weighing two talents, were in common use together with similar series of lion weights. The head is turned over the shoulder of the duck and pressed against its back. A number of ointment boxes from the 2nd millennium B.C. in the shape of a graceful duck with turned head have been found in Syria and Palestine. In Cyprus and Rhodes old jars in the shape of ducks were possibly related to the cult of Astarte-Aphrodite [1]). In Egypt the Nile god Hapimoou takes a bundle of hunted ducks as a tribute to Ra. The identification of the commonly depicted species will be given in various places. The legendary Diomedian birds are recognised since LENZ (1856 p. 411) as the common shell-duck (*Tadorna tadorna*).

M. Some other water birds. The pelican (mainly *Pelecanus onocrotalus,* also *P. crispus*) is little known until it enters the symbolic legends of the early fathers of the church; as feeding or reviving its young with its own blood. HORAPOLLO (1 : 5) tells: When their nest is surrounded by dry dung and this is set on fire, the parents fly into the fire, trying to extinguish it with their wings. But the fire grows and the singed birds are easily caught. Out of respect for this parental sacrifice the Egyptian priests do not eat its meat, which is freely consumed by the common people.

The cormorant (*Phalacrocorax carbo,* rarer the pigmy cormorant *P. pygmaeus*) is repeatedly depicted in Egypt and Palestine.

About gulls (*Laridae*) between the many species of which it is even difficult to distinguish in our days, we find in OPPIAN (*De aucupio* 2 : 4): The gulls are confiding in man and treat them as friends. When the fishermen draw in their nets, they fly around them, calling for their share. The fishermen throw them some fish, which is speedily devoured together with those which escaped from the net. They are believed to have been men, who invented fishery. Transformed by the gods into birds they retained their predilection for towns and harbours. Some gulls are white and similar to small 'divers', others are larger and with a thick cloth of feathers. A third species is still larger, and black on the tips of the claws and on the neck. All other gulls yield their place to them, as if they were kings. In age their feathers turn grey-blue. They nest on rocks, especially when drinkable water runs over them. Thus the young receive their food from the sea, their drink from sweet springs. No other bird equals the gull in speed of swimming.

And the following passage of OPPIAN (*De aucupio* 2 : 5) may refer to grebes (*Podicipidae*) or to smaller gulls: The 'divers' are enormously voracious and are never satiated. They feed on fishes and remain, whilst diving, for a long time under water. They live in the seas and in swamps, especially in the latter when storms drive them away from the sea. They are said to be the only birds without voice and hearing.

2. 13. REPTILES AND AMPHIBIANS

Tortoise representations are common in ancient art, but very often so conventional, that even turtles and tortoises cannot be distinguished. A round stamp of the Tell Asmar period in Babylon clearly depicts *Trionyx euphratica* (VAN BUREN 1939, fig. 95). PLUTARCH (*De solertia animalium, ed.* 1778 p. 85) describes the oviposition of sea-turtles: for oviposition the sea-turtle comes on land. As it can neither breed, nor remain for long beyond the water, it covers the eggs with fine sand. Some say, that they mark this place with their feet, others maintain that the female is turned by the male, thus a seal impressing with its carapace. Very astonishing is that they wait exactly forty days and then come back, when the young are formed, and tear their egg shells. Each turtle recognises its treasure, as no man his gold box, and opens it joyously. DIODORUS SICULUS (3 : 20) gives a lively description, how the 'chelonophagi', the inhabitants of some islands in the Indian Ocean, capture the big turtles.

The common sea-turtle (*Chelonia caretta*) and the freshwater-turtles (*Emys orbicularis*

---

1) Prof. B. MAZAR points out the correlation between this bird and the use of these cosmetic boxes by women.

and *Clemmys rivulata*) were connected with Astarte-Aphrodite. The benches in her temples were stamped with the image of a tortoise. One of AESOP's fables shows that the tortoise was held to be a symbol of domestic happiness, another aspect of this goddess. But, just as in Japan and China today, the connection with Astarte was based mainly on fertility, and perhaps also on the lewdness of the tortoise. Illustrations of turtles in river scenes are common in Assyria as well as in Egypt. Small tortoise weights are frequent in Mesopotamia, Syria and Palestine. The armour of the sea-turtle *Chelonia imbricata* served for the production of many ornaments from tortoise-shell. Entire armours of all tortoises were used for producing the so-called tortoise lyres. To them the riddle refers: What is without life, but gives a living sound?

The Nile crocodile (*Crocodilus niloticus*) is often referred to in the following pages. Much was written about it by the ancients, and we especially mention the plastic description in *Job* (40, 41), of the monster called leviathan. The Indian crocodile of the ancients is *Gavialis gangeticus*. TIGLATH-PILESAR I received a Nile crocodile as a gift from the pharaoh. Many crocodile cemeteries have been discovered in Egypt with mummies, sometimes of entire families, of crocodiles. The sacredness of the crocodiles was often mentioned. In later antiquity they were even part of the tourist industry. When the senator MUMMIUS visited Egypt, his arrival at a certain place was announced with the warning that gifts and bread for feeding the crocodiles be held in readiness. The gift of prophecy was ascribed to them. Thus we read in PLUTARCH (*l.c.* p. 86): The crocodile really reads the future. It proves this by laying its eggs every year exactly on the line which the coming Nile flood will reach. Every farmer, finding the nest, can thus know beforehand and tell others, how far the flood will reach. A crocodile hunt (an impossible topic for Egypt!) is shown on a small gnostic stele from Caesarea (Palestine; Coll. R. JONAS; Plate XXVII). Excrements of crocodiles were used in the ancient pharmacopoeia (Serapion of Alexandria).

Lizards are occasionally represented. A Bridled Skink (*Mabuia*) was found as a mummy in Egypt. Early Syro-Hellenistic symbolism connected lizards with the great summer heat, the Egyptian hieroglyphs with innumerableness (KELLER 1913 p. 27). The *scincus* of the ancients is the land crocodile (*Varanus griseus*), of whom PLINIUS (*Hist. Nat.* 28 : 8 : 30) says: The *scincus*, called the land-crocodile by some, is distinguished from the genuine crocodile by the cephalad direction of a row of scales. The Indian *scinci* are the biggest, followed in size by the Arabian. They are salted and imported. APELLES says that they are an antidote against arrow poison, when eaten before or after the poisoning. They are also components of various other antidotes of poisons.

The geckoes, these common and harmless inhabitants of houses, were regarded as poisonous. PLINIUS (*Hist. Anim.* 29 : 4 : 22) recommends pulverised scorpions against the poison of the geckoes. He also tells the following anecdote: When the gecko dies in wine, this wine produces freckles when drunk. Some jokers kill it in ointments, which they present to beautiful girls, the beauty of whom they want to spoil. Yellow of egg, honey and lye salt is the antidote.

Much has been written about the chameleon (*Chamaeleo chamaeleon*), which will be discussed in other places. ARISTOTLE's marvellous description of it is supposed to be a report from an Alexandrine friend or disciple (KELLER).

Snakes, feared by man since earliest times, are often represented. In Egypt especially two poisonous snakes are well recognisable: The asp or Uraeus snake (*Naja haje*), the symbol of the pharaoh, by its inflated neck, or at least by the not broadened head, and the horned viper (*Cerastes cerastes*) by its two horns. In the Bible the snake is described as subtle and cunning. The fiery snake (*nachash s'raph*) of the Bible was probably the efa (*Echis cari-*

natus). Interesting is the passage (*Numbers* 21 : 6 ff.): And the Lord sent fiery serpents among the people, and they bit the people, and many people of Israel died... And MOSES made a serpent of brass, and put it upon a pole, and it came to pass, that if a serpent had bitten any man, when he beheld the serpent of brass, he lived. This story is of special interest in connection with the discovery of two iron snakes in Palestine from the Israelite period. One of them doubtless refers to the asp. The other, larger one, may be the asp or a *Coluber jugularis,* the common, harmless, great black whip-snake of the country. But in this as in other cases not too much stress should be laid on specific identification. The very many snakes on Syrian incense altars, on Assyrian boundary stones, on pottery at Teleilat Ghassul, etc. are much too conventional to permit specific identification. The connection of the Aesculapius snake (*Elapha longissima*) and Aesculapius, the Greek god of health and medicine, is, of course, well-known. Interesting is the addition of a tuft behind the head in Assyrian seals and Greek serpent reliefs, as this convention was retained by travellers until modern times.

We conclude with a few snake lores. LUCIAN (*Pharsalia* 9 : 607 ff.) relates the African snakes with Medusa. When Perseus cut her head, the blood dropping on the sand caused the corning existence of terrible poisonous animals. First the deadly *aspis* (asp) with her broad neck sprung from the soil. It needs a hot climate, and never goes of its own to a cold country. It inhabits the sandy deserts up to the Nile. But the Roman is not ashamed of bringing this murderous beast to Italy for sale. Also the giant *Haemorrhois* snake sprung from Medusa's blood. The blood flows from the miserable one whom it bites. Further the *Chersyders* of the Syrtes came into existence; the *Chelyders* beneath whom the soil steams; the hidden *Cenchris* with coloured spots on the belly; the *Ammodytes,* whose colour is like that of the sand; the mobile *Cerastes;* the *Scytale,* which moults in the dew; the dry *Dipsas;* the dangerous, two-headed *Amphisbaena;* the *Natrix* infecting the water; the flying *Jaculus;* the *Pareas,* furrowing the soil, where it crawls, with its tail; the *Prester,* which voraciously opens its foaming mouth; the *Seps,* whose bite causes immediate decay of meat and bones; then the terrible *Basilisk,* which rules over all verminous beasts, frightens them by its mere hissing, and kills, before it poisons; also the dragons, which do damage nowhere in the world, are a terrible plague in the African heat: they fly high in the air, follow the flocks, wind around the biggest bulls and break their bones. Even the giant elephant is killed by them and the dragons are not poisonous. Amongst those terrible monsters CATO led his army through the dry desert of N. Africa and saw many of his soldiers die on small wounds. Also scorpions and *Solpugids* menaced and stung with their deadly poison. Neither by day nor by night rest was granted to the army. A number of test cases follow describing the death of soldiers by every one of these monsters. Finally they reached the country of the Psyllers, who know to conjure the serpents and are immune against them... This description is not a geographical enumeration, but tells us about all the dangerous snakes from all over the world known to the writer.

NICANDER (*Theriaca* 19, 157) describes some of the poisonous snakes. The horned viper (*Cerastes*) is like the common viper (*Vipera*), but easily distinguished from this hornless one by its four or two horns. The bite of the asp is almost invisible. When it hears a noise, it curls into a circle and from its centre raises its terrible head. Its neck is swelling, it hisses furiously and menaces with death, whomever it encounters. CELSUS (*De medicina* 5 : 27 : 3) gives a great deal of advice about the treatment of snake-bites: first, all the bitten limb has to be tied above the wound, but not too heavily, in order that the limb may not stiffen. Then the poison is extracted, which is best done by putting a glass over the wound. The surroundings of the wound may also be cut by a lancet, in order to extract more of the poisoned blood. Where no cupping glass is available, certainly a rare case, somebody has to suck the

poison from the wound. Snake-poison is without danger, when taken by the mouth..........
GALEN (*De Theriaca ad Pisonem* 8) informs us that when a criminal is judged to death at
Alexandria, and the death shall be an easy one, he is bitten by an asp on the breast. This
was, by the way, the manner of death chosen by Cleopatra.

We have to return to the winged snakes, which we mentioned before in connection with
the ibis. HERODOT reports (3 : 107 ff.): The winged serpents living in Arabia near Buto,
have the shape of water-snakes. The serpents migrate to Egypt every year, where they are
killed by the ibises. In Arabia they live in great numbers around each incense tree. They are
multicoloured, but not long. The serpents must first be driven away by styrax smoke, when
one wants to get at the incense. Fiery flying snakes are also mentioned by ISAIAH (14 : 29;
30 : 6). It is rather doubtful, and would be unique in all experience, if the small flying
dragon (*Draco volans*), a parachuting lizard of the Malayan area, were the background of this
legend, especially as these lizards are so difficult to keep, that very few have found their
way living into Europe until our days. We know of no other animal from that distant region,
which was known in the first millennium B.C. in the Middle East. The Babylonian snake,
the incorporation of the bad and the destructive, had no wings. Again from LUCIAN's quotation we learn that *Draco* was originally the giant python. We prefer to assume that early
in mythology wings were added to some snakes, just as in early Mesopotamian mythology
some lions were provided with wings, a transformation leading to the griffons. The quotation
by ISAIAH seems to indicate an old Semitic legend. Another cause for misunderstanding may
be the *Amphisbaena*. Monster snakes with two heads are occasionally found. But *Liber
monstrorum* (3 : 2) mentions Amphisbaenas from the Assyrian desert, with a second head
instead of a tail. This is something very different! KELLER (1913 p. 301) thinks it to be
the tiny worm-snake (*Typhlops vermicularis*). But we are not of the opinion that this
Typhlops was identified with a snake and distinguished from earthworms. The identity of
the anterior and posterior end of the sand-boa (*Eryx jaculus*), so common in sandy soils all
over the Middle East, seems to offer a much more likely interpretation.

For once we continue with an ancient exciting story about the capture of African
pythons. The report may deal with *Python sebae,* which reaches a length of up to six metres
in Africa. DIODORUS SICULUS (3 : 35 ff.): "Reports of snakes 100 ells long have been
obtained by the people living near to the negro country in Africa. This seems to me and to
other honest men to be a lie. They further say that this snake seen from afar when curled
up resembles a hill. If these are exaggerations, I will now tell about the giant snakes which
really have been seen and which have been brought to Alexandria in cages especially built.
PTOLEMY II., an enthusiastic lover of elephant hunts and generously rewarding those who
brought him giant animals, suggested to some hunters to co-operate in the dangerous undertaking of capturing a giant snake and to bring it to Alexandria alive. They had observed
one, which was thirty ells long, living in swamps and remaining motionless curled up, until
an animal came to the water. Then it suddenly sallied out, caught the animal with its jaws,
and twined round its prey so that it could not move any more. As the python was lazy, the
hunters hoped to overpower it by ropes and chains. Thus they freshly advanced. When they
had approached they were taken by terror and fear, seeing the fiery eye, the tongue moving
in all directions, the terrible rushing of its scales, the enormous teeth and the terrible mouth.
They still proceeded timidly to throw ropes on the tail. Now the monster turned with
terrible hissing, caught the foremost hunter with jaws by his head and devoured him alive.
It got the second, while he took flight, and twisted round his body. All others saved themselves by speedy flight.

In spite of this disaster, the hunters hoping for a great reward did not give up their undertaking. They now tried to obtain by ruse, what they failed to do by force. They made a *weir*-basket of thick branches, big enough to hold the monster. They had espied its hiding place as well as the hour when it left in search of prey and when it returned. When it had left, they obstructed the entrance of its hole with large stones and with earth, and dug another hole quite close to the earlier hole. Into this they brought the weir-basket in such a way, that its opening was turned outward. Then they posted, on the way, by which it used to return, archers, slingers, many horsemen, trumpeters and others. The returning python raised its head higher than that of the horsemen. Nobody dared to approach it. But when arrows and stones came upon it from all sides, and at the same time, the riders moved there and back, large packs of dogs yelped, the trumpets sounded, the python grew afraid and turned towards its recess. When it approached this, the noise of weapons, calls and trumpets increased considerably. The snake, finding its hole obstructed, entered the weir-basket. The horsemen hurried to the place and closed the basket, before the prisoner could leave it. The basket now was dug out and raised by crowbars. The serpent began to whimper loudly and to spit in its tight cage, lacerated the branches with its teeth and struck in all directions so that the carriers of the basket feared every moment that it would break out. They started to pick its tail, and then it left the branches alone and dealt with its tail. Finally it arrived in Alexandria and the hunters obtained the reward promised. The monster became feeble by long fasting and slowly became rather tame. Ptolemy kept this python and showed it to visiting strangers as his greatest curiosity."

Frogs (*Rana esculenta*) and toads (*Bufo viridis, B. regularis*) are often found as small figurines or as small weights. Toad figurines were also serving as apotropaia against the evil eye. Lamps in the shape of a frog appear in Hellenistic Egypt. As a hieroglyph the frog indicates the innumerable. The metamorphosis of the frog was well-known. The inclusion of frogs into the ten Egyptian plagues (*Exodus* 8) shows that they were regarded as detestable. AELIAN (*Var. Hist.* 1 : 2) calls the Egyptian frogs clever. When they meet a watersnake, they quickly bite off a stalk of reed, which they bear transversely in their mouth, holding it with their teeth as tightly as possible. Now it is impossible for the snake to devour the frog with the reed, as it cannot open its mouth so far. Thus the feeble frog overcomes the powerful snake.

Salamanders (*Salamandra salamandra*) are common in the northern mountains of the Middle East, south as far as Mt. Carmel. Many fables about it were current. Thus, PLINY (*Hist. Nat.* 10 : 67 : 86; 11 : 53 : 116) says (quite exact): Salamanders appear only after heavy rains and they are never seen in dry weather. Its shape is like that of a lizard with star-shaped spots. He is as cold as ice and extinguishes fire when he comes in contact with it.—Some not poisonous animals turn poisonous when they have eaten poisonous animals. Thus, everybody, who in the mountains of Pamphylia and of Cilicia eats part of a pig, which has eaten a salamander must die. The Babylonian *Talmud* has accepted all the fables about the relation between fire and the salamander. The salamander originates from fire, and he who smears himself with his blood is protected from fire (*Hagiga* 26a). The father of king HEZEKIAH wanted to drive him through the fire of Moloch. His mother smeared the blood of a salamander upon him and saved him (*Sanhedrin* 63b).

2. 14. FISHES AND FISHERY

We will begin with some quotations from the *Halieutica* of OPPIAN of Cilicia, perhaps to be distinguished from his contemporanean, OPPIAN of *Apamea,* whom we quoted so extensively before:

"For the toilsome fishermen their labours are uncertain, and unstable as a dream is the hope that flatters their hearts. Always they have to encounter the chill and wildly raging water. In tiny barks they wander obsequious to the stormy winds, their minds ever on the surging waves; always they scan the dark clouds and ever tremble at the blackening tract of sea; no shelter have they from raging winds nor any defence against the rain nor bulwark against summer heat. Moreover, they shudder at the terror awful to behold of the grim sea, even the sea-monsters which encounter them when they transverse the secret places of the deep. No hounds guide the fishers on their seaward path, nor do they see where the fish will encounter them and come within range of capture; for not by one path does the fish travel. In fable hairs and bent hooks of bronze and in reeds and nets the fishers have their strength. Yet not bereft of pleasure art thou, if pleasure you desirest, but sweet is the royal sport. (1 : 35 ff.).

First of all the fisher should have body and limps both swift and strong. And lightly he must leap from a rock, and dive into the deepest depths. Cunning and wise should he be, daring and dauntless and temperate. He must be found of labour and must love the sea. In the autumn fishing is best in the evening and when the morning star rises. In winter the fisher should set out with the spreading rays of the sun. In bloomy spring the whole day is prosperous. Look always for a wind that blows gentle and fair, lightly rolling a tranquil sea. For fishes fear and loathe violent winds and will not wheel over the sea, but with a temperate wind fishing is exceedingly favourable. All the fishes that swim the sea speed against wind and wave. But when the fisher puts to sea let him set his sail with the wind: northward when the wet southwind blows; southward when the north wind drives the sea. When the eastwind rises, towards the paths of the west wind; towards the east let the west wind bear his vessel; for so will infinite shoals meet him and his fishing will be blest with luck. Fourful modes of hunting their prey in the sea have fishermen devised. Some delight in hooks; and of these some fish with a well-twisted line of horse-hair fastened to long reeds, others simply cast a flaxen cord attached to their hands, another rejoices in leaded lines or in lines with many hooks. Others prefer to array nets; and of these there are those called casting-nets, and those called draw-nets—drag-nets and round bag-nets and seines. Others they call cover-nets, and, with the seines, there are those called ground-nets and ball-nets and the crooked trawl: innumerable are the various sorts of such crafty-bosomed nets. Others again have their minds set rather upon weels (a long basket of wickerwork) which bring joy to their masters while they sleep at ease, and great gain attends on little toil. Others with the long pronged trident wound the fish from the land or from a ship. The due measure and right ordering of all these they know certainly who contrive these things" (3 : 29 ff.).

Among rivers especially the Nile, the Araxes, the Euphrates and some Anatolian streams, among lakes the Moeris and the Genezareth lakes were famous for their abundance of fish. Fishing by spearing and by nets are often painted in Egypt. From Tell Halaf an angler is well represented. In one of the Moeris lakes 22 species of fish were found in such numbers that there were many more than could be fished. The pharaoh MOERIS gave the income from this lake to his wife for her toilet expenses (*Diodorus Siculus* 1 : 52). And HERODOT (2 : 93) mentions that the Egyptian migratory fishes live in lakes, but swim at certain seasons in shoals into the sea, the males first. Later they return, females first, which lay their eggs, from which the young fishes develop. When these fishes are caught when they swim toward the sea, they are all rubbed upon the left, when they return on the right side of their body. They crowd towards the left shore when going out, on the right one when coming back. When the Nile begins to rise the small grooves on its shores are speedily filled by the rising water and immediately are crowded with small fish. Probably these came out of the eggs which the fishes left during the flood of the preceding year. WILKINSON (II p. 23) says that only the poor Egyptians ate fish. About the holy fish of the Egyptians there is still much confusion. Herodot (2 : 72) reports the eel and the scaly *Lepidotus* as sacred. This seems entirely incorrect as regards the eel. The Lepidotes is the Nile barbel (*Barbus bynni*), a very popular and common, but apparently not a holy fish. The *Oxyrhynchus* (*Mormyrus oxyrhyn-*

chus) is mentioned by others. And LORTET and GAILLARD (1905) report only *Lates nilotica* as mummies. The solution is apparently that different fishes were hold sacred in various districts, as is also known for the sacred mammals and birds.

Herodot (1 : 200; 2 : 92) tells us that some tribes of Mesopotamia live on fishes only. This refers to the marsh rabs, who still largely subsist in this manner. Some Egyptians also live mainly on dried fishes. Dried and salted fish was an important food taken by the ancient Phoenicians and Carthaginians on their long sea-voyages. Tarichaea, the town of the salted fish, is *Migdal Nunaiia* (fish tower) in Hebrew. And Lake Hule is called by FLAVIUS JOSEPHUS *Zemachonitis, i.e.* fish lake (*Bell. Jud.* 4 : 1 : 1). Some towns called Tarichaea existed in the Pontus, one on the Lake of Galilee. Also Mendes in the delta of the Nile was famous for its salted fish. Fish ponds are early represented in Assyrian reliefs and in Egyptian paintings. The enormous piscines of the Romans are described by VARRO (*De re rustica* 3 : 17). From Anatolia to Egypt we here and there find old references to ponds of "holy" fish. Some of them still survive in connection with mosques, such as at Urfa, Tripolis, and elsewhere. XENOPHON (*Anabasis* 1 : 4 : 9) thus relates: CYRUS proceeded to the river Chalus (the Aleppo river or the Balikli Su), which is a *plethrum* wide, and full of large tame fish, which the Syrians looked upon as gods and which they did not allow to be hurt by any one, either them or the pigeons. These fish were connected with the Syrian goddess Atergatis. One stone is preserved from Smyrna with an inscription: Whoever will cause grief to the fishes of that pond, he shall meet disaster and he shall end as food for fish. When a fish died, a fruit sacrifice was brought on the same day. It seems that in old times fishes were not eaten at all by the Syrians. Not only Atergatis or Derketo of Sidon and Ascalon, but also many Mesopotamian gods had fishes on their steles, sometimes they were represented (longitudinally or horizontally) as half fish, half man. Even in the Ilias fish is not eaten. And in PLUTARCH (*De dea syra* 10) we read that many Syrians feared, even in Hellenistic times, the punishment of the great Syrian goddess, when they succumbed to the temptation to eat salted fish. The probable connection with the goddess was their great fertility, which also returns in the Egyptian hieroglyphics as fertility and wealth. In the old zodiacs the month of the fishes coincides with the beginning of the rainy season (KELLER 1913 p. 343 ff.). According to a cuneiform text from Niniveh the fishes of the ponds were used for obtaining *omina*. And Ea, the river god, was also the fish god. Holy fishes in Lycia were allured by flute tunes and asked about the future. Various sea-fishes appear on the oldest animal pottery of the Middle East, but so variable and conventional that an identification is scarcely possible. Freshwater fishes of the Varicorhinus-type appear as weights, small figurines as amulets and ornaments in Mesopotamia and Syria. Fish obtained a high importance in early Christian symbolism. This is based upon the anagrammatic interpretation of the Greek word ichthys as the beginning of Iesous christos theou hyios. But fishes are also found on the tombs of fishermen without reference to this symbolism.

We again conclude with a short selection from the five books of OPPIAN's *Halieutica* regarding some marine fish:

"Fishes differ in breed and habit, and not all fishes have like range. Some keep by the low shores, feeding on sand and what grows on sand, such as the sea-horse (*Hippocampus*), the swift cuckoo-fish (*Trigla*), the yellow *Erythinus* (*Pagellus*), the *Citharus* (a flat-fish), the red mullet (*Mullus*), and the feeble *Melanurus* (*Oblata*), the shoals of *Trachurus* (*Scomber, Trachurus*), and the sole (*Solea*), the *Platyurus* (a flat-fish), the weak ribbon-fish (*Cobitis*), the *Mormyrus* of varied hue (*Pagellus*), the mackerel (*Scomber*) and the carp (*Cyprinus*) and all that love the shores. Others feed in the mud and the shallows of the sea, such as the skate (*Raja*), the monster tribes of the ox-ray (? *Cephaloptera*), the terrible sting-ray (*Trygon*), the cramp-fish truly named (*Torpedo*), the turbot (*Rhombus*), the *Callarias* (a cod), the red mullet (*Mullus*), the *Oniscus* (a cod), the horse-mackerel (*Caranx*), the *Scepanus* (a thunny?), and whatsoever else feeds in mud. On the weedy beach under the green grasses feed the *Maenis* (*Maena*), the goat-fish (male of *Maena*), the *Atherine* (*Atherina*), the *Smaris* (*Smaris*) and the *blenny* (*Blennius*), the *Sparus* (*Sargus*), both bogues (*Box*), and whatsoever others love to feed on sea-weed. The grey mullets (*Mugil*), the most righteous race of the briny sea, the basse (*Labrax*), the bold Amia (*Pelamys*), the Chremes (*Sciaena*), the Pelamyd (one year old thunny), the conger (*Conger*), and the *Olisthus* (*Silurus*), these always dwell in the sea where it neighbours rivers or lakes, where the sweet water ceases from the brine, and where much alluvial silt is gathered, drawn from the land by the eddying current. There they feed on pleasant food and fatten on the sweet brine. The basse does not fail even from the rivers themselves but swims up out of the sea into the estuaries, while the eels come from the rivers and draw to the flat reefs of the sea. The sea-girt rocks are of many sorts. Some are wet and covered with seaweed, and about them grows abundant moss. About these feed the perch (*Serranus*) and the rainbow-wrasse (*Coris*), the *Channus* (*Serranus*), and withal the spangled saupe (*Box*), the slender thrush-wrasse (*Coricus*), the *Phycis* (*Crenilabrus*) and those which fishermen have nicknamed with the name of an effeminate man (a wrasse). Other rocks are low-lying beside the sandy sea and rough. About these dwell the *Cirrhis* (*Labrus*), the sea-swine (a flat-fish), the Basiliscus (?), and withal the *Mylus* (*Sciaena*) and the rosy tribes of the red mullet (*Mullus*). Other rocks again whose wet faces are green with grasses have for tenants the sargue (*Sargus*), the *Sciaena* (*Umbrina*), the dory (*Zeus*), the crow-fish (*Corvina*) named from its dusky colour, and the parrot-wrasse (*Scarus*), which alone among the voiceless fishes utters a liquid note and alone rejects its food back into its mouth, and feasts on it a second time, throwing up its food just as sheep and goats. Those rocks again which abound in clams or limpets (*Patella*) and in which there are chambers and abodes for fish to enter, on these abide the braize (*Pagrus*), the shameless wild braize (?), the *Cercurus* (?), the gluttonous and baleful *Muraena* (*Muraena*), the horse-mackerel (*Caranx*), the race of the late-dying *Merou* (*Serranus*), which of all others remain longest alive and wriggle even when cut in pieces with a knife. Others in the deeps under the sea abide in their lairs, such as the sea-sheep ?), the *Hepatus* (a cod) and the *Prepon* (?). Strong and large of body they are, but slowly they roll upon their way; wherefore also they never leave their own cleft, but just there they lie in wait beside their lair for any fish that may approach, and bring sudden doom on lesser fishes. Among these is also numbered the hake(?), which beyond all fishes shrinks from the bitter assault of the dog-star in summer, and remains retired within his dark recesses and comes not forth so long as the breath of the fierce star prevails. A fish there is which haunts the sea-washed rocks, yellow and build like a grey mullet, some call him Adonis, others the sleeper-out (*Blennius*), because he takes his sleep outside the sea and comes to the land, alone of them that have gills, those folds of the mouth, on either side. For when calm hushes the works of the glancing sea, he hastes with the hasting tide and, stretched upon the rocks, takes his rest in fine weather. But he fears the sea-birds, which are hostile to him; if he sees any of them approach, he hops like a dancer until, as he rolls on and on, the sea-wave receives him safe from the rocks. Others live both among the rocks and in the sands; such as the gilt-head (*Chrysophrys*) named from its beauty, the weever (*Trachinus*), the *Simus*(?), the *Glaucus* (?), the strong *Dentex* (*Dentex*), the rushing scorpion (*Scorpaena*), the long *Sphyraena* (*Sphyraena*) and the slender needlefish (*Belone*). The *Charax* (*Sargus*) likewise is there, the nimble tumbling goby (*Gobius*), and the savage sea-mice (*Balistes*), which are bold beyond all other fishes and contend even with men; not that they are so very large, but trusting chiefly to their hard hide and the serried teeth of their mouth, they fight with fishes and with mightier men. Others roam in the unmeasured seas far from the dry land, the dashing (*Thynnus*), most excellent among fishes for spring and speed, the sword-fish (*Xiphias*) truly so named, the coly-mackerel (*Scomber*) the *Hippurus* (*Coryphaena*). Among these too is the beauty-fish (?) truly named a holy fish, the pilot-fish (*Naucrates*) which sailors revere exceedingly, and they have given him this name for his convoying of ships. For they delight exceedingly in ships that run over the wet seas. Companion of the open seas likewise is the *Echineis* (*Echineis*). It is slender, a cubit long, of dusky colour and of the nature of the eel. When a ship is straining under stress of a strong wind, running with spread sails over the spaces of the sea, the fish gapes its tiny mouth and stays all the ship underneath, constraining it below the keel; and it cleaves the waves no more for all its haste but is firmly stayed, even as it were shut up in a tideless harbour. The pilchard (*Clupea*), the shad (*Alosa*) and the *Abramis* (a Nile *Mugil*) move in shoals, now in one path of the sea, now in another, round rocks or in the open sea, and they also run to the long shores, ever changing to a strange path like wanderers" (1 : 93 ff.).

We very much regret that we have to interrupt this splendid and beautiful ecological analysis of the fishes of the Levantine shores. No other description has been given until this day which by far could be compared with this vivid and beautiful language of a widely read and observant poet. We sincerely hope that the books of the two OPPIANS will increasingly become known as one of the most important sources for the natural history of the Middle East. A. W. MAIR, their editor and translator, deserves the highest praise for his careful work, for his erudite commentaries and for the adequate language of the translation (*Loeb Classical Library*).

DIODORUS SICULUS (3 : 21):

On the sea-shore south of Babylon the inhabitants have more fish than they are able to eat. They put into the sea, close to the shore, walls of reed-baskets with easily opening covers. When the flood rises, the covers open automatically and the flood brings the fish into them. At ebb the returning water shuts the covers on top of the baskets and the fishes remain on the bottom of the basket, crowding and kicking, and in this way are collected for food. Some people dig broad channels often deep into the land, up to their huts. A wall of the just described reed baskets is put at the beginning of the channel. They open the doors with beginning flood, and shut them when the ebb begins.

2. 15. TERRESTRIAL ANTHROPOIDS AND OTHER VERTEBRATES

A. *Vermin of man.* The nobles of Egypt always had their head and beard shaved. The priests even shaved their entire body every three days, as HERODOT (2 : 89) relates, in order to prevent the generation of lice on the servants of god. The beard as a "forest for lice" is mentioned by MARTIAL and JUVENAL. The Egyptian lice plague (*Exodus* 8 : 16 ff.) may well have been an allusion to this extreme aversion of the Egyptians against lice. There is no reason to assume that these lice are an error of translation for mosquitoes, as KELLER (1913 p. 397) supposes. An old Greek riddle of SYMPHOSIUS shows that lice were well-known:

Everybody hunts the prey, but its capture is peculiar:
Who succeeds to catch it, refuses to take it home,
Who does not catch it, certainly takes it home.

ARISTOTLE (*Hist. Anim.* 5 : 26) gives a good description of lice, but maintains that lice generate from meat, whilst bedbugs do from excessive body humidity, and fleas from dry decay. "Where lice are generating, first small pustules without pus are formed. When you puncture these lice come out of them. Sometimes this develops into a disease, when much humidity is in the body. Sometimes this disease has caused death, such as that of the poet ALKMAN and of PHEREDYKOS of Syros. Also in some diseases lice appear in abundance. Lice are more abundant on the head of children than of adults, more on those of women than of men." This leads to the reports on the lice-disease, called phthiriasis. We have at least three detailed reports on this rare disease. PLUTARCH (*Vita Syllae*) underlines the lewd manner of living of SULLA, until finally his body began to decay. Many lice generated and increased in numbers although they were collected from him day and night. All his clothes, the water of his bath, his food were overrun with lice, and no remedy could remove them until he died. Yet MOMMSEN (*Roman History*) maintains that SULLA died from haemorrhage and characterises his *phthiriasis* as an invention of SULLA's enemies. Also HEROD is often quoted as having died from *phthiriasis*. But FLAVIUS JOSEPHUS (*Bellum Judaicum* 1 : 33 : 5) gives a detailed description of his disease which today is interpreted as either *cirrhosis* or cancer of the liver (see, for instance, NEUBURGER, 1919). He only mentions worms (*skolekes*) produced by a putrid ulcer on his genitals as a very minor symptom. And in the second book of the Maccabaeans (9 : 6) we have the following report about the death of another pretended victim of *phthiriasis,* the Syrian king ANTIOCHUS EPIPHANES: He fell from his rolling chariot and suffered heavy pains from the fall. From his body grew maggots, and the meat ulcerated under heavy pain from his body and its stench molested all his army. Nothing of this description points to lice: a gangrene and fly-maggots may well have infested on the road his open wounds, which could not be treated as they should have been. The only medical authority for *phthiriasis* is apparently CELSUS (*De medicina* 6 : 15), who mentions a phthiriasis of the eyelashes, which may spread when the body is conditioned for it, and which may lead to blindness. Also here it is doubtful, if fly-maggots were not confused with an accidental occurrence of lice. To the best of our knowledge there does not exist any primary internal disease which manifests itself mainly by lice. Lice may abound when cleanness is disregarded. But this was certainly not the case in the three above-mentioned medical reports. Secondary eczemas may appear following excessive scratching in lice infection. The *Talmud* passage (*Temura* 31a) that many a handful of maggots (*rimah*) may come out of the body again refers to *myiasis*. Lice certainly were detestable: "Let me hear the crackling of my enemy" (*Sabbat* 12a)! Lice were killed by combs. *Nidda* (20b) mentions special combs by which lice are killed.

The bedbug (*Cimex lectularius*) was widely spread. The god Dionysus (ARISTOPHANES, *The Frogs* 114 f.) asks for night-quarters which may harbour the least possible number of bedbugs. And, according to the *Acta Johannis* (2nd century A.D.) even Christ suffered from them on his travels and said to them: "I say to you bedbugs: be clever and leave your haunts this night, be quiet and remain far from the servants of God", and the bugs obeyed. MARTIAL (*Epigr.* 11 : 57) sneers at the Stoic CHERAEMON: He has no property but bedbugs; no wonder that he does not fear death! Whilst very common in the wooden buildings of Anatolia and Greece, the bedbug is absent since ancient times from Mesopotamia, where even a word for it is wanting in Sumero-Accadian. Also in Palestine and Egypt they must have been relatively rare. But the bad smell of this insect was known (*Nidda* 58b).

The flea (*Pulex irritans*) was certainly known (cf. I. *Samuel* 24 : 14; 26 : 20). It molests man mainly in settlements, whilst lice prevail among the nomads. The *Talmud* forbids its killing on sabbath, as it propagates by copulation, whilst the louse may be killed on that day, as it originates from sweat without copulation.

Fly amulets and pendants appear quite often in ancient Mesopotamia and in Egypt, fly gems and coins with flies in the Greek world. As hieroglyphic ↔ the fly indicated impudence, but also courage. The military decoration for bravery in early Egypt was a fly. An old necklace from Palestine, exhibited in the Palestine Museum of Archaeology, is composed of two golden flies flanking an object which resembles most the maggot of a fly (Plate XVIII, 1). The knowledge of this metamorphosis is quite probable, and supported by the text on a slip of paper, found in the mouth of an Egyptian mummy (*Papyrus Gizeh* no. 18026 : 4 : 14) saying: The maggots will not turn into flies within you. Fly flaps are known from all periods all over the Middle East. Flies were also used in Mesopotamia and elsewhere for auguries. The Syrian god of the flies and other vermin, Baal-zebub, the god of Ekron, also the god of the summer heat, was widely accepted by the Greeks as Myiagros, as Zeus Apomyios, and as Apollo Smintheus. PLINY (*Nat. Hist.* 10 : 28 : 40) remarks about the Elaeans: They appeal to a god, whom they call fly-hunter (*Myiagros*) against the plague of flies. And as soon as they have brought him an agreeable sacrifice, he destroys the flies. HOMER often mentions flies quite naturalistically, for instance in *Iliad* 2 : 469; 16 : 639; 19 : 25). In the *Talmud* (*Bittin* 6b) we find a discussion about whether flies in the food are a valid motive for divorce. Prayers were said to avert fly plagues (*Tanit* 14a). They fly from sick to healthy persons and can be carriers of infection (*Ketuboth* 77b). They live less than one year (*Hulin* 58b). No flies appeared on the table of Eliahu and thus his house-keeper recognised him as a holy man (*Berachoth* 61a).

HERODOT (2 : 89) mentions mosquito-curtains from ancient Egypt: The Egyptians protect themselves against the abundance of mosquitoes in the following way. In the countries above the marsh-land they build towers to which they go when they want to sleep. The mosquitoes cannot fly high because of the winds. But in the marsh-lands everybody has a net, with which he fishes by day. At night however he pulls it around his bed and sleeps beneath it. If somebody sleeps in his clothes or beneath a cover of linen, he is stung by the midges. However, they even do not attempt to sting through these nets (perhaps by reason of smell!). The Talmudic word *kinuf* is derived from the Greek *konopeion*. They are able to kill a man when fettered (*Sanhedrin* 77a). Even in the tabernacle it is permitted to use a mosquito-curtain (*kila*) around the bed (*Sukka* 26a). They shall not be killed on sabbath. PAUSANIAS (7 : 2) says: The town Myus in Caria was situated on a bay of the sea. The Maeander river cut it off by mud and transformed this bay into a lake. When the water, later on, ceased to be salty, this lake generated innumerable swarms of mosquitoes, which forced the inhabitants to leave the town. They came to Miletus and at my time only a temple of Bacchus still remained there. JONES (1926) has written a most interesting book, in which he maintains that similar cases widely increased towards the end of antiquity, and that the subsequent spread of deadly malaria was one of the main reasons for the decadence of antiquity. Whilst it was a merit to expose the part which malaria undoubtedly has plaid locally, as well as its wider importance during certain rainy periods (of the secular cycles), it certainly is not correct to single out this one factor as the most important one for the regression of the Greek and Hellenistic cultures. Unfortunately we know very little about the diagnosis, spread and importance of this disease in antiquity, which can be diagnosed with certainty only since a few decades.

HORNETS (*Vespa orientalis*, in Greece (*V. crabro*) were not only feared because of their sting, AELIAN even reports (11 : 28) that the inhabitants of Phaselis in Lycia were forced to leave the country. And Cyprus was even called Sphekeia, the hornet island, by the Greeks. The saying of PLAUTUS (*Amph.* 2 : 75) "irritare crabrones" (to irritate hornets!) is well-known. Many writers underline the damage done by the hornets to the bees. In Egypt a *Hymenopteron* was the symbol of the ruler of lower Egypt ↔ since the first dynasty. The writer (1928 p. 27) could not decide for a long time if this symbol was intended as honey-bee, known since long to the Egyptians as "fly of the honey", or as a hornet. We are now much inclined to accept the latter identification. It is not only the deep incision between breast and abdomen, not only the alternate light and dark abdomen, but still more the symbolic interpretation, spreading fear before the powerful king. J. GARSTANG (1931 p. 258 f.) has vividly interpreted JOSHUA's verse (24 : 12): I sent the hornet to you which drove them out. GARSTANG shows how a consistent policy of tyranny and spoliation broke the land of Canaan and made it ripe for the Jewish conquest. E. B. POULTON and W. GARSTANG agree to the identification as hornet. The hieroglyphic may well have served both, the reading depending upon the context. The *Talmud* reports the death of a nine years old child as well as of some adults by hornet stings. The greatest cruelty of the inhabitants of Sodom was that they smeared a charity girl with honey and exposed her to the stings of the hornets (*Sanhedrin* 109b). Hornet stings were cured by putting a squashed fly on the wound. Public prayers were said in case of hornet plagues (*Tanit* 14a).

A spider spinning a long spiral thread was once represented on a cylinder seal from Ur (VAN BUREN 1939 p. 112). The natural history about them is well treated by ARISTOTLE (*Hist. Anim.* 5 : 22; 9 : 26). PLUTARCH (*De solert. an.*) holds the net of the spiders up as an example for weaving women and for fishermen in making their nets. The threads are fine, never break as they are put together by a sticky fluid, and have, to deceive the prey, the colour of the air. The net is thus arranged that the spider immediately feels, when a prey has come into it. And AELIAN (1 : 21) teaches that men have learned their weaving from the goddess Ergane, but the spiders from nature. They let the thread go from their belly and feed it with its help. The thread is more tender than the thinnest hair. KELLER (1913 p. 466) quotes an Alexandrine myth, about the origin of the art of weaving (see also OVID *Metamorph*. VI: 1 ff.). The arrogant but artful Arachne of Lydia was changed by the angered Pallas Athene into a spider. Although most spiders are feared and detested, few only are poisonous to mammals. JALKUT SHIMONI (to *Proverbia* fol. 145a) declares the spider to be the most hated of all creatures. *Sukka* (52a) compares passion at its beginning with a spider web, growing strong as the ropes of a chariot later. The most important poisonous spiders of the Middle East are: the giant "bird"-spider *Chaetopelma olivacea,* the dreaded black widow or the malmignatte (*Latrodectes lugubris*), *Tarantula spp.* and some related forms. Especially former has been believed to be deadly for man.

Besides scorpions and spiders the big, hairy Galeodid spiders (*Solifugae*) of the steppes and deserts are dreaded. STRABO (16 : 772) has well characterised them as four-jawed. In spite of their strong mandibles they are definitely not poisonous.

Scorpions represented a religious symbol in earliest Mesopotamia, where they abound to this day. Subsequently the scorpion was transferred into the zodiac. Scorpions are present on boundary stones (as in Rome), in scenes of animal contests, as symbols of the field, as amulets, on magic tablets and seals, as apotropaion against the malignant power of Lamashtu (VAN BUREN 1939 p. 111). We will find scorpion tails also in some of the old Mesopotamian mixed monsters. The Egyptian goddess of the scorpions is the originally Ethiopian Serk, who bears a scorpion with raised tail above her head, in later times also Isis. Falcons are honoured in Egypt, because they feed on scorpions (DIODORUS SICULUS 1 : 87). On later gnostic steles scorpions are connected with Serapis-Hermes. A scorpion appears on the arms of Syria Comagena. The scorpion of Adiabene in Syria was feared, so much that it was permitted to kill it on sabbath, even if it did not attack (*Sabbat* 121b).

Some tales of the ancients, such as those of PLINY or AELIAN, about scorpions have survived until our days. We therefore think it useful to give two quotations from modern observers (KELLER 1913 p. 472); which contradict their usual refutation as pure inventions. At Madras W. G. BIDDIE observed a big scorpion which he put under a bell-glass which he exposed to the bright sun. He concentrated the sun-rays on its back by means of a looking glass. It began to run to and fro furiously and to hiss. Suddenly it raised its tail and swift as lightening put its sting into its own back. Some fluid came out of the wound, and the scorpion was dead in less than half a minute. This is confirmed by A. THOMPSON for the Italian scorpion. C. J. WILLS put a big black scorpion in the midst of a circle of glowing coal near Shiras. It stood on the spot for a moment, moved in circles, now and then returned to the centre, raised its tail and stung itself some times into the head, and died immediately. It seems advisable to repeat these experiments under accurate conditions of experimentation.

Winged scorpions appear in a number of gems (KELLER 1913, fig. 144). These winged scorpions are, as it seems, connected with an old Mesopotamian legend. Thus the archer of the zodiac has sometimes wings and a scorpion tail. Hence the arching form of the scorpion on these gems.

Similar vermin was known, of course, from domestic stock. We mention two cases only. ARISTOTLE (*Hist. Anim.* 5 : 25) states that donkeys have neither lice nor ticks. It was a deed of the greatest moral courage, when FRANCESCO REDI in the 16th century published a figure of a donkey-louse (*Pediculus asini*), in spite of this authoritative declaration of the master. And we mention ticks, because they are common and often reappear in later traveller reports as "pharaoh's lice". PLINY (*Hist. Nat.* 11 : 34 : 40) describes it as an animal which sinks its head into the blood of the host to draw its food. It swells so strongly that it bursts, because it has no *exit* for the surplus of food, differing herein from all other animals.

Remedies against vermin were proposed since time immemorial. In Egypt Horus was the god protector against vermin, from lions and crocodiles down to "all worms which bite with their mouth, or which sting with their tail". The *Papyrus Ebers* (16th century B.C.) contains a series of remedies against vermin. The first prescription against flea and lice is: One part date flour and one part water shall be cooked to a portion of two *hennu* jars. Drink it warm and spit it out afterwards on the limbs where the vermin is.

Passing over the prescriptions of the Roman authors on agriculture, medicine, etc., we will now give the insect *pharmacopoeia* of DIOSCORIDES of Cilicia (about 50 A.D.), whose books were used for the medicine of the Middle East till far after the great Arab period of medicine. From his *Pharmacopoeia* we hear that bedbugs help to cure the four-day fever. Their smell awakes women who fainted from *uterus* cramps. Brought into the urinary duct, it cures urine detention (2 : 36). *Cockroaches* from bakeries, pulverised and mixed with oil, cure ear pains (2 : 38). Roasted cicadas help against diseases of the bladder (2 : 56). Also locusts, caterpillars and Spanish flies (*Meloidae*) are useful (2 : 57, 64, 65, 66). The *Kermes*-scale of the oaks is a good astringent (4 : 48), as are the oak galls (*Cynipidae*; 1 : 146). In another book on poisons and their antidotes DIOSCORIDES (1 : 1-3) deals, down to the smallest detail, with the treatment of poisoning by Spanish flies and by the hairs of the processionary pine caterpillar (*Thaumetopoea pini, T. wilkinsoni*) together with the symptoms of the poisoning, such as: "Who has swallowed the *pityocampa,* immediately feels a pain in the mouth and the palate. Heavy inflammation of the tongue, stomach and belly is followed by terrible pains of the intestines, as if they be lacerated. At the same time heat runs all over the body and a general nausea is felt...."

A short remark about intestinal worms may conclude this survey. At least the following human worms were distinguished: tapeworms (*Taenia*) and the two nemas *Enterobius* and *Ascaris*). CELSUS (*De medicina* 4 : 17) gives specified advice for their treatment. Leeches (especially *Hirudo medicinalis,* and in the south *Limnatis nilotica*) have at least since THEMISON (63 B.C.) served for cupping blood in a long series of diseases. This treatment, without doubt effective in quite a number of diseases, has even today not been entirely displaced by other methods. But the times are past, where annually almost incredible quantities of leeches were sent from Anatolian lakes to Europe for medical purposes. PLINY (*Hist. Nat.* 32 : 10 : 42) describes various applications of the leeches. They are used instead of cupping glasses, but have the draw-back that every year at the same season the desire for this treatment reappears. When they are satiated, they drop off, by the weight of the blood sucked, or they are forced to do so when salt is sprinkled on them. Sometimes the head sticks, and then causes incurable wounds and even death. Therefore the leeches are cut into two, whilst still sucking, by a scissor, the blood flows out, and slowly dying their head contracts and falls off. — Leeches are also a danger for man and animal who drink from wells infested by them. Many wells in Anatolia are known as '*sülüklü su*', as infested with leeches. When the leeches crawl into the trachea they sometimes cause serious pains and have to be removed by a specialist. As long as they are still in the mouth or the throat, CELSUS' old prescription (*De medicina* 5 : 16) holds good even today: 'Have you swallowed a leech, drink vinegar with salt!'

B. *Agricultural pests.* We hear about locust plagues from Mesopotamia already in its oldest times. Ancient locust prayers beg for protection from "the locusts that destroy the cereal fields and from the locusts that waste the fruit trees" (MACMILAN 1906 p. 567). A very beautiful enamel painting has been found at Ashur, showing an Assyrian noble praying to the god Ashur equipped with all his attributes and accompanied by a big locust (ANDRAE 1925 p. 29, pl. X). The writer, in studying locusts in Irak in the spring of 1943, had ample opportunity to see bordes of the Moroccan locust pass the very district of Ashur (now Kalaat Shergat), devastating all the fields. M. MEISSNER quotes from old Assyrian documents (1920 p. 195): "When in spring a locust swarm covers the land, it devours everything and devastates the land". Locust amulets were common all over the Middle East, as a rule used as pendants. A prayer of protection from locusts was also said by king Solomon at the opening ceremony of the first temple (I. *Kings* 8 : 37), and this was repeated in Talmudic times. Locusts are also found on lamps of the Hellenistic period.

Locusts also served as food. Thus we find locust-bearers among the food-bearers of the great royal banquet in the palace of Senaherib. The important locusts of the Middle East are the Moroccan locust (*Dociostaurus maroccanus*), locally increasing within the northern part of the area at irregular intervals (BODENHEIMER 1944), and the desert locust (*Schistocerca gregaria*) which invades the southern parts of the area at fairly regular intervals of about 13 years from the eastern Sudan or from southern Persia (BODENHEIMER 1929). Moroccan locusts, smaller and not eaten by man, are those of the Assyrian enamel work mentioned and recorded as destroyers of the cereal fields, whilst the bigger desert locusts, so often represented in Egypt, were those serving as food and damaging the fruit trees.

In the course of this book we will still often hear from locusts in Egypt (including the report in *Exodus* 10 : 13 ff.), and in Palestine (Megiddo seal; *Joel* 1, 2; MICAH, SVEN HEDIN, etc.), etc. The abundance of names for locusts in the Semitic languages is not surprising. Most of them refer to different stages, size and colour phases of locusts, a few may indicate grasshoppers, but of doubtful identity. Special rules for the sale of locusts as food are given in the *Talmud*. DIODORUS SICULUS (3 : 28) mentions a special tribe of locust eaters, the Acridophagoi from Libya, others are mentioned from Parthia and elsewhere. In Greece they served as food for the poor only. The report of locusts as food of JOHN the Baptist (*Matthews* 3 : 4) in the desert was much discussed later on by an incredulous European christianity. We end with a quotation from PAUSANIAS (1 : 24 : 8): The brass statue of Apollo on the Acropolis of Athens has been cast by PHIDIAS. This Apollo Parnopios is thus called because he promised to drive away the locusts (*parnopes*). The Athenians well know that he has kept his promise, but do not say how he did it. I know that the locusts have been thrice killed on mount Sipylus in Lydia, and every time in another way: once they have been blown away by a heavy storm; the second time they died from great heat following immediately upon heavy rains; the third time they were destroyed by a great cold.

Ants were known in the old animal fables as industrious, provident and subtle animals, such as in the *Proverbs* (30 : 24 ff.): There be four things which are little upon the earth, but they are exceedingly wise: the ants are a people not strong, yet they prepare their food in the summer. The conies are but a feeble folk, yet make they their houses in the rocks. The locusts have no king, yet go they forth all of them by bands. The gecko holds on to the walls by its felt, even in the king's palace. But the seed-collecting ants, such as the common *Messor semirufus,* cause damage in the fields, which is discussed in the *Mishnah. Moed Katan* (6b) even describes a kind of biological control: bring ants from a distance of 5 to 6 kilometres and throw them upon the nest that is injurious. In the following fight both groups will destroy one the other. And *Jebamoth* (76a) even tells about their use as surgical clamps: Large ants are allowed to bite into the adapted margins of a wound. Their body is cut off, the mandibles hold on and fix the position of the margins of the wound.

A few more pests are mentioned in the Bible. "All thy trees and fruit of thy land shall be the locust consume" (*Deuteronoy* 28 : 42). "Thou shalt plant vineyards, and dress them, but shalt neither drink of the wine, nor gather the grapes, for the worms shall eat them" (*Deuter.* 28 : 39). This may refer to the grapeberry moth *Polychrosis botrana,* so common from Palestine to Greece, or perhaps to the more conspicuous wine hawk moth *Chaerocampa celerio,* of which occasional heavy outbreaks are observed. The following passage may well refer to the olive fly (*Dacus oleae*): "Thou shalt have olive trees throughout all thy coasts, but thou shalt not anoint thyself with the oil, for thine olive shall cast his fruit". (*Deuter.* 28 : 40). Also the cloth moth (*Tineola biselliella*) is mentioned: "And he, as a rotten thing, consumeth, as a garment that is moth eaten, cf. *Job* 13 : 28; also *Isaiah* 50 : 9). We have dealt with the insect pests of ancient agriculture extensively elsewhere (BODENHEIMER 1928, 1930). We therefore wind up here with the following passage from THEOPHRAST of Lesbos (about 330 B.C.) *Natural History of Plants.* There we read about pests and diseases of fruit trees, for instance, (4 : 14): We do not know deadly diseases of wild trees, but they may suffer from cold and hot winds or from hail, but not from the normal winter. The tame (= cultivated) trees suffer from some diseases, some of which are common to all, others only concern special genera. All suffer from worms, from sun-rays and other causes. Some trees suffer more than others from worms, such as fig, apple and pear trees. As a rule, the trees with sharp and aromatic saps are less attacked by worms, but suffer equally from the rays. The fig wax scale (*Ceroplastes rusci,* called *scabies* by THEOPHRAST)and snails are diseases of the fig trees. But they are not always infested. It seems that just as in animals, the diseases of the trees depend upon the local climate. The wild fig tree is free from wax scale, worms, cancer, etc. which infect the cultivated form. Some of the worms of the fig trees are generated by themselves, other produce the longicorn beetle (*Niphona picticornis* and *Hesperophanes griseus*), into which they all change by metamorphosis. Some think that most diseases originate in wounds. The flower olive trees at Miletus are devastated by caterpillars: some species devours the leaves (*Glyphodes unionalis*) and those of another species the flowers (*Prays oleellus*), and the trees are bare. Another pest ruining the fruit is called *Arachnion* (still unidentified). Also various fruits are infested by worms, such as olives, pears and apples (*Carpocapsa pomonella*), medlar and pomegranate. The olive worm, which penetrates beneath the skin, destroys the fruit (*Dacus oleae*). But if it devours the kernel, it speeds it up to earlier maturity (*Oecophora oliviella* or *Rhynchites ruber*). Rain at the rise of the Arcturus prevents the generation of the olive fly. Also in spontaneously dropped olives worms will generate, which make the fruit worse for oil and which leads to decay. The worms of the olive-fly generate mainly at south winds and especially in humid localities.

C. *Honeybee, silkworm and Kermes.* Also for the early history of bee-keeping we have to refer to an earlier publication (BODENHEIMER 1928). Bee honey and dates were in antiquity the main sources for sugar, always a culinary dream of humanity. We will often recur to bees in the following pages. The main bee-races of our area are: *Apis liguistica* in Italy, *Apis syriaca* in Greece and on the Levantine coasts. This race has been subdivided into many subraces, the validity of which is doubtful. In the interior of the Balkans lives *Apis carniolica,* the influence of which reaches up to N.W. Anatolia, in Anatolia and Kurdistan *Apis remipes*. In Egypt lives *Apis unifasciata fasciata,* not belonging like all the others to the species *Apis mellifica,* but to the African honey-bee *Apis unifasciata*. The Syrian bee is famous for its stinging. Bees often appear on coins, on gems and as gold pendants in the Greek and Hellenistic world.

Most interesting is the occasional habit to make holes into a tombstone: (The tombstone had) many holes in order to invite the charming bees to come in and build their wax nests (KELLER 1913 p. 430). The same author remarks that to the neo-platonians the bee—leaving its home, yet not forgetting it—was the symbol of the soul, which tries to retain its purity in this life for its return to higher spheres.

Here only the mere outlines of bee-keeping in the Middle East can be given. A very detailed relief, now 5000 years old, from the temple of NE-USER-RE at Abusir in Egypt shows that then the same mud pipes served as hives, which are still common as bee-hives in Egypt. The details of sealing the honey in jars and of its use for preparing honey-vine (mead) are represented there. In Mesopotamia bee-keeping was unknown. An isolated attempt of SAMUS-RES-USUR, three thousand years ago, to introduce them, which will be described in detail later, remained without results. The ancient Hittites however, were well acquainted with bee-keeping (BODENHEIMER 1942, p. 5 ff.). The Hittite code of Boghazköy (1330 B.C.) contains a few paragraphs about the theft of bee-swarms and of inhabited and empty bee-hives. This code mentions that the fines for stealing bee-swarms were much higher in the older codes. This shows that bee-keeping was well established by them in Anatolia for at least some centuries. A bee-swarm was assessed as equal in value to a sheep. But the price of honey was fairly low, again pointing at a long established bee-keeping. The honey which was delivered in the midst of the second millennium B.C. to Egypt from Syria and Palestine was certainly honey collected from wild bees. In the Bible we do not find one definite reference to bee-keeping, but all passages indicate the hunting of wild honey. This will later be discussed in full. Hunting honey is still widely practised in many countries of the Middle East (see BODENHEIMER 1942 p. 44 ff., where also a modern revision of XENOPHON's remark on the poisonous honey of Trapezunt (*Anabasis* 4 : 8 : 19) is given). The Greeks and Romans had ample knowledge of bee-keeping as well as of the biology of the bees (ARISTOTLE, Pseudo-ARISTOTLE, PLINY, VARRO, VIRGIL, OVID, COLUMELLA, PALLADIUS). We especially recommend the reading of the seasonal calendar of the work on apiaries of HYGINUS, a contemporary of VIRGIL (cf. BODENHEIMER 1928 p. 101 ff.).

The silk of the ancient Greeks was gained mainly at Kos, where PAMPHILA invented its weaving. It was gained from the large, but poor cocoons of the Greek silkworm, the giant moth PACHYPASA OTUS (LASIOCAMPIDAE), whose caterpillars develop, as PLINY (*Hist. Nat.* 11 : 77) correctly informs us, on cypresses, therebintes, oaks and ashes. This industry must, however, have been fairly restricted. The real silk of the Chinese silkworm (*Bombyx mori*) began to appear in the Mediterranean world since the early days of the Roman empire. At that time, however, the knowledge of their biology was still very poor. Thus VIRGIL (*Georgica* 2 : 120) sings: I won't talk here about the fine wool, which the Seres comb from their trees. Or PAUSANIAS (6 : 26) who says: In the land of the Seres lives an animal, which is called *Ser* by the Greeks, but with another name by the Seres. It is twice as big as the largest beetle, for the rest similar to spiders, and also has eight legs. The Seres keep these animals in special buildings, which are fit for summer and winter. The web of these animals is tender, and they wrap it up around themselves with their legs. They are fed with millet for four years. But in the fifth year, when they are known not to live any longer, they receive green reed as food. This is delightful to them and they eat until they are thick and full, burst and die. Then many threads are still found within them.

At the times of EZEKIEL (16 : 10, 13) silk is first mentioned in the Bible as a great luxury. And Lampridius (*De Heliogabalo* 26) regards it as a very great extravagance that HELIOGABAL was the first Roman who wore clothes all silk whilst until that time only half-silk clothes were worn by Roman men. Only the Syrian AMMIANUS MARCELLUS (about 375 A.D.; *Hist.* 23 : 6), still maintaining that the Seres take the silk from their trees, states: before only the nobles had silk clothes, but now they are worn even by the common men. He continues: when foreigners come to the Seres to buy threads, the Seres spread their goods, and the bargain is concluded without any word being exchanged.

The first living Chinese silkworm-eggs were brought to Constantinople by two monks in 551 A.D., in the days of JUSTINIAN, (PROCOPIUS, *De bello Gothico* 4 : 17; about 560 A.D.; he was a native of Caesarea in Palestine). And the late Byzantine historian ZONARAS (*Chronicon* 14 : 9) confirms this: monks brought the eggs of the silkworm to Greece during the reign of JUSTINIAN. Only then they began to know something about these animals, their cocoons and the growing of silkworms. A number of passages of the *Talmud* tells us about three qualities of silk threads, showing that silk weaving was familiar in the Middle East at that period. Berytos and Tyre were famous early centres of this industry, before silkworm breeding was introduced. We intend to demonstrate later that Syria and Palestine were among the earliest centres of silkworm-breeding.

The dyeing industry of the *Kermes* scale for crimson colour will be treated later on. We here only quote the *Chronicles* (II : 2 : 7), where king SOLOMON asks from HIRAM of Tyr to send him a man able to work with purple and crimson.

D. *Some other insects.* Cicadas (*Cicada, Cicadatra, Melampsalta spp.*) were appreciated as beautiful singers by the Greek, an attitude not shared by the Syrians (cf. Syriac literature). ANACREON (*Ode* 43) calls the cicadas happy: You are loved by the farmer as the delightful prophet of summer, by the muses and by Phoebus, who has gifted you with song and voice. ARISTOTLE (*Hist. Anim., passim*) well describes their natural history. "At first the males taste better, later on, when full of eggs, the females." Also EUENOS of Askalon mentions the eating of cicadas. Even AELIAN (1 : 20) knows that they emit their sound from the hips. In Ionian Anatolia and in Athens the cicada was the symbol of autochthony. It was connected with Baal-zebub and with Apollo Smintheus as the announcer of the summer heat. The cicada appears in many animal fables, also on many coins, figurines and ornamental pendants, mainly in the Greek and Hellenistic world.

The sacred scarabaeus (*Scarabaeus sacer*), the kheper, is so common throughout Egyptian civilisation that he is almost the personification of ancient Egypt. The scarab seals outside Egypt are everywhere indicators of Egyptian influence or domination. The few scarabs from ancient Mesopotamia certainly are importations (VAN BUREN 1939 p. 113). It is an error to assume that a scarabaeus cult ever existed in Egypt. The beetle was connected with Ra, the sun god, and Ra is sometimes depicted as kheper with a scarab as head. The reason for this connection with the sun is obscure. The rolling of the spherical pills may have been the primary motivation. Another explanation is that the metamorphosis of the beetle, its being hatched from a mummy-like pupa, was taken as a symbol of the resurrection of the dead. This theory must be rejected. The metamorphosis of the *Scarabaeus* is very difficult to follow, and it was adequately described only fairly late by that incomparable observer JULES FABRE. The hint in PLINY (*Hist. Nat.* 11 : 28 : 34): some beetles make large pills of dung, roll them backward with their legs and lay small worms into them, from which new beetles are formed, is not sufficient to support that rather far-fetched theory (see BODENHEIMER 1928 p. 31 f.). All scarabs were regarded as males, and this may have to do with the custom of the Egyptian soldiers to wear scarab rings. This maleness of the beetles may have been another reason to devote it to Ra. Also some other species of *Scarabaeus* and related genera, such as *Copris,* were imitated on scarab seals. The enormous *Heliocopris* of the Sudan, one of the largest beetles with enormous pills, may perhaps still easier have impressed itself upon the mind of the people of Upper-Egypt, from where many of the Egyptian animal symbols took their origin, than the much smaller *Scarabaeus* and many related genera, so common in Lower Egypt.

The number of scarab seals and amulets, found wherever Egyptians lived, is enormous. The preference for scarabs was taken over by the gnostics of later Egypt. The scarabaeus entered into the symbolism of neo-platonism. And in the symbolism of the early fathers of the church it grew quite important. The beetle was even likened to Christ, as it knows to turn a vulgar matter into purity. The shape of the scarabs changes with the centuries and enables reliable dating of archaeological finds. The Palestine scarabs will be discussed later. Also in medicine the scarabaeus was applied. Thus we find the following prescription in the *Papyrus Ebers*: take a big scarab, cut off its head and its wings, boil it, put it in oil and apply it. Then cook its head and wings, put them in fat of snakes, boil it and give this drink to the sick.

Butterflies and moths are rare in Egyptian paintings. In Mesopotamia they are wanting. Neither does the Bible mention them (although it mentions the cloth moth). The animal fable of the ancients ignores them. And even ARISTOTLE and PLINY mention only a few common agricultural pests; their metamorphosis, however, was known (ARISTOTLE, *Hist. Anim.* 5 : 1 : 5; 5 : 17 : 1-4). But during the Mycenaean civilisation the psyche gained great importance. Many are the gold engravings of the moth since archaic times. It was undoubtedly a soul-bird. On an old Mycenaean mural painting we see the goddess of death striding over the asphodelos meadow of Hades, accompanied by a butterfly. IMMISCH (1915) studied the history of this myth. The original name of the moth was *phalaena*, derived from *phallos*. Hence the early tendency to exaggerate the size of the abdomen at the expense of the wings. Later only these flying *phalli* became the soul-birds, loving life, yet indidious of the living. Whilst the metamorphosis was known, we still are rather in doubt, whether the hatching of the moth from their pupa was a symbol for the resurrection of the dead. The moths swarming around the light, and over the cemeteries may have added to spread this myth in Greece. The simple love-life of the butterflies may have led to their late connection with Eros. Often we find the small god on gems torturing a butterfly. In early Christian symbolism the butterfly is on the one hand the prototype of vain and wordly soul, because of its playing all through its short life and by its coming into the flame which burns it. But, on the other hand, the hatching from the pupa served as a symbol of the purified soul, which released from material bonds enters the eternal happiness of heaven.

E. Significance of insects in dreams. ARTEMIDORUS of Daldos in Lydia (about 150 A.D.), in his *Oneirocritica* (Interpretation of dreams), gives a series of interpretations of dreams on insects.

Bees (2 : 22) are **a good augury** to the farmer and the bee-keeper, to other people they announce unrest through their humming, wounding, through their sting, disease through their honey and wax. When they sit on the head of the dreamer, they are favourable to a general or to a politician, to others they announce sufferings by a mob or by soldiers. To the sick they announce death when they sit on inanimate objects. Wasps are always a bad augury, spelling the company of bad and cruel men. Locusts and grasshoppers indicate a bad year to the farmer, to others a low woman. Dung-beetles, gold-beetles and glowworms are favourable only to people exercising a low and dirty profession, to others, especially to dealers in ointments and spices, they mean damage and poor business.

(2 : 13). Spiders, scorpions and centipedes mean evil men. (3 : 6). Winged ants spell disaster and dangerous travels. Apterous ants mean blessing to the farmer, indicating fertility, as no ants are seen on sterile places, also to people who earn their bread in large quantities. They are favourable to the sick, if they do not crawl over the dreamer's body. They are untiring workers. But when crawling over the dreamer's body, however, they announce death, as they are cold, black and sons of the soil. (3 : 7). To find and to kill a few lice on body or clothes is favourable, announcing release from every grief and sorrow. But if they appear in abundance, they mean disaster, long sickness, imprisonment or great poverty, as lice are increasing under these conditions. But if you get rid of them, there is hope of redemption from these evils. Yet when man awakens whilst still full of lice, there is no hope. (3 : 8). Bedbugs are the symbol of depression and sorrow, both of which will cause sleepless nights. They also cause irritation and discord with some members of the household, especially with women. Mosquitoes, gnats, and similar insects, indicate bad company, causing damage and bad reputation. But to keepers of taverns and sellers of wine they foretell transformation of the wine into vinegar, as they like vinegar.

(3 : 49). Cicadas mean musical men, yet in business useless people, babblers and makers of empty threats, as the cicadas possess nothing except their voice. To the sick they announce terrible thirst and unavoidable death, as they do not eat.

(5 : 64). Somebody dreamed that he found many large bedbugs in his cloth, and although he destested them he could not get rid of them, try as he would. The next day he learned that his wife had committed adultery. He felt very sore, but certain circumstances prevented him of getting rid of her. The cloth indicated his wife, the bedbugs the shame. Just as he could not get rid of the bugs in his dream, he could not get rid of his wife in life.

F. Other vertebrates. Here we may just mention the big snails which were eaten by the Romans. VARRO (*De re rustica* 3 : 14) gives an admirable instruction for the breeding of these snails (*Helix pomatia,* and others), part of which was introduced especially for this purpose.

2. 16. MARINE AND FLUVIATILE VERTEBRATES

A. Fluviatile animals. Among the fluviatiles we mention only the cancer of the zodiac. In all old zodiacs of the Middle East—and the zodiac is an invention of Mesopotamia—we definitely find only crabs, usually the fresh water crab *Potamion,* rarer marine crabs, such as *Maja.* The same crab occurs in Assyrian scenes of fresh water life. The crayfish (*Astacus*), which in Europe has replaced the crab in the zodiac, is restricted to S. Europe, the northern shores of Anatolia and to a river near Caesarea (Anatolia). This transformation is certainly secondary and of a late date. It is suggested that its retrograde (laterad) way of motion caused the old Babylonians to insert it into the zodiac, at the season when the sun begins its retrogression.

Freshwater shells were apparently not or little eaten by early man in this region. But in the oldest settlements we find ornaments of mother of pearl, made from the shells of *Unio* or *Leguminaia* (see Teleilat Ghassul). The freshwater pearl-shell was unknown in Europe, until CAESAR introduced it from N. Europe. Occasional pearls were known from Thrace and other regions.

B. Marine life: Crustaceans. We have a poor Assyrian illustration of marine life. (pl. XI). But we find beautiful scenes of marine life from the Hellenistic and Roman periods on mosaic pavements at Pompeji, Alexandria, Antiochia, etc. Among the fishes there appear crabs, crayfish, cuttle fish, sea stars, shells, and others, mainly the frutti da mare of the ancient fish markets. Cuttlefish were a favourite motive of Mycenaean art.

For the description of marine life we recur to OPPIAN of Anatolia and his *Halieutica,* *e.g.* where he sings of crustaceans (1 : 259 ff., 319 ff.):

"Two fishes whose limbs are fenced with hard coats swim in the gulfs of the sea: the spiny crayfish (*Palinurus vulgaris*) and the lobster (*Homarus vulgaris*). Both these dwell among the rocks and there they feed. The lobster holds in its heart a love for its own lair and he never leaves it willingly, but if you drag him away by force and carry him far away and let him go again in the sea, in no long time he returns to his own cleft eagerly. He will not choose a strange retreat, but seeks the home that he left and his native haunts and feeding ground. Thus even to the swimming tribes their own house, where they are born, instil in their hearts a sweet delight. To that kind also belong the wandering crab (general for *Decapoda brachyura*), the shoals of the prawn (shrimps such as *Crangon, Squilla, Palaemon*) and the shameless tribe of the edible crab (*Cancer pagurus*). All those whose body is set beneath a shell put off the old shell and another springs up from the nether flesh. The edible crabs, when feeling the coming moult, rush everywhere in their desire for food, that the separation of the slough may be easier when they have sated themselves. But when the sheath is rent and slips off, then at first they lie idly stretched upon the sands, mindful neither of food nor of aught else, thinking to be numbered with the dead and to breathe warm breath no more, and they tremble for their new-grown tender hide. Afterwards they recover their spirits again and take a little courage and eat of the sand; but they are weak and helpless of heart until a new shelter is compacted about their limbs. The hermit crabs (*Pagurus diogenes*) have no shell of their own from birth, but are born naked. Yet they devise for themselves an acquired home, covering their feeble bodies with a bastard shelter. For when they see a shell left all desolate, the tenant having left his home, they creep in below the alien mantle and settle there and dwell and take it for their home. And along with it they travel and move their shelter from within, whether it be some *Buccinum* that has left the shell or a *Cerithium*. Most of all they love the shells of the latter, as they are wide and light to carry. But when the hermit crab within grows and fills the cavity, it keeps that house no longer, but leaves it and seeks a wider shell-vessel to put on. Often battle arises among the hermit crabs about a hollow shell and the stronger drives out the weaker and puts herself on the fitting house."

(2 : 167 ff.). "And one who observes a crab among the mossy ledges will admire him for his cunning art. Heaven has given him wisdom to feed on oysters, a sweet and unlaborious food. The oysters open the bars of their doors and lick the mud, and in their desire for water sit wide open in the arms of the rocks. The crab now takes a pebble from the beach, and moving sideways, carries it clutched in his sharp claws. Stealthily he draws near and puts the stone in the middle of the oyster. Then he sits by and makes a pleasant feast. And the oyster is unable to shut his two valves, but gapes perforce until it dies and gluts his captor."

C. Marine molluscs. Cuttle fish and their ways were well-known to the ancients.

(2 : 389 ff.) "The spiny lobster (*Palinurus vulgaris*), prickly though he be and swift, is devoured by the octopus (*Octopus vulgaris*), albeit he is weaker and sluggish of motion. For when the octopus remarks him under the rocks sitting all motionless, stealthily he springs upon his back and casts his various bonds about him, oppressing him with the long chains of his strong feet and with the ends of his tentacles withal he constricts and strangles the warm channel in the midst of his mouth and suffers not his airy breath to pass either out or in (for fishes too draw the tide of the air), but holds him in his embrace. And the crayfish now swims, now halts, and again struggles. But the octopus relaxes not the contest of might, until life and strength forsake the other in death. Then the octopus sits by him on the sands and feasts, lapping the flesh of the crayfish, sucking and drawing it forth from its prickly vessel, and fills his belly with sweet food" (3 : 156 ff.). "The cuttle fish practise this craft: They (*Sepia vulgaris*) have seated in their heads a dark muddy fluid blacker than pitch, a mysterious

drug causing a watery cloud, which is their natural defence against destruction. When fear seizes them, immediately they discharge the dusky drops thereof and the cloudy fluid stains and obscures all around the paths of the sea and ruins all the view. And they straightway through the turbid waters easily escape man or haply mightier fish. The fluid of the squid (*Lòligo vulgaris*) is not black but reddish, but the device which they employ is similar (4 : 147 ff.). For catching the cuttle fishes merely trail in the waves a single female attached to the line. The cuttle fishes, when they behold it from afar, speedily come to meet it and twine about it and cling to it with their arms. And their passion not abates until the fishermen draw them forth upon the boat." (1 : 340 ff.). "One fish is covered with a hollow shell, in form like the octopus, which men call nautilus (*Argonauta argo*), so named because it sails of itself. It dwells in the sands and it rises to the surface of the water face downwards, so that the sea may not fill it. But when it swims above the waves, straightway it turns over and sails like a man skilled in sailing a boat. Two feet it stretches aloft by way of rigging and between these runs like a sail a fine membrane which is stretched by the wind: but underneath two feet touching the water, like rudders, guide and direct house and ship and fish. But when it fears some evil hard at hand, no longer does it trust the winds in its flight, but gathers in all its tackle, sails and rudders, and receives the full flood within and is weighed down and sunk by the rush of water."

Relatively little is reported about bivalves and snails:

(5 : 589) "As for the testacean tribes which crawl in the sea, they all are told to be in due cycle full of flesh when the moon is waxing and inhabit a rich dwelling, but when she wanes, again they become more meagre and wrinkled of limb: such compelling force resides in them. Of these men gather some from the sand with their hands, diving under the sea. Others they pull from the rocks to which they stubbornly cling, yet others the waves cast up on the very shores or in trenches digged in the sand. The purple shells (*Murex spp.*) again among shell-fish are eminently gluttonous, and by gluttony is the true manner of their capture. Small weels like baskets are made with close-set rushes, and the fishers gather and place in them snails and clams together. When the purple-fishes draw near, drunk with the lust of food, they put forth from within their chamber their long tongue, which is thin and sharp, and stretch it through the rushes, in quest of food and fatal feast they find. For the tongue, fixed in the close-set rushes, swells and is straitened by the mesh of withes and cannot any more draw back if it try but remains stretched in pain, until the fishers land the shell-fish while intent upon their tongue, bringing a colour most beautiful for purple cloths."

With these purple snails we will deal later in a special chapter. We have mentioned before that early men fed upon marine molluscs gathered along the shores, even if we do not find refuse hills of mussels as in Scandinavia, the famous *kjökkenmöddinger,* on the shores of the Levant. VIRCHOW succeeded to determine the following species from the refuse heaps of oldest Troja, which certainly had served as food: *Pecten, Pectunculus, Mytilus edulis, Cardium edule, Solen marginatus, Ostrea cristata* and *O. lamellosa.* At Mycenae even unbroken clams were put into the graves as food for the dead. The Romans in their practical way arranged artificial oyster-, and mussel-beds. That this food was even in later days not despised can be learned from a passage in XENOCRATES (*De nutrimento aquatico*): Rare are the oysters in the depths of the sea, and their value is small, as the sun does not shine upon them. They like a mixture of sweet water, and are most tasty in places, where a river flows into the sea. The best oysters are those found at the mouth of the Nile and at that of the KAYSTRUS near Ephesus.

The most important beds of pearl-oysters known to the ancient world were those on the Persian Gulf and between Toprabane (Ceylon) and India. Apparently they became introduced into the western world, at least to some considerable extent, only by ALEXANDER's expeditions. In Egypt the oldest pearls discovered date from the Hyksos period. They were also not unknown in ancient Mesopotamia, probably coming from the Indian or Persian trade. In ancient India pearls were abundant and at least the later Persians were great lovers of pearls. KELLER (1913 p. 559) points out, that the excavations in Phoenicia, Cyprus, Anatolia, Greece, Etrury and Carthage have so far not revealed any pearls before the date of Alexander. In the Old Testament we find allusions to pearls only in the book of *Job* and in the *Proverbs,* where they are referred to as something extremely valuable. CHRIST called the pearl the symbol of the kingdom of God and of the gospel. Well-known is his admonition not to throw pearls before the pigs.

The oldest literature is well compiled in ATHENAEUS (Dipnosoph. 3 : 45) : THEOPHRAST, Book of stones: Amongst the precious stones belongs the pearl. It is translucent and is used as a component of necklaces. It comes from shell-fishes similar to the *pinna* (undetermined bivalve), but smaller, being of the size of large fish eyes. ANDROSTHENES, a contemporary of ALEXANDER, in his description of the navigation on the Indian shores says: there exists a peculiar bivalve, called *berberi* by the natives, from which the pearl comes. It is highly appreciated in Asia, and is traded to Persia, and farther away. The shell-fish is similar to *Pecten,* but without furrows, smooth and rough; instead of the two earlike protuberances of *Pecten,* it has only one. The pearl originates in the flesh of the animal and is either as golden as gold or silvery or white as fish-eyes. CHARES of Mytilene (*Hist. Alexandri* 7): There are caught some shell-fish in the Indian Ocean, from which white bones are taken, called pearls, used as laces for neck, arms or feet, which are estimated higher than gold pendants in Persia, Media and Anatolia. And ISIDORUS of Charaxes, born himself near the Persian Gulf (*Descriptio Parthiae*): Many pearls are found in an island in the Persian Gulf. Hence many boats of reeds are in this island, from which the divers jump into the sea, up to 20 ells deep, in order to collect the shell-fish. The most and best pearls generate in the animals at thunderstorms and heavy rains. During winter the bivalves hide in the depths, in summer they open the valves by night and swim there and back, but close them by day. Those which are rooted on the rocks there produce the pearls. They feed with a peculiar organ with pincers, which apports the food: it looks like a small shrimp and is named *pinnophylax* (This is mixed up with the story of the *Pinnoteres veterum*). From it the meat extends to the middle of the shell-fish like a root; in this the pearl is generated, growing from the solid mass of the animal, as long as it is still connected with it. But if meat slowly grows between the pearl and the valve, this meat embraces the entire pearl, does not feed it, but makes it smoother, purer and more translucent. The pearls produced in the depth are the most shining, purest and biggest ones. The pearls of the swimming and of the shell-fish of shallow waters are worse in colour and smaller. People who put their hand between the valves of the shell-fish, run the risk that their fingers are cut when the valves close. Some die immediately. But if you put the hand obliquely into them, you easily can tear them from the rocks.

The scientific name of the pearl-oyster of the Indian Ocean is *Meleagrina meleagris.* About the incredible luxury of imperial Rome as regards pearls we find some informative anecdotes in PLINY (*Hist. Nat.* 9 : 35 : 58).

D. Other marine animals. "The star-fishes (*Asterias*) of the sea too have a device against oysters. They insert a rough limb into the middle of the open oyster. Thus the oyster is overcome, while the star-fish feeds" (*Halieutica* 2 : 180). "Wit and cunning also belong to the prickly sea-urchins (*Echinus esculentus*), which know when the violence of the wind and the fiercy storms are rising, and lift each of them upon their backs a stone of such weight as they can easily carry on their spines, that thus weighted they may withstand the driving of the wave. For they most dread that the swelling wave roll them on the shore."

About the common jelly-fish (*Aurelia aurita, Rhizostoma pulmo, Physophora*) PLINY

(9 : 45 : 68) writes: Although neither animal nor plant, they have a certain sensitivity I think. They wander at night, are like thick leaves and devour meat. When touching them, they burn like common stinging nettles. Sometimes they entirely contract. When a fish passes them, they extend their arms, embrace and devour it. At another occasion they appear to be feeble, let themselves drive by the water, by chance contact a fish which they immediately attack. At night they are looking for *Pecten* and sea-urchins.

The red coral (*Corallium rubrum*) was a popular ornament in all Mediterranean countries. Among the many places of fishery and coral manufacture Smyrna and Magnesia on the Ionian coast excelled. PLINY (*Hist. Nat.* 32 : 2 : 11) says that corals are valued in India as pearls with us. That is a fashion. The corals have the shape of a shrub and are green. Their berries are snow-white under water and soft. As soon as you take them out of the water, they grow hard and red. The corals are fished with nets or they are cut off with sharp iron tools. The best sort is entirely red and has many branches, smooth, without grooves, and solid. The prophets appreciate them as a protection against dangers. In India they are ornament and amulet in one. At present they are rare on the market and even in their regular sites few are found now. The small branches of the coral are put on children as an amulet. They are internally and externally used in medicine.

Also sponge fishery (of *Euspongia officinalis*) was rather well-known in the Levantine coasts in ancient times. Sponges were recognised as animals and sorted into four commercial qualities. The Anatolian and Syrian coasts were famous for sponge fishery until a relatively recent past. OPPIAN (*Hal.* 5 : 612) declares the task of the sponge-divers as hard and woeful.

„When they prepare themselves for their labour, they use more meagre food and drink. They do zealously take all watchful care that their breath may abide unscathed when they go down into the depths and that they may recover from past toil. But when they accomplish their mighty task, they make their vows to the blessed gods of the deep sea and pray that they ward from them all hurt from the monsters of the deep. And if they see a beauty-fish, then great courage comes into their hearts; for where these range there never yet a sea-monster appeared nor hurtful thing, but always they delight in clean and harmless paths: wherefore they also call it holy fish. Rejoicing in it they hasten to their labours. A man is girt with a long rope above his waist and, using both hands, in one he grasps a heavy mass of lead and in his right hand he holds a sharp bill, while in the jaws of his mouth he keeps white oil. Standing upon the prow he scans the waves of the sea, pondering his heavy task and the infinite water. His comrades incite and stir him to his work with encouraging words? But when he takes heart of courage, he leaps into the eddying waves and as he springs the force of the heavy grey lead drags him down. Now when he arrives at the bottom, he spits out the oil, and shines brightly and the gleam mingles with the water, even as a beacon showing its eye in the darkness of the night. Approaching the rocks he sees the sponges which grow on the ledges of the bottom, fixed fast to the rocks; and report tells that they have breath in them. Straightway rushing upon them with the bill in his stout hand, like a mower, he cuts the body of the sponges, and he loiters not, but quickly shakes the rope, signalling to his comrades to pull him up swiftly. For hateful blood is sprinkled straightway from the sponges and rolls about the man, and many a time the grievous fluid, clinging to his nostrils, chokes the man with noisome breath. Therefore swift as thought he is pulled to the surface. Beholding him escaped from the sea one would rejoice at once and grieve and pity: so much are his weak members relaxed and his limbs unstrung with fear and distressful labour. Often when the sponge-cutter has leapt into the deep waters of the sea and won his loathly and unkindly spoil, he comes up no more, unhappy man, having encountered some huge and hideous beast. Shaking repeatedly the rope he bids his comrades pull him up. And the mighty sea-monster and the companion of the fisher pull at his body rent in twain, a pitiful sight to see, still yearning for ship and shipmates. And they in sorrow speedily leave those waters and their mournful labour and return to land, weeping over the remains of their unhappy comrade."

2.2. THE ANIMAL IN THE LIFE OF ANCIENT MESOPOTAMIA

2.21. HUNTING AND ZOOLOGICAL PARKS

The royal hunters of Assyria and most probably also of other kingdoms of Irak, not only enjoyed the hunt, but they also collected animals in parks and showed them to "the people of their country". These parks not only included the big game of the country, but great efforts were made to introduce exotic animals from foreign countries. These were often added to the annual tribute of subjected peoples, to the exchange of royal correspondence, but were also often demanded especially from friendly neighbouring princes to be procured. Most kings boasted to have brought back from their foreign campaigns new agricultural and horticultural plants, new domestic and other animals and to have them planted and collected in special parks, some of which are partially depicted on big steles. The oldest zoological garden, of which a record is preserved, is that of TIGLATPILESER I:

> "In the days of cold, frost and rains, in the days of the burning Sirius, he caught in the mountains of Ashur and of Khana (near Sulaimaniye) and in the Armenian mountains: male and female wild goats, male and female deer with kids, collected them into herds and let them produce. He held these herds to be as valuable as small cattle. Leopards, bears, wild boar, large birds did he kill, together with the wild ass, gazelles and the cheetah."

From the land of Mussri, which often is interpreted as Egypt but is almost certainly a region in S. Anatolia, he received: some big monkeys, a rhinoceros and a crocodile. All these animals belong to the Indian, not to the African forms. Not only living, but also stuffed animals were ordered from foreign countries, in order "to be shown to the people of his land". ASURNASSIRPAL enumerates:

> In these days I received with the tribute small and large monkeys. I brought them to Ashur and let increase their herd at Kalach abundantly. I showed them to all my subjects. By stretching out my arm and by the courage of my heart did I catch 15 strong lions from the mountains and the forests. 50 lion cubs did I collect and put them into cages and let them increase. I caught living leopards with my hands. I brought herds of wild bulls, of elephants, living lions, monkeys, wild asses, gazelles, deer, bears and cheetahs into my town of Kalach and showed them to all my subjects.

His son SALMANASSAR received from the same Mussri: Bactrian camels, a wild bull, a rhinoceros, an antelope, she-elephants and two species of monkeys, all of the Indian races again. The great SANHERIB (ab. 690 B.C.) built artificial reed-beds in his gardens, which he populated with lions, wild boar, swans and other animals.

All these records not only show the very high, almost enthusiastic interest, which the old peoples of Irak had for at least the big animals of their realm, but also the abundance of this sort of animal life.

Hunting. Hunting was a royal sport in old Irak, apart from the hunting of professional hunters. The oldest hunting took place with nets. This is amply proven by the word '*ssaad*', which means hunting as well as catching of fish. The prey was caught by throwing nets over it or by catching it in specially prepared grooves. Bird-catchers also worked with nets. The wild ass was caught with lassos. The use of arrow and dart, of spear and lance, and, for short distances, of sword, dagger and club, perhaps also of slings, were probably secondary improvements. An old habit is certainly the hunting in groups. Later introductions were the hunting with dogs, the hunting from chariots, from horse-back, etc. Hunting with the cheetah and with falcons is also illustrated in reliefs.

The royal hunts are often described on illustrated steles. The compilation of a few of these official texts will give an impression of the abundance of many big game animals, which are extinct now:

TIGLATPILESER I (about 1000 B.C.) writes (LUCKENBILL I. 1926, I p. 85-87 no. 247, 248, 253. Prism inscription Col. VI. 247). The gods Urta and Nergal have given their terrible weapons and their majestic bow into my lordly grasp. At the bidding of Urta, who loves me, four wild bulls (aurochs), which were mighty and of monstrous size, in the resert, in the country of Mitani, and near to the city of Araziki, which is over against the land of Hatti, with my mighty bow, with my iron spear, and with my sharp darts, I killed. Their hides and their horns I brought unto my city Assur. Ten mighty bull-elephants I slew in the country of Harran, and in the district of the river Habur. Four elephants I caught alive. Their hides and their tusks, together with the live elephants, I brought unto my city Assur.

248. At the bidding of Urta, who loves me, I have slain 120 lions by my bold courage and by my strong attack, on foot; and 800 lions I have laid low from my chariot with javelins (?). I have brought down all (kinds of) beasts of the field, and birds of the heavens that fly, among my hunting spoils.

253. (Col. VII). Herds of horses, cattle and asses, which I seized with the help of Assur, my lord, in the lands which I brought under my sway, I have gathered together as the spoil of my hand; and herds of deer, stags, ibex, and wild goats, which Assur and Urta, the gods who love me, have given me for the chase, I have taken in the midst of the lofty hills. Herds of them I gathered and counted their number like unto that of a flock of sheep. Yearly I offered unto Assur, my lord, such of the young wild creatures which were born from them as my heart prompted me (to choose) together with my pure lambs, for sacrifice.

TUKULTI NINIB (early 9th century B.C.) killed 9 wild bulls near the Wadi Thirtar, in addition to deer (?gazelles) and game birds. ASURNASSIRPAL, his son, killed, during one expedition to the Upper Euphrates, 50 wild bulls and caught 8 of them, he killed 20 large game birds and caught 20 of them. In his life he killed 30 elephants with the bow, 257 wild bulls from the chariot, 370 lions with the spear. One room of the palace of SARGON was decorated with hunting scenes of birds and hares in a pine forest. An abundance of reliefs illustrating the royal hunt of lions, wild bulls and asses are preserved, some of them being of exquisite beauty.

ADAD-NIRARI II (I p. 121, 122 no. 392). The Broken Obelisk inscription Col. IV. The gods Urta and Nergal, who love his priesthood, granted him (the skill) to hunt in the field and he embarked in ships of the Arvadites and slew a *nahiru* (? dolphin) in the Great Sea. . . . . . mighty wild bulls near the city of Araziki, which lies opposite the land of Hatti, and at the foot of Mt. Lebanon, he slew. . . . . young of wild oxen he captured alive, and herds of them he collected. . . . . . elephants he brought down with his bow, and elephants he captured alive, and brought them to his city of Assur. 120 lions with his brave heart and with his courageous attack, he slew from his hunting (?) chariot, or on foot with the javelin, ... lions he brought down with the javelin (?). To hunt for them (the gods) in the high mountains, they (the gods) commanded him, and in the days of cold, and frost, and snow, (or) in the days of the ascendency of Sirius, which glowed like copper, in the mountains of Ebih, Urshe, Azameri, Ankurna, Pizitta, Parsagish (?) and Kashiari, mountains of the land of Assyria, (in) Mt. Hana on the border of the land of the Lulume, and in the mountains of Nairi, ... ibexes and mountain goats, ... hinds and stags, he captured in nets, and large herds of them he collected, he caused them to bring forth (young). Like flocks of sheep he counted them......leopards, ... *midini*, ... *asi,* and two (or 120) wild boars of the cane-brakes, ... *malshir*-birds he slew. . . . . . . onagers and gazelles, ... jackals, ...*simkurri* he brought down. A *burhish,* Bactrian camels, *tesheni,* -merchants he sent out, brought (them); he collected Bactrian camels, and he caused them to bring forth (young). Herds of them he caused the people of his land to behold. A great *pagutu,* a crocodile, a river ox (buffalo), creatures of the Great Sea, which the king of the land of Musre (usually identified with Egypt) sent, he caused the people of his land to behold. As for the remainder of the many wild beasts, and fowl of heaven that fly,—(his) dominion (?) over the field, the deeds of his hands, their names were not recorded with (those of) these (?) beasts, their numbers were not recorded with these numbers.

TUKULTI-URTA II (I p. 130 no. 410. Annals: frontal side).
.........30 camels, 50 cattle, 30 asses, 14 large birds, 200 lambs, food and drink, straw and fodder, I received as the gift of Amme-alaba of Hindanu. (There) I spent the night. Hindanu lies on the other side of the Euphrates. While roaming (about in) the desert I killed *ibur*-birds. The young *ibur*-birds I caught with my hands. While roaming (along) the banks of the Euphrates I killed deer (probably gazelles or antelopes). The young of the deer I caught with my hands.

ASSUR-NASIR-PAL (I p. 189 no. 518-520. Colossus from Calah. Col. IV).
518......At that time I received the tribute of the kings of the seacoast, of the Tyreans, the Sidonians, the Amorites, the Gebalites, the Mahalateans, the Kaisites, the Maisites, and of the city of Arvad, which is in the midst of the sea, — silver, gold, lead, copper, vessels of copper, garments of brightly coloured wool, linen garments, ivory, and a *nahiru* (?dolphin), a creature of the sea (cf. no. 298). I received at that time from them great and small *pagate,* together with their tribute. Unto my land of Assyria I brought them, and in the city of Calah I bred great herds of them, letting all the people of my land behold them.
519. By my outstretched arm and impetuous courage, 15 mighty lions from the mountains and the forests I seized with my hand, and 50 lion-cubs I carried away, and, in the city of Calah, and the palaces of my land, put them in cages, and I caused them to bring forth their cugs in abundance. URMINDINASH I captured alive with my hands, (and) herds of wild oxen, elephants and lions, and *malshir*-birds, male and female *pagate,* onagers, gazelles, stags, *asate* (?wolves), leopards, and *senkurri,* all the beasts of plain and mountain, I collected in my city of Calah, letting all the people of my land behold them.

520. O future prince among the kings, my sons, whom Assur shall call by name, or future peoples, or servants of the king, or noble, or high official: Thou shalt not abuse these creatures before Assur. Urta and Nergal, who love my priesthood, entrusted to me the wild creatures of the field, commanding me to follow the chase. 30 elephants from ambush I slew, and 257 mighty wild oxen in my hunting(?)-chariots (and by my lordly attack I brought down with my weapons, and 370 mighty lions, like caged birds, I slew with the javelin).

Lions must have been rather abundant at the beginning of the great empires in ancient Irak. In the account of the deluge the destruction of impudent humanity by an increase of lions is proposed as an equivalent alternative for the deluge. The laws of Hammurabi contain special paragraphs on the responsibility for hired cattle, which is killed by lions. The big lion hunter ASSURBANIPAL regards himself as a benefactor to his country (LUCKENBILL 1926 : 1025/26): "Since I ascended the throne of my father, Adad gave ample rains, Ea split (his sources), the forests increased and the reed-beds grew thick, and nobody may enter them. There increased the lions beyond numbers. They grew fierce by the feeding of small and big cattle and of men. Their roaring vibrated among the mountains, it terrified the beasts of the steppe. They killed the domestic cattle without end, and shed the blood of countless men. The corpses of dead men, of cattle are spread as after a defeat by the god of plague. The shepherds are crying and their overseers, that the lions are destroying all. Mourning is in the houses day and night. The misdeeds of these lions were announced to me. I entered their realm and destroyed their dens. I liberated the people of the town from this pest."

Illustrated inscriptions show ASSURBANIPAL killing a lion with a sword or with a spear. Other pictures show a number of lions which have been kept in cages and which are liberated for mass killing. Battles of gazelles and antelopes are also represented. Interesting is the beating-up of wild asses, which were hunted by riders and dogs or which were caught by means of a lasso by hunters on foot.

The following numbers 1021 to 1026 are from the famous lion-hunting reliefs of ASSURBANIPAL:

The king pours out a libation over four killed lions: I am Assurbanipal, king of the universe, king of Assyria, ... The lions which I slew,—the terrible bow of Ishtar, lady of battle, I aimed upon them ... (2, 1021).

The king seizes a lion by the ear and pierces its body with his lance: I am Assurbanipal, ... In my might, on foot I seized a fierced lion of the plain by its ears. With the aid of Assur and Ishtar, lady of the battle, I pierced his body with a lance of my hands (2, 1022).

The king seizes a lion by the tail and kills it with his club: I, Assurbanipal, ... in my lordly sport I seized a lion of the plain by its tail and at the command of Urta and Nergal, my allied gods, I smashed its skull with the club of my hands (2, 1023).

The king kills a lion with a dagger: I, Assurbanipal, ... in my lordly sport, they let a fierce lion of the plain out of his cage and on foot, with my spear(?)-shaft, I ... , but did not end its life. At the command of Nergal, king of the plain, who granted me strength (and) manliness, I stabbed him then with my iron girdle dagger and laid down its life (2, 1024).

The soldiers of the king kill lions with their spears: I, Assurbanipal, ... In an open space in the plain, fierce lions, dreadful children of the mountains, came out. They surrounded the chariot, my royal vehicle. At the command of Assur and Ishtar, the great gods, my lords, ... I shattered the might of these lions (2, 1025).

And a lion made for URTAKU, king of Elam, and he was scared and implored my majesty (for aid) (2, 1026).

SENNACHERIB built a channel for the waters of Musri: Following my plan, I added them to the Husur's waters for ever. I had all the orchards watered in summer ... To arrest the flow of these waters, I made a swamp, and set out a cane-break within it. Igiru-birds, wild swine, beasts of the forest, I turned loose therein (2, 401) ... The cane-breaks developed rapidly. The birds of the heaven, the igiru-birds, whose home is far away, built their nests. The wild swine and beasts of the forest brought forth young in abundance (2, 402).

And ESARHADDON describes the Bazu desert (probably the Sinai): Bazu, a district located far off, a desert stretch of salt-earth, a thirsty region: — 140 double hours of sand, thorn-bush and "gazelle-mouth" stones, 20 double hours of serpents and scorpions, with which the plane was filled as with ants, ... I left behind me (2, 537).

And SENNACHERIB writes about HEZEKIAH, king of Jerusalem: (Hezekiah, the Jew) like a caged bird, in Jerusalem, his royal city, I shut up (2, 312). And 200.150 people, grand and small, male and female, horses, mules, asses, camels, cattle and sheep, without number, I brought away (from the 46 strong cities of Hezekiah, the Jew) (2, 240).

The part of the beasts of burden in the army transport is illustrated by the remark of SARGON: I led my whole army load on horses, mules, camels and asses (in the mountains) (2, 165). But SARGON was also a promotor of agriculture: The ground of his uncultivated areas he made like a meadow, flooding it abundantly in spring, (and) grass and pasturage did not fail, winter and summer. Into stamping grounds for horses and herds he turned it. The camels in all of his submerged country he trained(?) and they pumped (the water into) ditches (2, 160).

And ASSURBANIPAL boasts: Adad sent his rains, Ea opened his fountains, the grain grew five cubits tall in the stalk, the ear was 5/6 of a cubit long, heavy crops and a plenteous yield made the fields continuously luxuriant, the orchards yielded a rich harvest, the cattle successfully brought forth their young. Much of the booty was in the form of cattle. And the many indications of their kind and number taken in the various part of the Middle East will serve one day to give a picture of the agriculture of those days. Also the tribute was largely imposed in the form of domestic animals. Thus ESARHADDON added 55 camels to the former tribute of the king of the Arabs (2, 518). Of the Medes he took: their riding-horses, cattle, sheep, asses and (Bactrian) camels (2, 540). And ASSURBANIPAL added 30 horses to the tribute of the Mannaeanse (2, 786). The yearly tribute of a king of the Arabs was mainly camels and stud-asses (2, 870). Another kind of tribute consisted not in a fixed number of animals, but: one from every 20 cattle and one from every twenty sheep as yearly tribute I laid upon them (SARGON 2, 31).

Two examples of booty are: (The Puduku) .., and the Assyrians carried off 90.580 people, 2500 horses, 610 mules, 854 camels, apart from cattle and sheep (2, 39). And from Hirimmu: 208.000 captives, 7200 horses and mules, 11003 asses, 5320 camels, 80050 cattle and 800.100 ewes (2, 267). The fixed tribute of the town for the gods of Assur was 1 ox and 10 lambs. (2, 266; 276). Among the horses we usually find the express remark: horses broken to the yoke (2, 144, etc.). Bactrian camels came mainly from Elam, dromedaries from the Arabs.

When SARGON entered his new palace, (2, 74), he sacrificed sleek bullocks, fat sheep, (barnyard) fowl, geese (?), doves, the brood of fishes and birds, the immeasurable wealth of the deep, wine and honey,... to the gods. He received important gifts from his people and his vassals on that occasion, such as violet and purple cloth, elephant hides, ivory, large Egyptian horses, broken to the yoke, mules, asses, camels and cattle. And he invited Nergal and the gods of Kalah to a sacrifice of large oxen, fat lambs, (barnyard) fowl, geese (?pesperu), birds which fly across the heavens (2, 138).

Animals appeared often in palace reliefs, as well as statues of them. Thus ESARHADDON mentions: Two wild oxen of silver, two wild oxen of copper and two suhufish of copper from one building (2, 761B). A very common composition is: one bronze bull, one bronze cow together with a bronze calf (2, 22; etc.). Another one is: 8 pairs of lions in bronze, mountain sheep as mighty protecting deities on palaces (2, 73; 84; 97; 367, etc.). Also bull colossi are often mentioned (2, 392, etc.). We would like to draw attention to the frequent mention of mulberry-trees, if the name musukanni really refers to this tree. It must be the black mulberry tree, as the white race, the better food for the silkworm must have been a rather late introduction (2, 73; 84; 97; 102; 265, etc.).

We may conclude this list with the booty of Musasir, as far as it refers to animals: Two horns of the great wild ox, whose inlay (were of gold?) and with (?) bands of gold completely surrounding their inlay . . . . Twelve great shields of silver, whose edges were ornamented with heads of dragons, lions and wild oxen . . . . One ivory couch, covered with jewels and gold, 139 ivory staves, ivory tables, ivory vegetable baskets, ivory daggers, poniards of ivory . . . . One bull, one cow together with its calf (in bronze)...One statue of Ursa with two of his horsemen, his charioteer, cast in bronze (2, 173).

Interesting is the organisation of the Assyrian army in its war arrangement, a description of which is found in the archives of ADADNIRARI III. (809-782 B.C.; cf. FRIEDRICH, MENZEL, UNGNAD and WEIDNER 1940 p. 167): Its smallest unit was a group (kita) of ten men under the command of rab es karta. The later had a chariot with four horses. Two asses were the animals of burden, and one ox with ten sheep formed a living provision of the detachment.

It may also be of interest to compare the relative value in money of the domestic animals in the Nuzi-texts (CROSS 1937 p. 16 ff.): Most common is the sheep (1.3 shekel silver), less so cattle (10 shekels each), rare are asses (6.7 sh.), also: horses (30 sh.) and goats (0.9 sh.).

2. 22. ANIMALS IN OMINA AND LITERATURE

Animal fables and animal tales. Fables could not possibly be regarded as part of the natural history of any nation. But if the actual knowledge of a people is only very fragmentary known, as is the case with the zoological knowledge of the old Sumerians, Babylonians and Assyrians and the copiousness of animal fables involves a considerable amount of accurate and perspicuous observations, it is worth while just to point out this wealth. A history of the zoology of the old Greeks would be incomplete, if it did not include a hint to the abundance of themes and observations in animal fables, culminating in Aesop. And EBELING (1927) had just demonstrated that the Greek animal and plant fables are in many cases translations or close paraphrases of older Babylonian texts. The future may show that many of these fables go back to the Sumerians. But even in this case Irak remains their background. Almost identical with an old Babylonian text is the epos of Kallimachos on the dispute between the datepalm and the tamarisk. A still better similarity exists for the fable, in which the mosquito asks the elephant, if it be too heavy a burden, where upon the elephant answers: "I did not know that you did sit on me. Who are you? I did not know that you left me".

These two examples illustrate the two types of Babylonian fables: epic poems and short fables illustrating a proverb.

Two larger epic animal poems have been published, so far. The first concerns the clever fox (shêlibu), who pretends to be naive and god-fearing in order to cheat his opponents. He is associated with the wolf (barbaru) against the shepherd-dog. His misdeeds lead him before the court of justice of Shamash, the sun god, where he defends himself in a touching manner. This fox motive reappears not only in Turkish and Greek fables, but still in the epos of Reinecke Fuchs. Another poem of this type is a discussion between the horse and the oxen.

We here give a few examples of the proverbial fable.

> "The swine is not pure, it fills with dirt what is behind it,
> besmears the streets and the houses".

The presence of mind of a mouse, falling from one evil into another, bigger one:
> "A mouse is fleeing before an enemy and enters a snake hole, with the words:
> The snake conjurer has sent me! Peace be with you!"

"A mouse living in the country meets a town mouse,
it abuses the starlings which feed on fruits."

"The spider laid an ambush for a fly,
the chamaeleon is indignant about the ambush for the fly."

"The wolf who does not know the exit of the town,
is persecuted in its street by the hogs."

"The horse in heat, who copulates with a she-mule, lisps in her ear:
The fillen which you will bear, will be ardent as myself,
not similar to an ass under the yoke".

This presumes a common knowledge of the sterility of such intercourse. Other topics are: The bird-catcher without fishes may catch them from the channels with his net. The dog, attacked by a wolf, advises him to select rather a piece of cattle as prey, as one dog will be insufficient to satisfy his hunger. Or the advice not to interfere in a struggle of others: the flea and the kuzazu-fly are quarrelling and advocate the arbitration of the jumping hametu-fly, but finally join forces against the latter.

In addition to the other proofs, this wealth of and pleasure in animal fables demonstrates a gift for and pleasure in observing animals, which are met with in daily life.

Also a number of proverbs concerning animals have been preserved, such as:

(From Assurbanipal's library, MEISSNER 1929):
"The scorpion has killed a man. What may be his advantage?
The cackling of the bird is an oracle of heaven, and nevertheless you cut his body.
A piece of linen is spread for a flea, a tissue for a moth, a granary for (a ?wasp) grain pests.
A duck, which has not been eaten at its proper time.
When you have saved yourself, you acted as a wild bull; when you have been caught you cajole like a dog.
The cattle of the neighbour feeds on grass, your own cattle rests on good pasture."

Omina. The origins of science in the Middle East, as elsewhere, were intimately interwoven with religion. The important discoveries in astronomy are not loosing their intrinsic value, on account of astrology being their main aim. In the same way an enormous amount of morphological and anatomical observations has been accumulated in old Irak in connection with prophecy. The omina have been systematically collected and many of the cuneiform tablets on omina are preserved. Many concern astronomical and weather omina. Others concern collections of unusual events, such as (Thompson 1900 p. XCI):

When a foetus (of a domestic animal) has 8 legs and 2 tails, the prince of the kingdom will seize power.

Very carefully collected details about the shape, colour and characters of all human physiognomic details, such as hairs, chin, etc. have been compared in detail together with their importance for the interpretation of the character and future prospects of the bearer (Kraus 1935). Still more penetrating are the anatomical data, which served as a basis for the omina from the ritual animal sacrifices. In order to give an idea of the wealth of accumulated observations we here reproduce the part concerning the "finger" (= processus pyramidalis) of the liver from the library of Assurbanipal. The liver is the most important internal organ which served as basis of such omina and the "finger" is just one of the parts of the liver which served as such:

When the finger is like a lion's ear, the prince will be without his equal.

When the finger is as the lion's ear, but its upper part is cleft, your army will be abandoned by the Gods at the beginning of the campain.

When the finger is like a lion's ear, but it lies in a groove, your army will be abandoned by its Gods at the beginning of the campaign.

When the finger is like a lion's ear, but the right part of the back is missing, the army of the enemy will be without its equal.

When the finger is like a lion's ear, but the left part of the back is missing, your army will be without its equal.

When the finger is like a cattle's tongue, the trusted friends of the prince will revolt.

When the finger is like a sheep's head, the prince will come to full power.

Fairly common are the omina which are based on observations of animals. Many of these observations have no scientific value. But even those show how much attention was paid to observing animals and to which animals where in the centre of popular attention.

The religious background of oracles and omina is the belief that the future is indicated by various phenomena, which are accessible to professional interpretation by systematic study. An enormous amount of such information was systematically arranged in long series of cuneiform tablets, amply preserved in the library of Assurbanipal. The latter is, for the greater part, inserted into the Kujunjik collection of the British Museum. These tablets have been collected by special castes of the baru-priests, who had specialised in their interpretation. Surprising is the wealth of characters and observations, on which these omina are based: body-shape, colour, weather, astrology, plants, behaviour of animals, body-fluids, oil-drops, birth of young of exceptional character, etc. Although rejecting the interpretation, we can only respectfully acknowledge this abundance of observations on natural phenomena. Remainders of this attitude and of these observations are still living among the peasants and bedawi of the country in our days.

HUNGER (1909 p. 10) summarizes the characters serving as the base of animal omina as follows: "The species and its character (large, strong, courageous, clever, or the reverse), the colour (dark, light, multicoloured), the sex, if gravid, the action (of flight, preying, menaced by an enemy, standing, sitting, flying or running), if and which voice is produced), whether the animals appear single or in numbers, in which place they are observed (e.g. in a palace or temple) the direction from which the animal appears (from right or left, from behind or from the front, etc.), eventually the hour or month of the animal's appearance, copulation among different species, all teratological births. Lion and eagle symbolise the king." Even a primitive theory on sex determination existed. Boys are conceived on fertile soil (garden, field), girls on uncultivated soil.

Most omina which have been published have been worked out by BOISSIER, BEZOLD, JASTROW, HUNGER, MEISSNER, a.o.

Bird omina seem to have been of special importance. A special group of the *baru* priests devoted themselves to their interpretation, and even special "eagle consulters" are mentioned. These bird omina were regarded as less important than the oracles from the liver show, those of the astrologers and perhaps also than those of the "oil show". Some authors still doubt, if only occasionally observed omina were interpreted or if special priests did go out with the intention to observe birds (JASTROW 1912 p. 801). But HUNGER (1909 p. 22) quotes the mention of a priest *"sha massarti"* (on the watch) and produces another text, where birds are allured to the desert by a specially prepared food. "You shall bring this into the steppe and offer them to Shamash. Three times shall you say the magic formula and you will see that a bird appears".

Relatively few of the bird omina are published so far. But it is certain that they did hold the first rank among animal omina. Originally most birds seem to have been collectively connected with omina. The many omina connected with special birds seem to be a later development. Day and month of appearance, direction of passing before the observer and activity are the most important characters.

The most ominous bird is *surdu,* the falcon. But there still is some discussion about the interpretation. HUNGER is of the opinion that it refers to the wild falcon, whilst MEISSNER regards it as referring to the royal sport of falconry. We follow MEISSNER, as there is no reason to doubt the very old age of falconry in the Middle East, where it was almost always reserved for princes. This is in accordance with the omina, which are usually favourable to princes and unfavourable to common men (JASTROW 1912 p. 804):

When . . . . ., the king will assemble his army and will reach the enemy country.
When . . . and the falcon reaches his prey, and he passes the king from his right to his left, the king will complete his purpose, wherever he goes.
When . . . and the falcon reaches his prey, carries off this prey and flies before the king, he will complete his purpose.
When . . . . and the falcon reaches his prey, he flies towards the king and drops his prey, the enemy will retire and make peace.
When . . . . and the falcon reaches his prey and drops it behind the king, he will not be successful, wherever he goes.
When . . . and the falcon reaches his prey and he circles around the king, his enemy will pierce the town-gate before him (or?) he will show clemency and the people of the country will be blessed.
When . . . and the falcon reaches his prey and tears it to pieces with his beak, and flies from the king, the king will be successful, wherever he goes and rule his enemies.
When . . . the falcon reaches his prey and carries his prey in his beak away from the king, the king will be successful wherever he goes and rule his enemy.
When . . . and a falcon and a raven fight together before the king and the falcon kills the raven, the army of the king will prevail over the might of the enemy, he will take the town of the enemy and live there in peace.
When . . . and a falcon and a raven fight together before the king and the raven kills the falcon, the army of the enemy will prevail, it will take the menaced town of the king and live there in peace."

Not all tablets with *surdu* omina are as favourable as this one. Some authors have considered the *surdu* as being owls. But the text of the omina makes this interpretation rather improbable. Possibly the "cave bird" (*issur churri*) is an owl. "When a dark cave bird is seen in a town, there will occur a sun eclipse, the approach of an enemy or a locust invasion within a month."

The few translated omina of the raven (*aribu*) seem to be more unfavourable. But more complete texts may change this impression.

"When an army starts its march and a raven caws before the army, it will not return from its march."

The raven is even favourable, if it takes something to a house. We reproduce the following response to a king's letter *in toto,* asking for the interpretation of such an omen:

"To the king, my master, from your servant Balasi. Salute to the king, my master! May Nabw and Marduk bless the king, my master!
With regard to the raven, about which my king asked me:
When a raven takes something to the house of a man, this man will be successful, whatever he undertakes.

When a falcon or a raven drops something which he carries on the house of a man or before this man, this house will grow rich.
When the bird carries meat or another bird something and drops it on the house of a man, this man will grow rich.
May Nabw and Marduk bless the king and grant him a long life and an abundant offspring...".

We mentioned before, that the eagle is the symbol of the king:
When eagles appear in great numbers, that town will be full of kings.
When eagles appear in great numbers, leopards will infest the town.

A few more, very incompletely published omina refer to the swallow and some still unidentified birds. Also doves and chicken have their omina. Very unfavourable is a crowing hen. When this occurs during a nuptial festivity, the hen has to be killed immediately.

Much rarer are omina about wild mammals. Wild cattle (aurochs) is repeatedly mentioned:
"When a wild oxen rests before the gate of a town, the enemy will besiege the town and this gate will be obstructed.
When a wild oxen penetrates the interior of a town, the enemy will destroy this town.
When a wild oxen joins the cattle and remains on their pasture, this is favourable; but if he leaves the cattle on the same day and runs away, this is unfavourable."

Omina about gazelles, lions, wild goats are rare and few have been published so far. They seem mainly to be connected with the appearance of such animals in unusual places. A few omina are derived from the movements of foxes (or jackals). A few omina about „kamunu" possibly refer to the mouse.

Domestic animals, of course, offer important omina. As regards horses they refer mainly to the number, sex and shape of colts, the part where a horse may bite a man, and omina about chariots. Sheep omina are very common, e.g.:
"When the sheep spring lustily, it will be well with the town.
When the sheep bleat, this pen will be destroyed."

The form of the lambs, teratological lambs, etc. are of importance, in addition to the shape of many body organs of the sacred sheep, which are sacrificed for oracles. The goat has few omina as compared with the sheep. The omina from swine are birth omina or connected with the behaviour in the sty. Of primary importance, again, are omina from dogs. Their colour is important: black dogs are always the worst omina, yellow and brown ones are more favourable. Dogs are usually favourable in temples, but unfavourable in palaces and houses. Howling, fighting, urination, resting in various places, etc. are other important criteria.

Snakes offer many omina. It is of high importance, in which month a snake is seen; if the snake sees the man before he sees the snake; if it appears from the right or the left, etc. JASTROW (1912 p. 784) points out that snakes are common during the warm season and that the appearance of a snake is especially unfortunate during the cool months, when snakes are rare. Almost all snake omina foreshadow an early death in the family. The only exception are children and sick persons, to whom they bring fortune and health. This old correlation of snake and healing of diseases is of special interest.

Scorpions are connected with many omina, mainly depending on the part of the body, which was stung. This list is very detailed and deals, e.g., with all the five toes of each foot. The events are by no means always unfavourable. A number of magic rites and of medicines against the sting of the scorpion are preserved. Less rare are other omina concerning the sight of a scorpion only.

There is much difference of opinion concerning a series of plates with omina about "*sasiru*". Locusts, crickets, beetles, cockroaches and ants are identifications of the *sasiru*. Considering the common occurrence of ants around houses in Irak, the variation of their colours (black, red, yellow, half black, half red, white—if termites are included), the presence of wingless and winged forms, the fighting of various forms of sasiru against each other and the mutual killing in these fights, the "breeding" of young in the house, respectively the transport of "eggs" (=*pupae*) and larvae from the house, we conclude that HUNGER (1909 p. 136) was correct in translating *sasiru* with ants.

The ideogram of the *ṣaṣiru* omina is different from that used for crickets, which usually are called *ṣaṣiru*. It indicates insects which appear in swarms ("d a g") and which have stings ("g i r"). This ideogram confirms our reasoning.

It is remarkable that most ant omina are unfavourable. Perhaps it helps to understand this when knowing that ants abound around the houses, but rarely only enter the deeply shaded brick or mud houses, which have little changed in construction since the oldest times. And all omina concern ants in houses. Even termites are rare in houses, when no wooden structures are present in the house. As these omina are rather typical, we give one plate rather completely, following the publication of JASTROW (1912 p. 829 ff.):

"When dark and black ants appear in the house of a man, the owner of the house or his wife will die.
When black ants appear in the house of a man, he will reach an extraordinary old age.
When black ants with wings are seen in the house of a man, the house will be destroyed and his son will die.
When small black ants with wings are seen in the house of a man, the son of the owner will die.
When black and dark red ants with wings are seen in the house of a man, his wife will die and the house be destroyed.
When black and multicoloured ants are seen in the house of a man, he will die.
When black and yellow ants are seen in the house of a man, . . . disaster, and the house will be destroyed.
When white ants are seen in the house of a man, the house will collapse.
When large white ants with wings appear in a house, this will be destroyed.
When white and dark red ants are seen in a house, it will be destroyed.
When white and dark red (or small) ants are seen in a house, the back part of the house will perish.
When small white and dark red ants are seen in a house, it will collapse.
When yellow ants are seen in a house, . . . disaster, the house will be destroyed and the owner not prosper.
When yellow ants with wings are seen in a house, the house will be destroyed and the owner will die.
When black ants kill dark red ants in the house of a man, joyful cries will be heard in that house.
When dark red ants kill black ants in a house, disaster will occur in it.
When white ants kill dark red ants in a house, mourning will occur.
When white ants kill black ants in a house, mourning will occur.
When yellow ants kill dark red ants in a house, the house will be destroyed, or fratricide will occur in it.
When . . . . . ants settle in a house and fight, the owner or his wife will suffer.
When . . . . . ants aggregate in a house and make a nest, the owner will die and his house be lonely.
When the nest of the . . . . . ants is laid open in a house, the events in it will be slow.
When the nest of . . . . . ants are seen in a house, offspring will be produced, but nothing of the property will remain.
When the nest of . . . . . ants is destroyed in a house, in that house a change of mind will occur.
When the nests of white ants wings are seen on the sides, the house will be destroyed.

When the nests of white or black ants are seen in the house of a man, the owner will die and nothing will remain of his property.
When many ants appear in a house, the owner will die and the house be destroyed.
When the nest of ants is seen in a house and black ants kill multicoloured ants, a bad event will occur.
When ants make a nest in a house, the events will slow down.
When ants breed in a house, it will be destroyed.
When ants transport their "eggs" from a house, the house will prosper.
When small ants enter a house and fight, there will be discord in the house.
When ants are seen on the entrance of the outer door, the house will fall.
When ants are seen on the inner side of the outer door, need will disappear from the house.
When ants are seen above the outer door, the house will be destroyed.
When ants are seen on the threshold of the outer door, the house will be destroyed, but distress will leave the family.
When an ant burrows in a house, the owner will die.
When ants are seen in a certain tool, prosperity will be destroyed.
When ants are seen in the passage of a house, events will slow down or change.
When an ant appears above a certain tool, the house will be pillaged.
When an ant breeds in a tool in a house, the house will collapse.
When an ant is seen in a jar, the house will be pillaged.
When ants are seen on a rafter of the house, the house will be pillaged.
When ants are seen in the grain store, the full stores will be emptied.
When ants are seen in the sesame store of a house, the owner will suffer want.
When ants are seen in the oil store of a house, the house will not prosper.
When ants appear in a certain vessel, the owner will die, but offspring will be produced.
When ants are seen in a certain vessel, the owner will die, but his house will rule a palace.
When black ants are seen in a house of mourning, the mourning will be less.
When ants are seen on a pillar of a house, the mourning will be less.
When ants are seen on the front wall of a house, an event will occur.
When ants are seen on the south wall of a house, discord will rage within.
When ants are seen on the north wall of a house, there will be discord between man and wife.
When ants are seen on the cornice of a house, need will be strong.
When ants run on the inner walls of a house, the house will be destroyed.
When ants in a house .... toothache will occur."

Few other insects appear in omina. Especially the honeybee is absent. Probably the cloth moth is referred to in the following omina as "sasu":

"The presence of the moth is favourable for a house.
When the moth destroys a garment, this is favourable.
When the moth destroys a woollen garment, this is favourable.
When the moth destroys a women's dress, this is favourable."

The kulilu of some omina are usually interpreted as dragonflies.

"When kulilu rises, the interior of the country will be well.
When white kulilus rise, this means damage to the country.
When black kulilus rise, the interior of the country will be well.
When red kulilus rise, the enemy will fall.
When yellow kulilus rise, the country will be destroyed, etc."

"When at the season of the high water of the river the sâchu flies hatch and fly, the date-crop will be good." [It is quite possible that this omen refers to *Palingenia,* a big Ephemerid.]

Hardly any complete fish omen has been preserved or at least been published, except:

"When the fish stands in the river, this means a quiet life for the country."

Considering the very great importance of fishery in the country and the prominent rôle of the sea-god Ea, it must be assumed that a very comprehensive system of fish omina existed. But it has to be remembered that fish omina are rare among most peoples.

We do not go into the details of birth omina, where the teratological character of the young is interpreted. The lists of these omina are rather extensive.—A few occasional omina are also preserved with regard to the interpretation of animals which appeared in dreams, including the gift of fat of various animals.

Primitive pictographs, the earliest forerunners of the cuneiform writing, contain a number of primitive animal pictures, which were tried to be made as naturalistic as possible. They are signs for bird, sheep, fish, ox, camel, etc. The final ideograms of the cuneiform writing are much changed and do not show such realistic illustrations any more.

A rather pertinent remark on old "bookworms" is made by CHIERA (39 p. 20): "Worse is the fate (of the tablets) if, while they are soft in the moist ground, they find themselves in the path of small rodents or earthworms. Many earthworms, which lived millennia ago, have immortalized themselves through their work. In the course of their wanderings underground they encounter a tablet. Sometimes, in spite of the tablet's comparative softness, they find the clay too hard for their liking, and so they go around the obstacle, eating as they go, until they reach softer ground. At other times they pass right through, undaunted by the added difficulty they meet. We used to call these earthworms that damaged our tablets the original bookworms. I prefer those which go right through to their goal without being diverted by difficulties."

After Xenophon (Anabasis I : 5) the next important source on animal life in C. Irak is the Babylonian Talmud, which was brought to a conclusion about 500. A. D. LEWYSOHN, in his pioneer book on the zoology of the Talmud, did neither distinguish between the Palestinian sources and the Iraki ones, nor did the zoogeographists of those days realise that the fauna of Irak is not necessarily the same as that of Europe. No thorough revision was planned. But Mr. Damast, a student of the writer, kindly undertook to separate the Palestine and Irak sources of some interesting quotations. The following list is thus ascertained to have been quoted from rabbis living in C. Irak. Also a better knowledge of the present and earlier fauna of Irak made a more critical attitude towards some of the earlier identification necessary. The following is a list of animals, which thus have been mentioned in the Talmud from C. Irak. A long list of unidentifiable *nomina nuda* and of doubtful animals have been omitted. *Mammals:* lion, leopard, hyena, fox, wolf, marten, mongoose, hedgehog, vole, house-mouse, hare, roe deer, fallow deer?, wild goat, aurochs, wild ass, wild boar, and oryx. *Birds:* owl, buzzard, falcon, eagle, vulture, crane, egret, flamingo, stork, raven, crow, gull, starling, sparrow, swallow, some larks, pelican, bustard, ostrich, wild duck and geese, some species of pigeons and doves, quail, chukar, ?black partridge.

The "hardoun" (may be *Uromastyx*), some snakes and many fishes. Dolphin and sperm whale are mentioned. Among insects many pests are mentioned. An abundance of names is given to locusts and grasshoppers. Honeybees are also mentioned.

Gazelles and wild fowls were extensively trapped by traps, nets of various kinds and snares. Less common was hunting with the arrow, as prey hunted in such a way was usually not fit for consumption according to the ritual laws. But NEWMAN (1932 p. 142) reports some cases, where Jewish hunters were so skilled that they killed birds by arrows according to the prescriptions.

2. 23. MAMMALS IN THE ART OF ANCIENT IRAQ
2. 231. WILD MAMMALS

Animal representations abound in the ancient art of Irak in all periods from Tell Halaf in the north to Ur in the south. The animals represented vary according to place and period. In most periods the tendency, especially in reliefs, much less so on the cylindric seals, was to make the animals too heavy. Mainly on seals animals with anthropomorphic heads are common. All mythical animals, such as the famous dragons of Babylon, the winged bulls, etc., are, of course, not included into the frame of this sketch. Most beautiful are some of the big and small hunting scenes, especially of the lion, the aurochs, the red deer, the onager, of gazelles and antelopes, etc. Of domestic animals some milking scenes are of special importance for the history of domestication, even if this preceded the illustration considerably.

Especially beautiful are the preserved illustrations of scenes of lion hunting throughout all periods and throughout the country. Many reliefs and seals illustrating lion hunts and lion fights of the Assyrian kings must be mentioned. The frequent occurrence of lions in ancient times is sufficiently illustrated by some of the documents quoted before. The Iraki lion of the north was characterised by a heavy mane, also on the belly. He belonged to the Persian lion (*Panthera leo persica* FISCH.). He was still fairly common in many parts of the country during the 19th century, whilst he must be regarded as extinct by now. Rumours that a single lion was still recently seen in one or another part of the southern jungles and marshes are not substantiated by skins. In ancient illustrations sometimes a lion without mane is represented.

We still have to mention the most beautiful mural painting from an Assyrian palace at the time of ASSURBANIPAL, discovered by THUREAU-DANGIN (1926) at Tell Barsib or Tell Ahmar. In the bathroom of the palace is a scene showing the king standing in a quadriga chariot with galloping horses, the left hand protected by a leather glove, bending his bow toward a crouching lion, who has been hit before by three arrows, one sticking out from his throut. Two riders behind the royal chariot step over a dead lion, laying on the soil, killed by arrows. Two chariots follow, each transporting a dead lion. All faces in this splendid painting are unfortunately mutilated.

The leopard (*Panthera pardus tulliana*) is represented in Iraki art a few times only. At Tell Halaf a leopard with a collar is represented on an orthostat. The large round ring shaped spots, the relatively large head and especially the shortness of the forelegs characterise it as this species (not as a cheetah, WEIDENREICH 1933 p. 22). HILZHEIMER (1929) identifies an animal on a seal of Uruk IV (WEBER 20 no. 515) as cheetah (*Acinonyx jubatus*). In a picture of a wild goat hunt one of the hunters holds in leash a big beast with long legs, pointed ears and a tail raised vertically above its back. Against its being a cheetah points the long head, in its favour: the erected tail with curving only at the tip, the light body which is not pinched in at the groin like that of a dog (VAN BUREN 39 p. 13). Also the legs, the erected ears and the tail are not in agreement with a seluki greyhound. HILZHEIMER's theory seems, therefore, acceptable. This would then be the oldest document on the domestication of the hunting cheetah. A jungle cat (*Felis chaus*) is probably figured in a Babylonian relief (VAN BUREN 39 p. 12).

From the Jemdat Nasr period the head of a wolf (*Canis lupus*) is preserved. This seems to be the only representation of the wolf (VAN BUREN 39 p. 13). Foxes (*Vulpes vulpes*) and jackals (*Canis aureus*) are quite often figured, but they are not always easy to distinguish from each other. The safest character seems to be the tail, which is long and horizontal in the fox, drooping or erect in the jackal. Also the ears of the fox should be longer, the legs shorter.

Small animal figurines from various sources have repeatedly been interpreted as marten (*Martes foina*) or related animals. There is too little similarity to be sure of this interpretation (VAN BUREN 39 p. 20).

The boar (*Ursus syriacus*) is repeatedly represented quite clearly, but a few times in S. Irak, where he never occurred. He is represented on an orthostat at Tell Halaf.

Bats are common in Irak, but they are figured once only, and even here we are not sure, on an alabaster lamp from Ur (VAN BUREN 39 p. 24). Hedgehogs are occasionally figured (and very dubiously once a porcupine). Hares are abundant and are depicted in ornamental rows, as prey for the table, hunted by dogs, or as a prey of eagles. The hare of the lowlands of Irak is *Lepus connori*. It is just possible that another form may occur in the mountainous area, from where no specimen has yet been subjected to scientific study. VAN BUREN's remark (39 p. 1) that "certain creatures, and in particular the hare were introduced into Mesopotamia about 2000 B.C. by newcomers who penetrated from a more mountainous region" is either a misprint for "horse", or else an error. Mice (*Mus musculus*) and rats (*Rattus rattus*) were perhaps abundant, but appear only now and then in illustrations. The jerboa (*Jaculus loftusi*) is common in the deserts and steppes. A few animal caricatures and figures of the animal orchestras are interpreted, apparently rightly, by VAN BUREN (39 fig. 28, 29) as being this rodent. The long tail and hind-legs support this identification.

Three species of deer have occurred in Irak and of all of them we have representations. Most common are illustrations of the red deer (*Cervus elaphus*). The species is still not uncommon in N. Anatolia and probably a few still survive in some mountainous areas of S. Anatolia. In Irak it is extinct since long, as antlers are unknown to most Arabs and Kurds. It was much hunted in ancient times. The red deer is easily recognisable in the male sex by its long, many-tined and pointedly ending antlers. The tail is short, knob-like and the skin is never spotted, except in early youth. In the specimens of the Zoo at Ankara the light spots had disappeared during the first year after birth. The fallow deer (*Dama mesopotamica* BROOKE) was also much hunted and is definitely extinct in Irak. It is characterised by the large, based palmated, flattened antlers. The tail is about 25 cm long and the skin is often spotted. This giant form of fallow deer was common in prehistorical times all over Asia Anterior. Today it is apparently restricted to the southern Zagros mountains of Luristan. HILZHEIMER (1929 p. 193) states that, to the people of ancient Irak, „both species of fallow deer were well-known". He quotes examples of both European (*Dama dama* L.) and Persian fallow deer (*D. mesopotamica*). The European form is considerably smaller and the antlers are distinctly longer than the head, whilst in the Persian form they are about as long as the head. The roe deer (*Capreolus capreolus*) is the only one of the three species which has survived in the mountains of Iraqi Kurdistan until our days. But, unfortunately, intensive hunting will exterminate this pretty species rather soon. Protective laws would have little value in the Kurdish mountains. It has relatively long ears and short, three-tined antlers. The tail is very short. The hunt of roe deer was less spectacular and this is probably the reason, why it was so very rarely figured.

Gazelles are still as common in Irak today as they were in ancient times. They are well represented in hunting scenes and elsewhere. They represent the species which are still common, *Gazella marica* and *G. subgutturosa*. It is quite possible that in the western steppes a representative of the *G. dorcas*-group, which abounded until recently in the western steppes of the Syrian desert and the Jezireh, also occurred. But it is impossible to identify the species from the illustrations.

Abundant are the representations of antelopes. The oryx (*Oryx leucoryx*) with its long horns stretching straight backwards and with a rather long tail, ending in a tuft of longer hairs, is pictured on some seals. The oryx is an inhabitant of the desert, which presumably was not uncommon in the deserts of S. Irak in ancient times. Its area has been rapidly contracting during the past century and it is now restricted to a few areas in Arabia. CARRUTHERS (1935) followed the oryx there and collected much valuable information. It is not impossible that rare stray animals may still occasionally penetrate Irak. No reliable information about such strays is, however, available from recent times. More abundant are the illustrations of antelopes (mainly *Antilope cervicapra*). But it is by no means certain that this is the only antelope then present and figured. They are easily distinguished from the oryx by the undulation of their long horns.

The ibex (*Capra nubiana*) and the wild goat (*Capra hircus aegagrus*) both occurred in N. Irak. The latter is still fairly common. The former still occurs in the Taurus mountains and it is quite possible that a few still survive on the higher mountains of both sides of the northern and north-eastern Irak border. They are often difficult to distinguish in illustrations. In life, the most reliable difference is offered by the horns. Those of *Capra aegagrus* have a smooth surface broken by a few widely spaced protuberances which give an angular appearance to the upper edge. The horns of *C. nubiana* are less angular and apparently thicker. They sweep back in a sabre-like curve, are flattened underneath and show on the upper surface a number of riblike transversal thick protuberances (up to 12) with short intervals. The name ibex is applied today by local sportsmen incorrectly to *C. aegagrus*. In some illustrations, where both species appear, it is often only possible to state that obviously two species are figured, which may also refer to the two sexes. It seems, however, that in ancient times also *C. nubiana* was sufficiently abundant to be a preferred game.

Wild sheep are also depicted. It is doubtful which forms occurred. In the northern mountains forms of the Anatolian mouflon (*Ovis musiman*) occurred, whilst *Ovis laristanica* may have intruded into the western foothills of the Zagros along the eastern border. Wild sheep have repeatedly been represented in hunting scenes. One kind of wild sheep is still living in or close to the north-eastern borders of Irak. The small mouflon is repeatedly figured on seals. Wild sheep as well as gazelles are easily distinguished from wild goat and ibex by the absence of the goat's beard.

Three forms of wild cattle occurred in ancient Irak: the aurochs (*Bos primigenius*), the arni-buffalo (*Bubalus bubalis*) and the wisent (*Bison bonasus*). The presence of the wisent has only recently been proven (HILZHEIMER 1926). The wisent is characterised by a flat hump in the shoulder region, a very heavy mane which develops into a beard beneath the chin, and a short triangular head with short, crescent-like horns. The latter are half as long as the head. HILZHEIMER enumerates a number of old seals on which this species is definitely represented and more often still the figure of a "wisent man" appears (HILZHEIMER 26 p. 12). All these seals belong to the third millennium B.C. The Sumerian ideogram for cattle, a small triangle, with its base turned upwards with two short vertical bars above it, has been taken from the wisent. He is not represented in later illustrations. The wisent belongs to the fauna of cooler climates. He may have been a relic from the northward migration of his species from a Himalayan centre and have extended his range again slightly southwards during the cooler pluvial periods. The wisent died out before 2000 B.C., possibly in connection with climatical changes. The arni-buffalo is a large, thinly haired piece of cattle with a strongly sloping crupper, a relatively fine muzzle and with mighty, crescent-shaped horns. These are twice as long as the head, triangular in cross-section and with regular transversal protuberances on the front or upper side. He was the first of the wild cattle to die out (about 2500 B.C.). The arni-buffalo is an inhabitant of tropical swamps and jungles, such as probably existed widely in S. Irak during the period of land formation in C. and S. Irak.

The most common kind of wild cattle in historical times is the aurochs. DUERST (1899) has first pointed out that illustrations of the arni-buffalo are relatively common in archaic times, but are wanting in the latter periods. The aurochs shows just the reverse. He has a long, not too plump rump with straight back, no mane and a long, narrow head. The horns are as long as the head. The aurochs was apparently quite common in Asia Anterior in pre-historic times. The hunting of *"rimu"* was a preferred sport of the Assyrian kings. Its presence in Talmudic times in the lowlands is doubtful, as the philology is not clear. Many authors still understand the *"rem"* as oryx, which conception certainly is not correct. Persistent rumours reach the traveller in N. Kurdistan that still a few individuals are surviving in remote mountain valleys of Kurdistan, of Hakkari or Siirt. WIGRAM (1936 p. 282) has still seen, early in this century on the front of a house at Amadiya, the horns of a piece wild cattle, which can only have been this species. If these rumours should prove to be true, there certainly is a strong reason for energetic and combined action on the part of the governments of Irak and Turkey in attempting to preserve the species, if it is still possible.

STEGMANN (24 p. 250) believes that the hunting scene in the reliefs of Kujundjik, which represent an onager, is really a wild horse. We doubt this interpretation very much: 1) because of the definite ass form of the tail, 2) because all observers of the onager in nature agree that it gives as a whole much more the impression of a horse than of an ass. Until bones of a wild horse are found in N. Irak, it seems safe to refer these hunting scenes to the onager, about whose domestication as a chariot animal we will talk later. The hunt of the onager (*Asinus hemionus hemippus*) seems to have common and some beautiful illustrations of it are preserved.

The wild pig (*Sus ?scrofa*) and its hunt are not uncommonly represented from Tell Halaf to the south. On one seal a bear is seen breaking out of thick reed bed, on another it is shown to be hunted by boat. The hunt was by lance.

The elephant (*Elephas maximus*) has been hunted and captured alive by at least four Assyrian kings: TIGLATPILESER I, ADADNIRARI II, SALMANASSAR III and ASURNASIRPAL. Elephants have lived apparently on the banks of the Upper Euphrates until about 800 B.C. VAN BUREN (39 p. 77) calls the attention to the fact that "so imposing a beast was never illustrated in early Mesopotamian art." An archaic seal from Tell Asmar, where the Indian elephant appears in the company of the Asiatic rhinoceros and a crocodile, is influenced by Indian art (Mohenjo Dare culture) and the seal may actually have been imported from the Indus valley. The well-known picture of an Indian elephant on the black obelisk of SALMA-NASSAR III is a tribute from Mussri. Bones of extinct species of elephants have been found in layers of the Pleistocene in Palestine and Syria. Elephants have also been common north of the Sahara in parts of N. Africa in historical times. There is no reason to doubt the actual occurrence of wild elephants in N. Irak in historical times. Our assumption that it was an Indian elephant is based—apart from the body shape in profile—on the fact that other animals, such as the arni-buffalo, also have occurred in Irak. HILZHEIMER (29 p. 192) adds further strength to this argument: "The Indian elephant on the stele of the Egyptian governor Rekhmere was almost certainly Euphrates elephant." This is confirmed by the analysis of the ivory.

Among the marine mammals TIGLATPILESER I and ADADNIRARI II report the killing of *"nahiru"* in the midst of the sea. These may have been sperm whales (*Physeter catodon*) from the Eastern Mediterranean. If it happened in the Persian Gulf, it might have been *Balaenoptera musculus*. A basalt figurine from Assur (about 1075 B.C.) is assumed to re-present a seal (*Monachus monachus*), which still occurs in the Persian Gulf. The damaged fragment of a dolphin must be regarded as a doubtful identification.

A number of the animals pictured was doubtless introduced into Irak. We have heard before about the anxiety with which some Assyrian kings collected foreign specimens for their zoological parks. Among such animals we have to mention monkeys first. Most fre-quently represented is the hanuman (*Presbytis entellus* L.) of India. Rarer are illustrations which have been interpreted as those of an Indian gibbon (*Hylobates sp.*) and as of two Ethiopian species, a baboon (*Papio cynocephalus* L.) and the hamadryas (*Papio hamadryas* L.). Another imported animal is the singlehorned Indian rhinoceros. It is represented twice: as a figurine at Tell Asmar and on the black obelisk of SALMANASSAR III.

A new period of investigation into prehistoric zoology in Irak will begin when systematic excavations will start in the caves of the Kurdish mountains. This very promising field of research, especially regarding the smaller mammals, has not yet been touched, except for some preliminary work of Miss GARROD. We end this chapter with the impressive list of large mammals, which, still in historical times, abounded in Irak and which are extinct to all practical purposes, many only during the second half of the past century:

Lion (*Panthera leo*)	Fallow deer (*Dama mediterranea*)
Antelope (*Antilope cervicapra*)	Aurochs (*Bos primigenius*)
Oryx (*Oryx leucoryx*)	Arni-buffalo (*Bubalus bubalis*)
Ibex (*Capra nubiana*)	Wisent (*Bison bonasus*)
Wild sheep (mouflon and red sheep)	Onager (*Asinus hemippus*)
Red deer (*Cervus elaphus*)	Indian elephant (*Elephas maximus*)

To this impressive list we add the ostrich (*Struthio camelus syriacus*) among the birds.

2. 232. OTHER ANIMALS IN ANCIENT ART

We can be short about the other animals illustrated in ancient art in Irak. It would be futile to identify the many snake figures specifically. *Cerastes cerastes* was regarded as the symbol of Ningizzida, the patron deity of king GUDEA. The illustrations, which the author has seen, do not permit an identification. The common dotted snake depicted is probably *Coluber ventrimaculatus,* the most common snake of Irak, or *Sphalerosopis diadema*. But it is useless to speculate about specific identifications in the absence of other characters. Once a sea-serpent has been represented, swimming in the midst of the sea.

Lizards are never figured with sufficient neatness to permit identification. It may only be surmised that most of the larger lizards represent the "land crocodile" (*Varanus griseus*), which abounds all over Irak, up to the mountains.

The crocodile is only figured once on the seal from Tell Asmar, which we mentioned before as perhaps being imported from N.W. India. We have no indication that it lived in Irak, whilst in N. Syria and Palestine it only recently died out.

Tortoises are rarely figured. They are, of course, *Testudo greaca* HERM. (which name now replaces *T. ibera* auct.). A good example of a big fresh water turtle is *Trionyx euphratica* DAUD. (VAN BUREN 39 fig. 95). The turtle in fresh water is *Clemmys caspica,* and sea-turtles also are depicted.

Frogs are common, especially as figurines. Usually they refer to *Rana esculenta* or to *Hyla arborea*. Fig. 105 of VAN BUREN (1939) seems to be *Bufo viridis*.

Fishes abound in Irak. Fish ponds have been represented as well as the spearing of fish. King GUDEA filled "channels with running water and let s u k h u r - fish in the ponds". Detailed contracts on the lease of fish ponds are preserved (MEISSNER 1920 p. 326). Angling is represented on the orthostats of Tell Halaf. Fish-nets are mentioned and must have been the professional instrument for catching fish. An old relief from Tello shows a, probably amateur, fisher with bundles of three fish each on a ring in both hands, just as many amateur fishers as still today take their catch into town. No specialist has yet attempted to identify the many fish in ancient illustrations. HILZHEIMER (1929) quotes the following genera as represented:

marine fish: *Scyaena, Labrax, Conger* or *Muraena, Mugil, Synodontus;*
fresh water fish: shads, carps, *Barbus, Labeo;*
Molluscs seem not to appear in representations, but HILZHEIMER (1929) reports that the shell of *Cassa sp.* served as weight; the fresh water crab (*Potamion fluviatile*) is the cancer of the zodiac.

Insects in art. Locusts are rather frequently represented in ancient art (cf. VAN BUREN 39 p. 109). On seals, on golden daggers, etc. locusts are figured. A lead figurine of a locust, of natural size and of great accuracy, was excavated from the temple Asur in Kar-Tukulti-Ninurta. It was probably connected with locust prayers, either for protection given or expected. The splendid coloured illustration of such a locust prayer has been preserved and excavated from a dwelling-house in Ashur (ANDRAE 25 p. 29, pl. X). Of this small enamel painting (56 × 27,5 cm) a colour reconstruction has been published by BODENHEIMER (1944 p. 1). "It represents Ashur, the chief national god, being worshipped by an Assyrian noble. The meaning of the prayer is represented forcibly enough: protection from a plague of locusts, for which he is either petitioning or returning thanks. A locust, wonderfully hit off in the simplicity of the drawing, is above the worshipper in front of the god. Whoever has seen, as we have, this plague invading the fields of Ashur, and has experienced the helplessness of men against the swarming millions, will understand why such a costly picture was dedicated to such an event." (ANDRAE 1925 p. 28). Exactly the same figure of god and worshipper with locusts feeding on a shrub is reproduced on a old Babylonian seal (BODENHEIMER 1928 p. 36, fig. 21).

Locusts are also figuring in a banquet scene in SANHERIB's palace at Niniveh: servants appear bearing locusts arranged on sticks (*ibidem*). MEISSNER (1920 p. 195) quotes the following old records of locusts: "More important is the locust plague. If "in spring a locust swarm invades the land", it devours everything and "devastates the fields"."

Locusts are mentioned in omina. Magic omina for keeping them off seem to have been in use (MEISSNER 1925 p. 237). Regular prayers for protection from evil include the special request for protection from locusts, as in the following fragment (MACMILLAN 1906 p. 567); preceded by a prayer for protection from diseases and other evils:

> "The big (or stinging) locusts that destroy the grain,
> The small (or evil) locusts that waste the fruit trees."

The former refers to the Moroccan, the second to the desert locust as ROOKE (1930) thinks. It is true that the Moroccan locust feeds on cereals, the desert locust largely on herbs and fruit-trees in Irak, but the sizes are reversed: the bigger species is the desert locust.

Flies appear not uncommonly on seals, etc. No specific identification can be attempted. Scarabaei apparently were introduced, but VAN BUREN (1939 p. 112) thinks that some indefinite insects on seals and figurines may represent beetles.

Spiders and centipedes (VAN BUREN 1939 p. 112) are rarely illustrated, whilst scorpions are very common.

Why honeybees do not figure frequently will easily be understood from the following declaration of a governor on the Middle Euphrates 3000 years ago: "I, SHAMASH-RES-USUR, the governor of Sukhi and Ma'er, have brought the bees (honey-flies) which collect honey and which none has seen since the days of my forefathers, from the mountains of the Kabkha-people. I have settled them in the gardens of the town Gabberini (?), so that they may collect honey and wax(?). I know the preparation of the honey and of the wax(?), and the gardeners also know it. Whoever may come later, may ask from the elders of this country: "Is it true, that SHAMASH-RES-USUR, the governor of Sukhi, has introduced the honeybee into the land of Sukhi?" The introduction seems, however, not to have been very successful, as little other information is available on bee-keeping in ancient times. In Talmudic times bee-keeping was quite common in C. Irak (cf. NEWMAN 1932 p. 135, LEWYSOHN 1858, p. 301, BODENHEIMER 1928 p. 42). Many practices of bee-keeping (smoking, care of swarms, winter food for bees, watering of bees, treatment of bee-stings, use of honey as meat and on wounds, falsification of honey, sterilisation of hives by sharp food) are mentioned. Bee-honey should have been forbidden as the product of an unclean animal. But the Talmud authorities decide that the bee secretes as honey the unchanged nectar of the plants, whilst the wasps and hornets add from their saliva and make their honey unclean thereby. The writer has misinterpreted the form of the Talmudic hive (1928 p. 42), because he was unfamiliar at that time with the native bee-hives of Asia Anterior. He has had opportunity to study in the mean time those from Anatolia and Irak (BODENHEIMER 1943, 1944). There is no doubt that the hive from "reeds or straw" was a plaited cylinder, laying horizontally on the soil, in accordance with those from the two just mentioned regions. This is confirmed by Ohaloth 9 (DANBY 1933 p. 661 ff.).

2. 24. THE H A R - R A = *HUBULLU*, THE OLDEST BOOK ON ZOOLOGY

A. *General introduction.* If only those sources for the animal life in ancient Irak would have been preserved, with which we have dealt so far, the material should already be characterised as abundant. But, in addition, the oldest book on zoology is preserved on some cuneiform tablets of old Assyrian libraries. To these tablets we have to turn our attention now.

LANDSBERGER (1934) has recently published the first translation of the 14th tablet of the series H a r - r a = *Hubullu*. This is one of the many lexicographical dictionaries of the Accadian period. They contain systematically arranged lists of Sumerian names with their current Accadian translation in the corresponding column. Most of the fragments of this series were discovered in the big library of ASSURBANIPAL (7th century B.C.). They are compiled from old liturgical and other books of the Sumerians. Whilst old in origin, the compilation must have taken place at a relatively late date, as many of the Sumerian words have obviously been misinterpreted. The sequence of the matters and names probably follows a certain tradition, apart from that enforced by the Sumerian denominative prefixes.

The 14th tablet of the h a r - r a = *hubullu* aims at including all wild terrestrial animals. Most of the domestic animals are treated on tablet 13. Birds (including bats) and fishes (including probably all other marine and fresh water animals) are enumerated in the following plates.

LANDSBERGER (1934) makes the following remarks with regard to the philological as well as the zoological side of his interpretations and identifications: "Our lists originate from Sumerian lists, such as were used in the period of HAMMURABI, but which developed from much older lists. They were dragged—by literary tradition or by inertia—even through the Sumerian linguistic tradition, whilst the language had ceased to live. The Sumerian lists not only enumerate zoological species, but also refer to differences such as: large and small, various colours, etc. They make use of popular epitheta ornantia, such as: furious or refer to typical habitats ("snake of the grass", etc.). In adding the Accadian equivalents to this original list of Sumerian names, either the Sumerian name was mechanically translated although we do not know if they still understood the real meaning of the word. Or Sumerian words were used for the interpretation or the current Accadian name of the respective animal was offered. Generally, this procedure was certainly based on good tradition, but occasionally some criticism is necessary e.g., when mush. sig. sig, the yellow (green) snake is identified as urun (= waran) or when the "bad snake" is taken as a zoological species. In the first case the identification by the Assyrian scientist is doubtful, in the second case the old Sumerian name was probably not connected with any single species. A strict analysis should treat the Sumerian names and their Accadian equivalents separately".

In the Sumerian column the list definitely follows a traditional zoological arrangement. This is expressed in two ways: by the sequence of the names and by denominative prefixes. The prefix "mush", e.g., characterises the following name as that of a snake, "buru" as an orthopterous insect, etc. It seems that these prefixes were only written, but not pronounced. The Accadian animal names have no prefix, denominating the taxonomic position of the animal, nor is their sequence of importance, as they are intended to follow strictly that of the Sumerian column. In the following discussion we are therefore only concerned with the taxonomic views of Sumerian science and not the often divergent interpretations of the Accadians.

We first give a survey of the main animal groups of Sumerian zoology as expressed by sequence and prefixes. This permits a first view of the general taxonomy of the Sumerians, always considering that neither birds nor animals of the fresh water or of the sea are included in this part of the list. We are eager after waiting the continuation of the work, i.e. the translation and publishing of the following two as well as of the 13th tablet. This list will be followed by a short discussion of those species on which some remarks are needed from the zoological point of view. Then we reproduce a list of the leading name for all more or less acceptable identifications with their Sumerian and Accadian name, following the enumeration of LANDSBERGER (1934). The writer regrets that in this discussion he often has to question or to reject many of the ingenious suggestions made by LANDSBERGER and nevertheless is not able to add better or more reliable interpretations of his own. But it seems safer to have less specific identifications of Sumero-Accadian names than to identify many species on the ground of insufficient, doubtful or just ingenious characters. The fundamental book of LANDSBERGER remains the most valuable guide for anybody who wants to occupy himself with animals of ancient Irak, especially as regards philological and literary sources.

The following list of taxonomic units as characterised by the prefixes begins with snakes, possibly because they are nearest to the soil. The fact that not-winged insects and insect larvae precede the adult insects lends support to this view. A more potent reason may have been the fear of snakes, in which many snakes and dragons are included. Danger to man seems to have been an important motive for the sequence of the list. The other vertebrates are arranged in a general way from large to small species. This is also the leading principle in the Historia Naturalis of Pliny. The list of the more important Sumerian denominative animal prefixes runs as follows:

Prefix	Zoological group	No. in *Landsberger*'s edition
mush	Snakes	1—46
am (+ sun + silam)	Wild cattle	48—60
ur (+ sal)	Dogs, wolf, a.o.	61—98
sa	Small wild cats	108—115
az	Bear	120
ug	Lion	121—136
lu (+ si)	Deers	145—146
dara	Wild goat, ibex	147—150
mash	Gazelles	151—153
shakh (+ sal, = tab)	Pig	159—183

pesh	Small rodents	184—198
nin	mungo a.o. small carnivora	200—204
bar	? Hedgehog, ? ratel	205—206
erne (+ kun)	Lizards	207—215
ilu	Crab	225—226
buru	Most Orthoptera	228—244
uh	Vermin of men, stores, agriculture	253—272
za (+ ush)	? Caterpillars or beetles	273—279
mar	Earthworms	283—289
girish	Lepidoptera	296—298 (—303)
num	Diptera, Hymenoptera	304—332
mul	Mollusca	340a—345
kuli	Odonata	347
kishi	Ants	352—359
gir	Scorpions	361—370
ne	Amphibia	376—379
u, nig, gar	Animals in general	387—409

The following notes give the commentary of a zoologist, who has a certain knowledge of Irak and its present fauna, on the identifications of the philologists. Where an accepted identification is not quoted, this name is rejected. The numbers refer to the line and enumeration in LANDSBERGER's edition. (S) and (A) refer to the Sumerian respectively to the Assyrian column.

B. *Mammalia*. No. 48-52, 57-60. "aurochs, a. of the mountain, ferocious a., a. with projecting, erected or open horns" (S), "horned aurochs" (A) are obviously *Bos primigenius*. No. 57-60 refer to the cows.

No. 53-56 are translated as follows:

No. 53, 54. "horned aurochs" (S), elephant (A), elephant of the mountains (A + S).

No. 55, 56. "horned aurochs of the mountain, camel of the travel" (S), camel (A).

There is not the slightest doubt, that the Assyrian words piilu and ilibu refer to elephant and camel, which should figure at the beginning of the animal list in accordance with their size. But there is no indication that the Sumerian words are intended for the same animals. This possibility is not excluded, and a living tradition may have induced the Assyrian translation. But the latter may just as well be inserted here, because the author of the list felt that these animals should be added and that in a prominent place. Possibly additional Sumerian texts may elucidate this point in future.

No. 61-103 is the group with the dog prefix. Most of the epitheta obviously refer to the domestic dog (largest, small, tied, female, bitting, pregnant dog, dog of the hound pack, dog of Elan, dog of Marash (S) = dog of Parash (A), etc (A + S).

A few references to other species are included in the dog group:

No. 68, 69. "strange dog" (S), wolf (A).

No. 70-74. "? dog, dog of the reeds, dog with a pattern" (S), "a species of lion (? tiger)" (A). Cf. LANDSBERGER (1934 p. 7).

No. 74a. "?" (S), tiger or cheetah (A) (LANDSBERGER ibidem).

No. 85. "water dog" (S), beaver or otter (A) (LANDSBERGER ibidem).

No. 86. "dog of the soil" (S), "dog of the spice mortar" (A) is interpreted as badger or ratel (LANDSBERGER 1934 p. 8).

Whilst it is probable that especially the wolf and also beaver or otter and badger are included in the original Sumerian series, it is rather improbable that large cats have found their place here, whilst other names soon follow. The wolf certainly belonged to this group. The waterdog (ura, kalab mee) (no. 85) corresponds to the actual Arab name for otter (*Lutra lutra*). LANDSBERGER (1934 p. 85) notes that this species caused damage and disasters comparable to those caused by the lion. He thinks that beaver dams may have interfered with navigation. With regard to the badger LANDSBERGER (1934 p. 86) suggests that the gallery is of this animal may have been compared in form with a spice mortar.

No. 104-106. The hyena (*Hyaena hyaena*).

no. 107. The fox (*Vulpes vulpes*).

No. 108-115 include the smaller cats. No. 108 simply refers to a cat, which LANDS-BERGER thinks it to be a domestic cat. This is, however, improbable, perhaps it is a wild cat. The Sumerian epitheta of this list are: predatory, large, horned, yellow cat. The most common wild cats of Irak are the jungle cat (*Felis chaus*) and the wild cat (*Felis sp. libyca*), of which two forms occur. LANDSBERGER refers the Assyrian names no. 109-110 to *Felis lybica*, 111-114 to *Felis caracal*, 115 to *F. chaus*. The sequence of abundance is in the northern mountains wild cat, jungle cat, in C. Irak jungle cat, cat, caracal. The attribution to the various species therefore needs revision, but it is not beyond doubt that the Assyrian names are not always identical with the original Sumerian list.

No. 116-119 are the monkeys in the Assyrian list, whilst the Sumerian names are too incomplete to permit full reading.

No. 120. The bear (*Ursus arctos*).

No. 121-136 is the lion group. Epitheta are: mouth-opening, double-toothed, terrible, ferocious, ?spotted, small lion. The two last numbers are translated as leopard (niimri) on the Assyrian column.

No. 137 introduces a name for the eagle.

No. 138-141 is the jackal (*Canis aureus*), of which this country is the *terra typica*.

No. 142-143. The wild sheep (*Ovis spp.*).

No. 144. "alim" (S), "ditanu" (A) is suggested by LANDSBERGER (1934 p. 92) as being the wisent (*Bos bonasus*).

No. 145-146 "deer, stared horn" (S = A). No differentiation of the three species of deer attempted by LANDSBERGER, whilst at least red and fallow deer are well-known from artistic representations.

No. 147-150 is the wild goat group. The Sumerian epitheta are: strange, gazelle-like, shy wild goat. The Assyrian equivalents read different: wild goat, red deer (aalu) and probably roe deer (naalu). LANDSBERGER (1934 p. 95) points out correctly that it would seem from literary sources that the ibex and the wild goat may well have been differentiated. The problem needs further study.

No. 151-153. Gazelles (male, young) (S + A). Also here the absence of the big antelopes should be pointed out, which abound in the hunting scenes of art illustrations.

No. 154-155 may refer to the hare (*Lepus connori*) in both columns.

No. 156-157. "pig like" (S), bear (A). This "identification" may, of course, be based on tradition.

No. 158-183. The pig group. In contrast with the usual method followed in the list, here obviously the domestic pig is included and most names and epitheta refer to it. The domestic pig must have been rather popular in Sumer. In the pig group possibly the following three species of wild animals are included:

No. 161 "pig of the reeds" (S), "wild pig" (A).

No. 162 "reed eating pig" (S), porcupine (A) cf. LANDSBERGER (1934 p. 103).

No. 164a "roof hog" (S), ?dormouse (A) cf. LANDSBERGER (1934 p. 107).

There is no reason not to assume that no. 161, 162 both have designated the wild bear (*Sus scrofa*) in the Sumerian list. The identification for porcupine is derived from the Assyrian ideogram which means: fur like that of a bird and pig like. The "roof hog" (164a) does not invite to a zoological identification and least of all to a dormouse, which is unknown so far in Irak. If the name refers to rats, the Sumerian name is of doubtful equivalence.

No. 184-198 (199) include the smaller rodents. The Sumerian epitheta are: mouse of the mountains, small mouse, mouse of the reed, reed or sesame eating mouse, mouse of the roof, mouse of the field, multicoloured, destructive, bad mouse, a mouse which changes its place, collecting mouse. The Assyrian names have been specifically interpreted in many cases by LANDSBERGER (1934 p. 105 ff.):

No. 189 "the small mouse" (S) may be the house-mouse. *Mus musculus bactrianus* is the common house-mouse of Irak, where it lives wild in large numbers.

No. 190, 190a "mouse of the reed" (S). The identification as dormouse or porcupine seems to be artificial and improbable (see also the pig group). The same is true for no. 193.

No 191. The "reed eating mouse" (S) is certainly not the rat. A typical reed-eater is *Nesokia buxtoni,* which is regarded as a delicacy by the bedawis of Irak and Palestine until this day.

No. 192 "sesame eating mouse" (S). We see no reason to identify this description with the rat.

No. 194 "mouse of the field" (S + A). The most common field mouse of C. Irak is *Tatera bailwardi.* In N. Irak vole-outbreaks occur, but no specimens are available. It is probably *Microtus socialis.*

No. 196 „mouse of destruction" may refer as well to the rat (*Rattus*) as to the vole.

No. 197. We see no reason for the identification as *Sorex.*

No. 197b "collecting mouse" (S + A) may be a hamster. We received *Cricetulus nigrescens* from the extreme north. But voles as well as hamsters prepare stores in their galleries. It is doubtful if the name is specific.

No. 200-204 is the mongoose group. The Sumerian epitheta are strange mongoose, m. of the forest, m. of the steppes. The Assyrian names are interpreted by LANDSBERGER (1934 p. 110 ff.). No. 200 is the mongoose (*Herpestes auropunctatus pallipes*) himself. No. 202, the mongoose of the forest, m. of the steppes, weased, neither of which occurs in Irak. If the "mongoose of the steppe" is a specific animal, it may be *Vormela peregusna,* which how-ever has not been yet reported from Irak.

No. 205, 206 are referred to in the Assyrian text as "hedgehog" (*Erinaceus*). This name is possibly not identical with the Sumerian "animal (a. of the mountains) with multi-coloured fur".

It is to be hoped that future progress will permit a better understanding of the Sumerian and Assyrian knowledge of zoology. How inadequate even this rather impressing list of the animals of the h a r - r a = *hubullu* is, can be concluded: 1) from the lack of names for a few groups which were well-known to the old inhabitants of Irak, such as goat and ibex, the various species of deer and of wild sheep, etc. 2) from the absence of a number of impressive animals, such as onager, antelopes and oryx, squirrels, a.o. In the mean time the historian of zoology has to be extremely grateful to Prof. LANDSBERGER for his masterly and laborious pioneer work in publishing the tablet 14 of this lexicographical list.

The thirteenth tablet of the H a r - r a = *hubullu* has recently been published by A. L. OPPENHEIM and L. F. HARTMAN (1945). The list is translated, but without any commentaries. And more unfortunate still, the list is obviously incomplete. Horse and pig and dog are missing, the latter perhaps on purpose, as they are contained in tablet XIV. This incompleteness, obviously based on the incompleteness of the preserved tablets, is the more regrettable as the names of the camel, if present, would have been of the highest importance. The names as they are published concern:

No.	1—192 domestic sheep,	No. 262—279	kid,
	193—239 domestic goat,	280—353	domestic cattle,
	240—261 lamb,	354—382	donkey and mule.

C. *Reptilia and Amphibia.* No. 3, 4 "giant snake, big snake" (S + A) may refer, if not mythological, to one of the three Iraqi snakes which reach or surpass 2 m in length: *Coluber asianus jugularis, Sphalerosopis diadema* or *Malpolon monspessulensis.*

No. 7 "womb snake" (S). LANDSBERGER (1934 p. 56) points out that this name may possibly refer to one of the viviparous *Hydrophinae.* But he correctly adds that it is rather questionable if the Sumerians were sufficiently sharp observers for this discovery. The Accadian synonyms for no. 7 and 8 refer to mythical, poisonous snakes. All the Iraqi sea snakes are poisonous.

No. 8 "sea snake" (S) = *Hydrophinae.*

No. 9. There is no obvious reason why the "snake of the snake god" (S) which appears so frequently on the boundary stones beneath the emblems of the gods and which had a definitely apotropaic character, should be identified as *Natrix tesselatus,* which is almost restricted to fresh water. In some cases these snakes are horned, i.e. refer to *Cerastes cerastes.* For the not-horned specimens there is still the possibility that the same species was meant, as many *Cerastes* are not-horned in Irak, as well as it may refer to any other snake. If it is identical with no. 10 "small snake" (S) it is one of the smaller snakes, such as *Eirenis, Echis,* etc.

No. 11, 12 "girdle snake, big girdle snake" (S + A). These names may denominate species with black transversal bands around the back, such as *Lytorhynchus diadema* a.o. It is improbable that a python was meant, which does not occur in Irak anyhow. Or should snake-skins have been made into luxury articles such as girdles?

No. 13 "tortoise snake" (S + A). This is certainly not the cobra of Irak (*Naja,* probably more correctly *Atract aspis morgani*), as has been assumed by LANDSBERGER (1934 p. 3), as this species does not inflate its neck.

No. 14. "Eel snake" (S), eel (A). If a fish is intended, it refers to *Conger* or *Muraena.* If a terrestrial snake is intended, it may well refer to *Eryx jaculus.*

No. 15. The "yellow (green) snake" (S), waran (A). Corkill (1932 p. 17) points out correctly that the Sumerian reference to a yellow or green snake almost certainly concerns the very common *Coluber ventrimaculatus.* The Accadian "urnu" is, of course philologically identical with the Arab word "waran".

No. 18 "horn-bearing snake" (S + A). This is obviously *Cerastes cerastes,* even though many specimens of the *Cerastes* are hornless in Irak.

No. 20-22 "wild or vicious snake" (S) does not eo ipso lead to viper, as LANDSBERGER (1934 p. 3) translates. Exactly the most vicious and feared are some of the not-poisonous, ones e.g. common whip-snakes, such as *Coluber asiana, C. ventrimaculatus,* a.o., which because of their "furious" temper have in German received the name "Zornnattern".

No. 23-25 "blind snake" (S + A) is almost certainly not *Typhlops vermicularis* (LANDS-BERGER 1934 p. 3): 1) The species is rather rare and inconspicuous. Only about 5 specimens have been collected so far. 2) The similarity with the earth-worm in size, shape and colour is so great that it is more than doubtful, if this species was recognised as a snake. 3) The absence of eyes in these miniature snakes is very difficult to observe for anybody whose attention has not been turned especially to this character. But very old snakes are occasionally blind on one or both eyes. The same occurs in tortoises. The author caught, near Ankara, two old specimens of *Testudo graeca,* one of which was blind, the other one-eyed. At present the mole-rat (*Spalax sp.*) is called "father of the blind" in N. Irak.

No. 26-28, 36-45. (S + A, part.) contain names chosen from habitats, such as "snake of the mountains, of the wet places, of fallow land, etc." No. 42, the "snake of the nest" is interesting, as snakes hunting bird's nests are still playing a rôle in recent popular medicine. It probably refers to *Coluber* and *Tarbophis.* No. 43. The "water snake" (S + A) is doubt-less the common *Natrix tesselatus.* But this is not the only fresh water snake of Irak. In late spring and early summer, during the flood season, we caught some specimens of *Coluber ventrimaculatus* in the Tigris near Baghdad.

No. 34. The "snake of the night" (S + A) must refer to *Tarbophis martini.*

No. 409 "a snake in the state of enlarging" (S), a "snake" (A) is referred to a cobra by LANDSBERGER (1934 p. 65). It may perhaps rather describe the moulting (casting the shun) of a snake, a rather common phenomenon in Irak.

No. 46, 47 the "mouse-snake" (S) is, according to oral information from Prof. LANDS-BERGER, an animal half-snake, half-mouse, definitely not a mouse-eating snake. Identification with the Amphisbaenid *Pachycalamus zarudnyi* makes no sense and the species is very rare.

We now turn to the other reptiles:

No. 207, 208 "rugged tail" (S) fits the *Uromastyx* very well, three species of which genus occur in Irak. LANDSBERGER (1934 p. 17) refers it to a Scincid, for which this name is out of place. The "rugged tail of the fruits" (S + A) may well be a big *Agama,* such as the writer has seen in oak-woods in Kurdistan.

No. 210-215. We agree with LANDSBERGER that the names of lizards were usually used in a general way. No. 215 "lizard of the steppe" (S), small lizard (A) may refer to the common *Ophisops elegans,* perhaps, much less probably to *Agama ruderata.* No. 213 "lizard with two tails" (S), "forked tail" (A) describes lizards where a lost tail was regenerated by double tail formation. This occurs not too rarely among the common *Ophisops.* No. 211 "lizard of the walls" (S + A) means the common gecko *Hemidactylus turcicus.*

No. 223 "(land)crocodile" (S + A) can only designate the common waran (*Varanus griseus*), for which no other word of the Sumerian list seems suitable. Cf. also no. 15.

No. 372-375. In spite of the position in the list, far away from the other lizards, LANDS-BERGER (1934 p. 115 f.) identifies no. 372-374 as geckoes. His philological and literary quotations make it quite probable that lizards are meant under the "snake like, snake like of the fruits" (S). As these animals are grouped together with the frogs and toads, there is a strong possibility that Amphibia Urodela, two species of which occur in Kurdistan (*Neuergus crocatus, Triturus vittatus*) may have been meant. Another possibility is a reference to Agamids or geckoes. The writer caught a specimen of *Agama ruderata* near the Tuz göl in Anatolia and the driver of the car exclaimed: "By god! I don't know if this animal is a frog or a lizard!"

No. 216-222 denominate the land tortoise *Testudo graeca* in various sizes and its eggs. The fresh water turtle (*Clemmys caspica*) and probably also the marine turtles have a fish-determinative as prefix.

No. 375. We very much doubt the identification of "small toad" (S) "humbabalike (gecko)" (A) as chameleon. This animal is unknown in Irak.

The *Amphibia* include:

No. 376-381. The last two numbers mentioning the croaking do not refer to the orange-speckled toad, which is unknown in Irak, but to the common *Rana esculenta*, whose croaking gives a common evening-concert along all fresh-waters of the country. It is possible that no. 377 "big frog" (S) is meant for the toad (*Bufo viridis*), another common inhabitant of Irak.

D. *Insecta.* The insects are rather well represented in the h a r - r a = *hubullu* list with 111 of the 396 names. It is obvious that we can expect still much less specific identifications among the insect names than among those of the mammals.

No. 227-244. The list begins with the buru-group, the *Orthoptera*.

List of the buru-group in the har-ra = hubullu.

No.	Sumerian name	Translation	Accadian name	Translation
227	*buru*	locust	*eri-bu*	locust
228	*buru sag*	head locust	*si in-na-ra-bu*	locust
229	*buru gal*	large locust	*si in-na-ra-bu*	—
230	*buru gal*	large locust	*hi-li-mu*	—
230a	*buru tur*	small locust	*zi-i-ru-*	—
231	*buru tur. tur*	very small locust	*zir-zir-ru*	—
232	*buru sahar. ra*	dust locust	*e-rib-tur-bu-ti*	dust locust
233	*buru a. ab. ba*	sea locust	*e-rib-tem-tin*	—
233a	*buru id*	river locust	*erib-na-a-ri*	—
234	*buru id. da*	river locust	*ku-li-lum*	dragon fly
235	*buru gan. na*	field locust	*zi-za-nu*	grasshopper
236	*buru gan. tir. ra*	forest locust	*zi-za nu-qish-tum*	
236a	*buru za. pa. ag*	noisy locust	*sa-si-ru*	cricket
236b	*buru za'pa. ag. ti. ra*	noisy forest locust	*sa si-ru-qish-ie*	forest cricket
237	*buru en. me li*	consultant (of death)	*sa-'i-lu*	mantis
238	*buru en. me. lis. sha. (g) ga*	dto. of field	*sa-'i-lu'-eq-lu*	field mantis
239	*buru ir. gi. lum*	grasshopper	*shu-lum*	—
240	*buru ir. gi. zum*	grasshopper	*shu-zum*	—
241	*buru sa. a. sa. a*	grasshopper	*si-ig|k-du*	—
242	*buru ma. su. (d). ud. da*	grasshopper	*a-du-dil-lum*	mantis
242a	*buru du. hu*	grasshopper	*(x)-ih-tu*	?
242b	*buru sa. kal*	grasshopper	*(x)-ti-tu*	?
243	*buru ha. mun*	noisy grasshopper	*lal-la-ri-tum*	lamenting woman
244	*buru balag. ga. na*	"harp of the field"	*sar-sa-ri*	Cricket

The great number of names in use for locusts and grasshoppers is nothing unusual. The Bible, the Talmud and the mediaeval Arab authors comply with this habit. An exact identification of these names is almost impossible. The philological indications are insufficient. The enormous economic importance of locusts in Irak, which is invaded at intervals by the desert locust (*Schistocerca gregaria* Forsk.) from the south and where the Moroccan locust (*Docio-staurus maroccanus* Thnbg.) increases at similar intervals in the north, justifies and explains this variety of names. The names by themselves do not even permit to verify whether these two kinds of locusts were distinguished from each other. Certainly separate names were given to various stages and colour phases. Nos. 230a and 231 probably refer to hoppers.

In addition to locusts and grasshoppers apparently praying mantids and crickets were included in the buru group. No. 333 "ubpad: the lacerator of plants" (S) is claimed by

LANDSBERGER (1934 p. 135) to be the mole-cricket (*Gryllotalpa gryllotalpa*), because of the heavy damage done by this insect. The name describes the activities of the mole-cricket rather badly. It does not lacerate plants, but cuts their roots and the plants wilt and die. The name may just as well be applied for noctuid caterpillars but it is probably safer to abstain from any interpretation of the name.

Some other groups are:

No. 232 "dust locust" (S + A) refers, according to LANDSBERGER (1934 p. 123), to a very small species, not to locust swarms.

No. 233 "sea locust (S + A) is almost certainly a crustaceous marine animal of the *Squilla mantis* group.

No. 233a, 234 "river locust" (S) has, as Assyrian equivalent, "river locust" in the former, dragonfly in the second case. The former may refer to the larvae of Odonata or to fresh water shrimps. Possibly they refer to the large Ephemerid *Palingenia euphratica* Mos., which because of the huge swarms in which it appears over the river may have well been inserted into this group.

No. 235, 236 the "zizanu" are described in a medical commentary as having big jumping legs (or eventually long antennae). In both readings this would refer to the long-horned grasshoppers (*Tettigoniidae*). Cf. LANDSBERGER (1934 p. 123).

No. 236 a, b, 243, 244, 247. The "noisy locust" (S) is translated into the Assyrian for cricket (*Gryllidae*). We would suggest, however, that the "harp of the field" or one of the other last mentioned names, in Assyrian sarsari instead of sasiru, may refer to the cicada. This noisy group producing a chirping which, in summer, dominates the landscape of most inhabited parts of Irak and which was regarded as a very pleasant noise by the ancient Greeks, certainly deserved to have a name.

No. 237, 238, 242 "consultant of death, dto. of the field" (S + A) is translated by LANDSBERGER (1934 p. 124) as praying mantis (*Mantidae*). This identification seems only to be based on the similarity of the popular name, which by itself is insufficient.

No. 249-272, 293-295. The next, the uh-group, includes all pests. First the human vermin are mentioned:

249	uhuh	uplu	head-lice	251	imuh	kalmatum	body-lice
250	liuh	naabu	nits	252	mubiuh	purshuu	fleas

No. 253 to 255 contain other variants of the same names, especially of the former. Lice and fleas are common vermin among the poorer population of Irak until today. Surprising is the absence of the bedbug especially as Prof. LANDSBERGER and the writer discussed this question at Ankara. Anatolia is, of course, the seat of the king of bugs. The simple explanation is that the bedbug is really absent in Irak. Even in Kurdistan the writer has never been disturbed by this vermin. The ecological reasons are discussed elsewhere. The only possible reference to this species was found by LANDSBERGER (1934 p. 41, no. 48) in a medical commentary, where line 48 reads: "samanu sha igari = red insect of the walls" (S), "tultu saamtu = red worm" (A).

The following names describe pests of crops and stored products, such as pests of the field, of the forest, of the cereals, of sesame, of dates (probably referring to *Ephestia cautella*). If this interpretation is correct, it would support the endemicity of this species in the Middle East. Pests of water, of wood, of beams, of vegetables, of flour, of clothes, of dead fish, of wool (*Tineola pellionella,* the cloth-moth) are followed again by meat and disease pests. The uh-group is thus identical with current popular names, such as "bugs" in

American slang or the "dudi" in modern Arabic. It is useless to try a specific identification beyond the few remarks made just before.

No. 272-283. The zana- and ushu-groups are interpreted as caterpillars by LANDSBERGER (1934 p. 23, 128) (S). The Assyrian word "munu" appears in another Assyrian text (AMT 104, 105) as "flying munu of the field". LANDSBERGER (p. 128) assumes that this and other similar texts prove that larvae and caterpillars had been recognized as development stages of winged insects. We do not see the slightest proof for such an assumption, just as the assumed knowledge of the old Egyptians on the life cycle of the *Scarabaeus* has been shown to be entirely unfounded. But we take this epitheton to be a hint not to apply the munu group to caterpillars, but to beetles (*Coleoptera*). Most of the conspicuous Tenebrionid and Carabid beetles of Irak, as well as *Meloe* and other beetles are wingless. This would be sufficient to secure them a position in the list before the winged insects. Winged and apterous forms of the same group again occur in the ants. no. 275, the "stared munu" would then apply to the big Scarabaeids with horns, such as *Oryctes*. It is impossible that the beetles are entirely absent from the list. In the medical commentary (LANDSBERGER 1934 p. 130) kanzuzu = muqappil occurs, which is interpreted as "rolling balls". This would refer to *Scarabaeus* and related genera. Nos 292-295 have the Sumerian prefix uh, but are translated into moth in the Assyrian saassu.

No. 296-303 the girish or butterfly group. The epitheta do not add much evidence for specific identification, except perhaps: "horned butterfly" or "bat", which may refer to a nocturnal moth. It is quite possible that the butterflies reappear in the list of bird names and the editor of the bird tablet of the har-ra = hubullu should pay attention to this possibility. The Assyrian names apparently distinguish saassu = moth from butterfly: "kurmittum and turzu". Also the "eggs of the butterfly" are mentioned.

No. 304-332 the num-group, containing *Diptera* and *Hymenoptera*. The "flies of the lion, wolf, cattle" refer probably to *Tabanidae*. The "fly of the cucumbers" may be *Myiopardalis pardalina,* but with reservation. The "green fly" is *Lucilia,* the blue one *Calliphora erythrocephala.* The "toothed fly" (S), "biting fly" (A) is *Stomoxys* and *Hyperosia.* The "dog fly" (S + A) may be *Hippobosca.* The "trembling fly" may be a Syrphid, the "collecting fly" a Bombyliid, but both with reservation. No. 316 has an ideogram of mosquito and blood-fly. Together with the baqqu (A) it forms the mosquito group. The identification of no. 318-320 with *Sirex* (LANDSBERGER 34 p. 132) is impossible, as this family is so far unknown in Irak. The identification of no. 321, 322 with *Ammophila* must also be rejected. No. 325-327 332, the numlal or honeyfly is, of course, *Apis mellifera.* No. 327 (A) and 328 (S + A) are wasps, which refers to *Vespa orientalis,* the hornet. There remains no. 331, the "running fly" (S), the "harvester of the water surface" (A), which must be *Gerris* or *Hydrometra.* We have no identifications for the "vegetable, the water, and the stone flies".

No. 347-350. The "kallat il shamash", (A) the "bride of the sun", may well refer to *Odonata*, as LANDSBERGER has translated (1934 p. 28).

No. 352-359, the kishi or ant group. A "flying ant" is mentioned, as well as ants of the mountains, light, dark, brown, multicoloured, yellow ants. The two last mentioned may refer to *Messor semirufus,* a very common species, which is half-black, half-red, and to *Dorylus punicus.*

E. *Alia Evertebrata.* We follow the original sequence of the names in the har-ra = hubullu and not the taxonomic arrangement.

No. 225, 226. The crab (S + A). This is the freshwater crab *Potamion fluviatile.* No cancer is known to occur in Irak (except in the Persian Gulf). *Potamion* is found occasionally along the shores of fresh waters on rainy or cool days. This explains its inclusion in the list of terrestrial animals. The name is identical with that of the corresponding sign of the zodiac, which must therefore be correctly named "crab" instead of "cancer" (cf. also LANDS-BERGER 1934 p. 121).

No. 283-289 designate the "worm" group: "worm, big worm, big worm of the loamy soil" (S + A). LANDSBERGER here includes (1934 p. 129) the earth-worm and the leech. Doubtful are: "mubattiru", the disease vermin, which name may refer to intestinal worms as well as to maggots infesting wounds. "Igigula" is an eye-disease, which possibly is caused by a worm. If this conjecture is correct, it probably refers to the maggots of *Oestrus ovis* L., which fly not unfrequently lays its eggs in the Middle East, in the corner of the eye, causing conjunctivitis.

No. 336-340 "spider" (S + A). No specific identification of the names seems possible. It is difficult to decide if the "spinner" (A), the "plant spinner or mouth spinner" (S) (no. 334, 335) belong here or to the *Lepidoptera*. In the former case the "plant spinner" may refer to the common *Theridium aulicum*, whose webs often cover trees and shrubs in gardens.

No. 340a-346 include the *Mollusca*. Here also no specific identification seems possible. A few names indicate the amphibious character of the animal. This scarcity of names corresponds to the scarcity of terrestrial snails in Irak.

No. 360-371 refer to the scorpions (S + A). The Sumerian epitheta are: light, dark, red (= brown), multicoloured, yellow, flying scorpion. These colours, in combination with the abundance of certain species, will permit a specific identification in some cases. The insufficient knowledge of this group in Irak induces us to abstain at the present moment from any attempt to identify them. The "flying scorpion" (no. 370) may well be the big water bug *Belostoma nilotica,* which comes to the light not unfrequently when near water. No. 371, the "child leading scorpion" refers, of course, to the habit of the first larva to stay on the mother's back.

We resume the names of the har-ra = hubullu in their quantitative distribution on modern taxonomic units:

Mammalia. Total: 179 names.

Unguiculata	71
Carnivora	87
Rodentia	19
Insectivora	2

Reptilia and Amphibia. Total: 75 names.

Ophidia	48
Lacertilia	13
Chelonia	8
Amphibia	6

Insecta. Total 121 names.

Orthoptera	25
Pests	33

Insecta. Total 121 names.

?Coleoptera	12
Lepidoptera	8
Diptera/	
Hymenoptera	31
Odonata	4
Formicidae	8

Alia Evertebrata: 32 names.

Crustacea	2
Vermes	7
Arachnida	5
Mollusca	6
Scorpions	12

We have tried to find places for important and well-known, popular groups, such as beetles, cicadas, a.o., which had been omitted so far. Other animals which probably are included in the list are *Solifugidae*, ticks, etc. The taxonomic principles were rather simple and resemble those applied by PLINY. They are much less progressive than the early Greek taxonomy, such as represented by ARISTOTLE. The taxonomic conception of the Sumerians, as exposed here, was maintained for a long time in the Middle East. The zoology of the Talmud was still entirely based on them. And from a short analysis of the mediaeval Arab writers it appears that they also still seem to accept it in a general way as a base of their taxonomic arrangement. It is however possible that the knowledge of the ancient Sumerians, Babylonians and Assyrians was much superior to the impression which we get from the analysis of these bare lists of names.

2. 25. BIRDS IN ANCIENT IRAQ

Bird illlustrations abound in ancient Irak art. But they are usually of such a generalised and conventional or plump design that it is impossible to identify the family, and a specific identification is very seldom possible. HOUGHTON (1885), to whom we owe the almost unique comprehensive study of the Assyrian birds, gives some good illustrations of these difficulties. One family after the other is rejected, and finally what is assumed to be meant, as a rook, he adds, and this quite rightly, that quite another bird may have been meant. The base of most identifications is purely philological, either in the field of comparative philology or interpretation of the popular name by the meaning of the root. Some of these identifications seem untenable and the majority at least doubtful. The art representations of birds have been carefully compiled and interpreted by VAN BUREN (1939 p. 84 ff.).

Indefinable eagles, often in heraldic application, are frequently figured. Eagles have to be assumed, when the wings of big birds of prey are rounded, the tail short and rounded. HOUGHTON (1885 p. 58) could not find a word distinguishing the eagles from the common vulture (*Gyps fulvus*). The Egyptian vulture (*Neophron percnopterus*) is distinguished (HOUGHTON 1885 p. 59) and the same author follows DELITZSCH in the recognition of the Laemmergeier (*Gypaetus barbatus*). Also HILZHEIMER (cf. VAN BUREN 1939 p. 84) identifies some of the accipitres with long tail, elongated body and slender, pointed wings as the Laemmergeier. HOUGHTON hints at the "raven of the gods" and the "antelope attacker" being *Gypaetus*. But the former may as well be the raven, the latter a falcon. Vultures in company of crows, feeding on the corpses of the slain, are common in illustrations of battle fields the latter especially picking at the eyes. Falcons and kestrels are certainly represented, but so far specifically unidentified (cf. WEBER 1920 no. 566). LAYARD (1853 p. 483) reports that at Khorosabad he saw a relief in which a falconer was apparently represented with a falcon sitting on his wrist. This relief, unfortunately, has disappeared. For other figures of falcons see VAN BUREN (1939 p. 85). Owls are rarely identifiable. One of the figurines reproduced by VAN BUREN (1939 fig. 93, left) may be *Tyto alba*. HOUGHTON (1885 p. 62) distinguishes between the eagle owl (*Bubo bubo*), the barn owl (*Tyto alba*) and a small owl (*Athene* or *Scops*).

The few illustrations of the raven group can only in a few cases be ascribed to a definite species. The many small birds, which so frequently are depicted, are most probably, as VAN BUREN correctly points out, not intended to represent any special bird, but birds in general. Only a few of them have been tentatively interpreted as starlings (*Sturnus vulgaris*) or as swallows (*Hirundo rustica*) (cf. VAN BUREN 1939 p. 86, 87).

The crane (*Grus grus*) has been repeatedly represented from Tell Halaf to Uruk. This also holds good for the heron (*Ardea cinerea*) an the swan (*Cygnus olor*). Gulls (*Larus*) are suggested for the birds on two seals, which are picking at fish (VAN BUREN 1939 p. 96). A houbara or a great bustard may be meant on another seal (VAN BUREN 39 fig. 37). The chukar (*Alectoris graeca*) is represented together with locusts and hares in a banquet scene in the palace of SANHERIB at Niniveh. Wild geese and ducks are plentifully illustrated. Both were widely used as models of weight stones. Geese, indicated by long legs and a curved neck, are e.g. the birds on the seals nos. 65, 110, 115 of WEBER (1920). Ostrich, falcon, houbara or bustard, geese and ducks, crane and stork or swan are well represented in the orthostats of Tell Halaf (OPPENHEIM 1931 pl. 25, e.g.). In SALMANASSAR's palace at Babylon the hunting of small birds with bow and arrow is illustrated, as well as on some seals.

The ostrich (*Struthio camelus*) is not often figured. Three seals are especially remarkable. Some more illustrations of similar birds with much shorter neck and legs should not be referred as being those of ostriches, as has repeatedly been done, but of birds of prey. On one seal the god Ashur strangles two ostriches, on another the god Marduk kills an ostrich with a scimitar. These figures hint at a possible ritual sacrifice in connection with ostriches. Another seal cylinder shows an ostrich on the point of attacking a man with widespread wings and raised left foot. The man tries to lure the bird a piece of fruit, which he holds in his right hand, while behind his back he hides a deadly scimitar in his left (LAUFER 1926 p. 8). Recent excavations at Kish and elsewhere, have brought to light a number of ostrich egg-shell cups with rich ornamentation. Such cups were valued objects of foreign trade with China.

In order to give an idea of the ornithological knowledge of the ancient inhabitants of Irak, whilst the bird plate of the "h a r - r a = *hubullu*" has not yet been published (which also includes the bats, as Prof. LANDSBERGER kindly informed the writer), we compile the list produced by HOUGHTON (1885 p. 134 ff.), with all its philological insufficiencies, which also is based on bi- resp. trilingual lexicographical name lists:

Assyrian bird names and identifications (from HOUGHTON)

ASSYRIAN NAME	ACCADIAN NAME	LATIN AND ENGLISH NAME
1. eruu, naasru zaaikhu	idkhu, eru(?)	Eagles + Griffon vulture (*Gyps fulvus*)
2. lakhantuv	qasuqudda	a screaming bird of prey.
3. qatimatuv, eruulluv	—	Egyptian vulture (*Neophron percnopterus*).
4. tasbaluv, khakharili, kariib, barkhati	—	Laemmergeier (*Gypaetus barbatus*)
5. Sarrad qipri, lalla qippar	adimma	??? (*Pernis apivorus*).
6. ziibu, kharrukhani	nuumma	a screaming bird of prey
7. esebu, khusii	—	Eagle owl (*Bubo bubo*)
8. marratuv, itstsurtu-baqi	—	small owl (*Otus scops* or *Athene noctua*)
9. kaduu, aqquu	—	Barn owl (*Tyto alba*)
10. qililuv, qulili	—	Woodpeckers (*Dendrolimus syriacus*,
11. anpatuv	gissir	??? *Picus viridis*)
12. dulimmassat	sibtirra	*Dendrolimus syriacus*
13. khazuu, khuuku	sulu	cuckoos (*Cuculus canorus*, *Clamator glandarius*)
14. nambuubtuv, adammumu	—	Hoopoe (*Upupa epops*) or *Vanellus cristatus*
15. asqiqituv, abqinini-nituv,	—	Swallow (*Hirundo rustica*)
tsapitav	tsapitav	
khatsibaruv, bulili	khurub baqugudurra gungil	swallows, martins, swifts.
16. tsulamu, tsalamdu, itstsurmusi	— akhu	Nightingale (*Lusciola luscinia*) or *Acrocephalus phragmitis*

17. kipsu, tsitsildu itstsurkiisi	kipsu nambirgizi	*Acrocephalus arundinaceus* or *A. stentorius.*
18. maaqlat ubla, khurat-sanituv	gamuundu	(Golden oriole: *Oriolus oriolus*)
19. sa eqil	khumes	(finches etc.)
20. diikdiku, duqduqqu, itstsur samedi	qu	Sparrow (*Passer domesticus*)
21. allalluv	sibtur	Starling (*Sturnus vulgaris*)
22. rihu	sib	? rook (*Corvus frugilegus*)
23. 'eribu	khurub	Locust bird (*Pastor roseus*)
24. aribu, khakhar	—	Raven (*Corvus corax*)
25. kakuu, tarmazilu	—	a cawing bird
26. pahu, kakanu	—	Hooded crow (*Corvus cornix*)
27. qasid qabruv, qasid qabarti	—	Jackdaw (*Corvus monedula*)
28. tasballuv, khaakhkhu, tuballaats	—	a bluish-brown cawing bird: ? roller (*Coracias garrula*)
29. ballutsituv, tuballaats, qinasa (its nest)	—	Magpie (*Pica pica*)
30. ursanu, taamsilu	sak	Wood pigeon (*Columba palumbus*)
31. tarru, qaqabaanu	igimul	Turtle dove (*Streptopelia turtur*)
32. irqabu, rigabu	—	Rock pigeon (*Columba livia*)
33. suum (matu ?)	suummu	Domestic pigeon
34. siliingu, buridu	illumbi	(Snowfinch, *Montifringilla alpicola*)
35. kakuulluv, qulukuku, qilippu	—	Chukar (*Alectoris graeca*) and Black Partridge (*Francolinus vulgaris*)
36. sudinnu, giilgidanu	—	Bustard (*Otus tarda*) or houbara (*Chlamydotis undulata*)
37. urnigu, qaliu	kesda	Crane (*Grus grus*)
38. rakraku, lakalaka	—	storks (*Ciconia alba* and *C. nigra*)
39. ummi mi 'i, abaya	amaa	Ibis (*Threskiornis aethiopicus*) and the Hermit ibis (*Comatibis eremita*)
40. —	ua	Buff-backed heron (*Ardeola ibis*)
41. naadhru	agus	Heron (*Ardea cinerea* or *A. alba*)
42. dhar lugalluv	dudurranu	Flamingo (*Phoenicopterus antiquorum*)
43. tus, qumuu, abuunnu, ataan nari	nambirmukhdilluv, raggussa	Pelican (*Pelecanus onocrotalus*)
44. qunipu, 'ezizu, dilbat	agusse, saggusu	Domestic fowl
45. sakatuv, gamgamu, seip ariq.	girigidda, gamgam (khu)	Ostrich (*Struthio camelus*)

We have pointed out before that identifications are mainly based on philological argumentations, which leads not always to the correct zoological result. We may add that 60 years ago the science of Assyriology was still in its infancy and that the ornis of Irak was very incompletely known by then. We have preserved in the list the identifications of HOUGHTON to which we wish to add a few remarks. The only change is the introduction of modern synonymy for those species of birds which occur in Irak. In looking over this bird list we miss a series of very obvious and common birds, which certainly should appear, such as all larks (*Galerida, Alauda,* etc.), the bee-eater (*Merops*), the bulbul (*Pycnonotus leucotis*) and the pin-tailed sandgrouse (*Pterocles alchata*). The common roller (*Coracias garrula*) is only mentioned with a question mark. It is impossible for us to attempt a revision of HOUGHTON's list, but we hope that a complete revision of the ornithological knowledge in ancient Irak will be made when the bird plate of the h a r - r a = *hubullu* will be published. In the mean time we limit ourselves to a few remarks.

The determinative prefixes or affixes are khu and pak (the later being connected with flying) in the Sumerian, nam bir in the Accadian languages (Khu bir, read: khu rub, identifies insect names).

Accipitres (no. 1-6): The identification of the various vultures seems still provisional. *Gyps fulvus* is a dark vulture, for which denomination "black" would suit (as it would for the common black kite), which has been referred to the lammergeyer. No. 5 is certainly not *Pernis apivorus*, which is rare. And bee-keeping was restricted in time and extent to such a degree, that as a honey bee-eating bird it should be neglected. HOUGHTON himself (1885 p. 109, 142) proposes in a note to read "queen of the regions" for "terror of the regions" and to suggest as "bird of heavenly beauty" the bee-eater (*Merops*), for which we propose an apparently more suited name.

STRIGES (no. 7-9): The eagle-owl is called the "bird of evil".

No. 10-12: All the names for woodpeckers seem doubtful, not only with regard to species, but with regard to the group in general. The only species fairly abundant although restricted to the north, is the Syrian woodpecker.

No. 13: The onomatopoeic name khuuku for the cuckoos is quite suggestive.

No. 14: may be the hoopoe (*Upupa epops*) which is quite an obvious and common passing migrant.

No. 15: If the names are based on other grounds than on the onomatopoeic name alone, the identification as swallow may be correct. This abundant summer breeder, which is so intimately connected with human dwellings, had certainly a special name.

No. 16, 17. Are almost certainly misidentifications. The "bird of the night" does not characterise any of the nightingales and warblers. Tristram correctly remarks that *Cettia cetti* is the most common warbler (HOUGHTON 1885 p. 142). The reed-birds of the Irak marshes, if small singing birds are meant, are *Acrocephalus arundinaceus* and *A. griseldis*.

No. 18: The golden oriole cannot possibly be the "golden coloured worm-eater". He is only a passing migrant for a very short period. But the name excellently fits the metallic green Persian bee-eater (*Merops persicus*).

No. 19, 20: refer to "birds injurious to the crops". If some names are put aside for the house sparrow (*Passer domesticus*) and the starling, the other names should be reserved for the various larks, such as *Galerida cristata, Melanocorypha calandra, Calandrella spp., Alauda arvensis*. These are most injurious bird pests of field crops in Irak (BODENHEIMER, in press). The crested lark (*Galerida*), the commonest bird of Irak almost certainly had a special name.

No. 21: is assumed to refer to the starling (*Sturnus vulgaris*). It may rather refer to a lark.

No. 22: The rook as "shepherd bird" is doubtful. Tristram (HOUGHTON 1885 p. 142) thinks it is the jackdaw.

No. 23: The "locust bird" is certainly *Pastor roseus*, which sporadically invades Irak during heavy locust outbreaks (cf. ROOKE 1930).

No. 24-29: We have no opinion how far the specific identification of the raven birds is justified. It is highly probable that the "bluish-brown cawing bird" (no. 28) refers to the roller (*Coracias garrula*), but *Garrulus glandarius* is equally well suited to that description.

No. 30-33: refer to doves. We are of the opinion that three names should be reserved: one for *Columba livia,* one for *Streptopelia turtur* and the last for *Columba palumbus,* but we cannot decide which is which. On philological and onomatopoeic grounds "turru" seems to design the turtle dove. We do not know on which foundation the name for the rock or the domestic pigeons is based.

No. 34: The snowfinch is certainly a misidentification, which has not been satisfactorily explained (HOUGHTON 1885 p. 101).

No. 35: Among game birds, the rock-partridge is abounding in the hills and mountains of the north and east, whilst the black partridge is rarer there, but quite common in C. Irak. It would be astonishing if these common game birds had not obtained separate names.

No. 36: refers probably rather to the common houbara (*Chlamydotis undulata*) than to the great bustard (*Otus tarda*), which occurs more sporadically.

No. 37, 38: The references to crane and stork are probably correct. The onomatopoeic name *lakalaka* is of special interest, as the present name of the stork is still *haji laglag*.

No. 39: refers possibly to an ibis (*Plegadis falcinellus*).

No. 40, 41: for the herons are probably correct. The same is true for the four following numbers (flamingo, pelican, domestic fowl and ostrich).

18 more names are discussed, most of which remained unidentified (HOUGHTON 1885 p. 101 ff.). The following four names are however identified:

a) *dhaabbi'u,* qaqis na'ari indicates a diving bird. This may rather be the Smyrna kingfisher (*Halcyon smyrnensis*) than the grebes, but the trallid *Fulica atra* is quite common in settlements in winter in small channels. HOUGHTON suggests *Podiceps*.

b) suurduu, qasuru, a falcon, is probably the hunting falcon, as has been discussed under omina. TRISTRAM (HOUGHTON 1885 p. 103, 142) notes that *Falco sacer* is the hunting falcon of Irak.

c) *dudu, ibbiltuv* is referred again to the turtle dove as the sacred bird of Astarte.

d) *urinnu* is interpreted as peacock (*Pavo cristatus*). This bird does and did not belong to the native fauna of Irak. It was introduced from India.

2.3. THE ANIMAL IN THE LIFE OF ANCIENT EGYPT

2. 31. THE DOCUMENTS ON CHANGES IN THE FAUNAL COMPOSITION

The title of this chapter is not well chosen. We do not intend to give a survey of the fauna of ancient Egypt, but merely to give some documentation on those animals which have disappeared from the country since the palaeolithic. Animals common then as now will therefore not be mentioned. The Tertiary history of the Egyptian fauna has been sketched out before (p. 23). We only remind the reader that the early Quaternary fauna—at least of Upper Egypt—is a typical savanna fauna, with giraffes, hartebeests, elephants, hippos, etc., the last remnants of the southward drift of the ancient Pikermi fauna. For the study of the fauna of recent Egypt a number of splendid publications are available. Among them may be mentioned those about mammals (J. ANDERSON, 1902; S. S. FLOWER, 1932), about birds (E. MEINERTZHAGEN-M. NICOLIS, 1930); about reptiles and amphibians (J. ANDERSON, 1906; S. S. FLOWER, 1932); about fishes (C. GAILLARD, 1928).

The remnants of the savanna animals still lingered in Upper Egypt all predynastic and early dynastic times. M. HILZHEIMER (1926, *et alia*) has earned much commendation for his careful analysis of the early archaeological documents. The status of some of the monkeys is uncertain. The hamadryas (*Papio hamadryas*), appears—apart from other figures—in a marvellous series on the obelisk of Luxor (Louvre), praying to the sun. BREHM points out that many peoples of the East-African steppes and of Abyssinia have chosen their hairdress after that of the hamadryas. DÜMICHEN has described the sacredness at which the animal was held in ancient Egypt. The hamadryas, as well as Anubis-baboon, babuin and *Erythrocebus pyrrhonotus* are still living in the Sudan. It is certain that in dynastic times they were introduced in large quantities into Egypt. This does not exclude that some of these species were still inhabiting Upper Egypt in predynastic times.

A nice illustration of the Ethiopian hedgehog (*Parechinus aethiopicus*), still occurring in the Sudan, has been published by DÜMICHEN from the tomb of PTAHHOTEP (2500 B.C.): A pair coming out of the earth, one devouring a locust.

Lions were common at least until the Middle empire. AMENOPHIS III published a special nuptial scarab announcing that until that day he had killed over hundred lions, not necessarily all in Egypt. The lion hunts of the Egyptian kings found a monographer in WIEDEMANN (1926). The spotted wild dog (*Lycaon pictus*), used for hunting gazelles in the third millennium B.C., then replaced by the dog, disappears and now lives south of the Sahara. The gennet, now extinct, appears in some of the ancient marsh scenes. The mention of the otter by HERODOT may be a mistake.

The most conspicuous changes have taken place in the ungulates. TUT-EN-KHAMON (1350 B.C.) and RAMSES III (1180 B.C.) were among the last which hunted wild asses in Egypt. HILZHEIMER (1926 p. 151) comes to the conclusion that a wild grey ass (*Equus asinus*), a subspecies different from the Nubian and from the Somali asses, inhabited all N. Africa in alluvial times. A beautiful illustration is found in a mosaic of *Hippo Regius* (Bone) in Algeria. The N. African ass had the shouldercross (perhaps even doubled) of the Nubian and the colour and the leg striation of the Somali ass.

The deer of the Egyptian monuments was long regarded as representing the Barbary deer (*Cervus elaphus barbarus*), which still lives in the mountain forests of the Atlas. Yet HILZHEIMER (1926 p. 152) has described it as a new form of fallow deer (*Dama schaeferi*). The last document of this deer is a head from the tomb of MENTU-HIR-HOPSET (19th Dynasty). The Egyptian fallow deer had no palmated antlers and a long face. The remainders of a unique recent specimen of this deer, probably from Tripolitania, has been found by HILZHEIMER in the Zoological Museum at Berlin. But no later illustration exists after the 19th Dynasty. The old illustrations (cf. PATON 1925 p. 13) strongly support HILZHEIMER's view. Thus the Barbary deer has, unless new discoveries would show otherwise, to be struck out from the list of ancient Egyptian mammals.

Some good reliefs of giraffes are preserved from the fourth millennium B.C., such as those on the cosmetic pallets of Menes (3200 B.C.). In these times the giraffe also appears as a hieroglyph. All later illustrations refer to giraffes offered as a tribute or as gifts from southern countries.

The figures of some gazelles, now living in the Sudan, such as *Gazella dama* and/or *G. soemmeringi*, occur on old monuments (cf. PATON 1925 p. 14). The North-African Hartebeest (*Alcelaphus buselaphus*) was not only found on monuments, but also as a mummy (LORTET and GAILLARD 1905 p. 14). All these species do not exist in Egypt any more. Documentation is presented about two other great mammals from N.W. Africa, but not from Egypt, so far: The *Bubalus antiquus,* a relative of the arni-buffalo, and a rhinoceros, related to the African *Diceros.*

The aurochs (*Bos primigenius*) certainly lived in early Egypt. This is the correct interpretation of HILZHEIMER of an animal in the tomb of SAHURE (fifth Dynasty), and of other animal illustrations. Whilst in the predynastic era the bulls have curved horns with tips turned inward, the later figures have lyre-shaped horns with tips turned outward. The aurochs was rare during the reign of THUTMOSE III. When the presence of a herd was announced to the king, he immediately embarked at Memphis, and after a night's travel, hurried by chariots to the place indicated. There, in a four days hunt, he killed 75 out of a herd of 176 aurochsen. This killing is described on a special hunting scarab (HILZHEIMER 1926 p. 159). The last document concerning the aurochs is a magnificent hunting scene of RAMSES III, chasing the bulls by chariot.

And, last not least, another important discovery of HILZHEIMER (1926 p. 140 ff.): The African elephant (*Loxodon*), which inhabited Numidia still at the Roman era, undoubtedly lived in Egypt. About seven, partly splendid reliefs and paintings of African elephants are known from early times until the end of the first dynasty. The elephant also occurred as a hieroglyph. For over 2000 years we then only find elephants introduced for carrying tributes in the representations, until the use of war elephants in Ptolemaic times brought the animal back to Egypt in large quantities.

MOREAU (1930 p. 58 ff.) has carefully gone through the bird list from ancient tomb decorations. He states that the highest standard in both execution and truth of life is found in the earliest dynasties. The decline begins with the fifth Dynasty, and after the twelfth only inefficient copies without inspiration are found. The following species have been identified from the monuments:

1. *Lanius collurio* (Red-backed shrike). Beni Hassan.
2. *Lanius nubicus* (Masked shrike). Beni Hassan.
3. *Phoenicurus phoenicurus* (Redstart). Beni Hassan.
4. *Hirundo rustica savignii* (Egyptian swallow). Common hieroglyph.
5. *Cotile rupestris obsoleta* (Pale Crag martin). Hieroglyph in Medum.

6. *Upupa epops* (Hoopoe). Beni Hassan, hieroglyph, etc.
7. *Ceryle rudis* (Pied kingfisher). In many marsh scenes.
8. *Caprimulgus sp.* (Nightjar). An ivorine figurine.
9. *Tyto alba* (Barn owl). Common hieroglyph.
10. *Gyps fulvus* (Griffon vulture). Common hieroglyph.
11. *Neophron percnopterus* (Egyptian vulture). Common hieroglyph.
12. *Phalacrocorax ?pygmaeus* (?Pigmy cormorant). Ti, Sakkara, Beni Hassan, etc.
13. *Pelecanus sp.* (Pelican). Only in the tomb of Mera at Sakkara.
14. *Anser albifrons* (White-fronted goose). Common in marsh scenes and as hieroglyph. Three species of geese excellently on tomb of Ne-fermaat at Medum of the first dynasty.
15. *Anser fabalis* (Bean goose). Medum.
16. *Branta ruficollis* (Red-breasted goose). Medum.
17. *Chenalopex aegyptiacus* (Egyptian goose). Common in marsh scenes.
18. *Cygnus sp.* (Swan). Once at Sakkara.
19. *Tadorna tadorna* (Shelduck). At Bersheh.
20. *Anas crecca* (Teal). Bersheh.
21. *Anas platyrhyncha* (Mallard). Bersheh.
22. *Anas acuta* (Pintail). More common.
23. *Anas penelope* (Wigeon). Medum.
24. *Nyroca ferina* (Pochard). Bersheh.
25. *Nyroca fuligula* (Tufted duck). Ti.
26. *Phoenicopterus antiquorum* (Flamingo). Medum, rare hieroglyph.
27. *Ardea cinerea* (Grey heron). Thebes.
28. *Ardea garzetta* (Little egret). Ti, El Bahari, Sakkara, etc.
29. *Ardeola ibis* (Buff-backed egret). Beni Hassan.
30. *Nycticorax nycticorax* (Night heron). Beni Hassan.
31. *Balaeniceps rex* (Shoe-bill).
32. *Plataliea leucorodia* (Spoonbill). Beni Hassan, etc.
33. *Threskiornis aethiopica* (Sacred ibis).
34. *Comatibis eremita* (Hermit ibis). Hieroglyph.
35. *Grus grus* (Crane). Common as domestic bird from 5th to 18th dynasty.
36. *Anthropoides virgo* (Demoiselle crane). Together with 35.
37. *Hoplopterus spinosus* (Spur-winged plover). Ti.
38. *Recurvirostra avosetta* (Avocet). Bersheh.
39. *Vanellus vanellus* (Lapwing). Medum, hieroglyph.
40. *Podiceps ruficollis* (Little grebe). Ti.
41. *Porphyrio madagascariensis* (Violet gallinule). Medum, Beni Hassan.
42. *Turtur turtur* (Turtle dove). Beni Hassan.
43. *Columba sp.* (Rock dove). Common.
44. *Coturnix coturnix* (Quail). Sakkara.
45. *Struthio camelus* (Ostrich). Bersheh.

The birds of prey are usually unidentifiable, as pointed out before. Of course, there are plenty of foreign birds from Palestine and elsewhere, such as those in the Botanical Garden of THUTMOSE III. Among this group the phoenix, whose hieroglyph characterises it as the golden pheasant of Eastern Asia (*Phasianus pictus*; cf. KELLER 1913 p. 147) is prominent.

More interpretations which probably are correct are (KELLER, WILKINSON): *Haliaeetus albicilla,* kestrels, sparrow-hawk, peregrine falcon, lammergeyer, brown-necked raven, domestic fowl (late), various plovers, such as the Egyptian plover, black-winged stilt, curlew, black-tailed godwit, black stork, landrail, great shearwater, a tern, and silver gull. HILZHEIMER (1926 p. 141) adds the saddle-stork (*Ephippiorhynchus senegalensis*) from a cosmetic tablet dating about 3200 B.C. Also the marabu *Leptopilos crumeniferus* has been illustrated at Beni Hassan (KELLER 1513 p. 157, 63). Birds introduced in later periods are: the Colchian pheasant (*Phasianus colchicus*), the paroquet *Palaeornis torquatus,* the peacock

(*Pavo cristatus*), domestic fowl (*Gallus domesticus*), the guinea fowl (*Numida meleagris*), and—a few centuries ago—the turkey (*Meleagris gallopavo*).

2. 32. ANIMAL MUMMIES AND ANIMAL CULTS IN EGYPT

These have been carefully studied by LORTET and GAILLARD (1905), mainly from the enormous animal hypogea near Roda, Thebes, Sakkara, Abusir, Gize, Kom-Ombo, Esne, and others. These authors quite properly reject the theory, so often pronounced by Greek writers that the ancient Egyptians worshipped various animals as gods. They refer to a remark by HERODOT (2 : 123): The Egyptians are the first who talked about the doctrine that the human soul be immortal and enters—after the destruction of the body—into another living being. When the soul has travelled through all the animals of the land, the sea, through all the birds of the air, then it returns into a human body. This complete cycle lasts three thousand years. The soul enters a new animal or man, when those are born. And certain chapters in the famous Egyptian Book of the Dead actually describe the entrance of human souls into hawks, lapwings, swallows, serpents, crocodiles, lotus plants, etc.

Most animal hypogea or cemeteries belong to the Graeco-Roman period. Many of the mummified animals are found in abundance in some places and are rare or absent elsewhere. Those mono-specific cemeteries are usually close to the temples of the deities to which each of them was sacred. New excavations may add animals either entirely wanting or poorly represented in the earlier finds. HERODOT and other ancient writers stress repeatedly the localisation of the sacred animals. The different provinces or nomes were often characterised by a certain animal. Especially in Upper-Egypt this may be a relic of ancient totems and taboos, perhaps under Ethiopian influences. FRAZER (G.B. 1945 p. 87) gives another, not necessarily conflicting interpretation: In ancient Egypt the sacred kings were blamed, as in many African tribes they are until now, for the failure of the crops, but the sacred beasts were also held responsible for the course of nature. When pestilence and other calamities had fallen on the land, in consequence of a long and severe drought, the priests took the animals by night and threatened them, but if the evil did not abate they slew the sacred beasts. As most of the mummified animals were neither old nor sick, to all appearence, they may have been killed on purpose. This strengthens the view promoted by FRAZER. Totemistic reminiscences are probable. But others may have been mummified in reverence to the souls of deceased relatives. One of the numerous classes of priests may even have specialised in announcing the animal into which the soul of the dead had entered, and asked for the mummification of an individual of that species. A. WIEDEMANN (1912) insists on another explanation of the Egyptian animal cult. Local tradition of it is very old and dates back to the first dynasties. He explains that these cults were most popular with the common people in early days, whilst they were often neglected by the upper classes. None of the big temples would dare to abandon the sacred animals in the temple sanctuaries. Some of these cults, as that of the apis, the crocodiles and the falcons, were widely spread, whilst most other animal cults remained more or less locally restricted.

The popularity of the animal cults grew, when in the first millennium the gods actually did not sufficiently support Egypt's foreign policy any more. The successful conqueror of Jerusalem, SHESHONK I, the SISAK of the Bible (about 950 B.C.), originated from Bubastis, near Zagazig, where his relatives were the main supporters of the cult of Bastis, the cat-goddess. The greatest impulse for encouraging these cults was, in the opinion of WIEDE-MANN, the reaction towards foreign penetration after 700 B.C. In contrast to the cosmopolitan Olymp of the Greeks, the Egyptians more and more concentrated purposely on the animal cults, so obviously strange to all foreigners. Still CLEMENS of Alexandria (about 200 A.D.) says: "When entering the holy of holies, the priests show a cat, a crocodile, a snake as the god of the temple." The naos of the holy of holies contained in most cases a cage with the animal, in others galleries leading to their rooms. The killing of a sacred animal, such as a cat or an ibis, was an unforgivable crime. About 60 B.C. a Roman killed a cat by accident in Alexandria. Neither the fear of Rome nor the intervention of the king could save the unlucky one from being executed.

Only one or very few individuals among those maintained in the main temples, were really regarded as gods. All other individuals of the same species were just sacred. The taboo of most sacred animals was locally restricted. The different districts (nomes) had each their own sacred animal, which also appeared on the military standards of the nome. Serious local strifes between neighbouring districts, adherents of different animal gods, were not unusual. Under the Psammetichids and the Ptolemies the animal cults reached their pinnacle. The people of Oxyrhynchos once grew furious about those of Kynopolis, as these ate their holy fish, the oxyrhynchos. They therefore caught some of the sacred dogs of Kynopolis, slaughtered them and ate them at a sacrifice banquet. This led to troubles of such an extent that the Romans—usually very reluctant to interfere in religious strifes—had to crush them by heavy punishment.

The assumption that only a few individuals were true gods, the others only sacred, explains the small number of animals buried sometimes with gold ornaments as gifts.
We may quote a few passages from AELIAN as illustration to this conception of *Wiedemann*.

(7 : 9). On the sparrow-hawk (or falcon) of Egypt. The servants of Apollo in Egypt say that some people are called fosterers of sparrow-hawks, as they have to wait upon those birds and to feed them. All these birds are sacred to Apollo, but some individuals are fed with special food as holy in the temples. The keepers say that they breed in a holy grove. Of these breeders they take special care. To the just hatched young they offer the brains of caught birds, a very suitable food for the tender young.

(10 : 46). The oxyrhynchus (= pointed nose) fish has its name from the shape of its face. He lives in the Nile and is sacred in one district named after it. The inhabitants do not eat angled fish, as they fear that their holy fish may be wounded by the angle hook. When they fish with nets, they carefully look if no oxyrhynchus is amongst it and they prefer a bad catch without the holy fish. They say this fish has originated from the wounds of Osiris, who is one with the Nile.

(11 : 10). Apis is held as the most conspicuous Egyptian god. He is born from a cow, which has been touched and thus fertilised by a heavenly ray. The Egyptians enumerate 29 different characters which distinguish the holy bull, each connected in a symbolic way with the stars. One announces the flood of the Nile, another the shape of the world, one that darkness is older than light, another the moon, etc. As soon as the rumour goes that a new god has been born, one of the holy scribes, well acquainted with all those characters, visits the place and builds a house for him there. He is nourished with milk for four months. Then the holy scribes and prophets go to him at the rising moon. Every year they decorate a holy ship and on this they bring him to Memphis, his preferred site. There he has places for his pleasure, for running, for standing, for exercises and rooms with beautiful cows, which he may visit at his pleasure, a well and a spring. It would be too long to enumerate the processions, the sacrifices, the dances, the banquets and the feasts in his honour, and how towns and villages rejoice. The owner of the herd, from which the apis has been born, is held as lucky and is admired. The apis is also a good prophet. Whilst the preacher asks him his questions, boys play around and enthusiastically answer every question in rhythms. The Egyptians compare him with Horus, the giver of fertility and good luck. But what the Egyptians have written about him, does not appear to me to correspond with the truth and with the character of this animal.

The process of mummification itself shows many variations (LORTET and GAILLARD 1905). Some animals, most of the paria dogs for instance, were simply thrown into a soda bath, then dried and roughly wrapped up in a piece of linen. Others seem to have been dried first, then smeared with bitumen. But there are many other animals which were mummified with great care, were carefully wrapped up in long strips of linen, enclosed into often highly artistic mummy boxes, these again into sarcophagi of wood or stone or into jars, and then put into the hypogeum, together with many hundreds of thousands of its kind.

These mummies are most valuable for the history of some domestic animals, such as dog, cat, cattle, sheep and goats. But these will be dealt with later. Among the wild mammals two kinds of jackals only were found among the many dogs, but more kinds of wild cats (*Felis libyca*) than the slightly feebler domestic cats. Two species of shrews (*Crocidura olivieri* and *C. religiosa*) were even first described from such mummies, when they were still living in Egypt. The embalmed ungulates include two antelopes (*Alcelaphus buselaphus*), about twenty gazelles (*Gazella dorcas,* more common in Lower Egypt, and *G. arabica,* more common in Upper Egypt), and one Barbary sheep (*Ammotragus lervia*).

From about thousand bird mummies more than half were young birds in too bad a condition to permit identification. The most common species are the sacred ibis and some birds of prey (kestrel, buzzard, spotted eagle, kite). A small book by SAVIGNY, the zoologist of Napoleon's expedition (1805 p. 70), was devoted to the sacred ibis and to its veneration by the ancient Egyptians. He explains it by the coincidence of the rise of the Nile with the arrival of the ibis. This coincidence connected this bird intimately with the fertility of the country, and thus the ibis became the symbol of the Nile. Whilst the birds of prey all show a very primitive type of mummification, being roughly wrapped up in linen and often in groups of four to forty in one "parcel", the ibis mummies are all carefully wrapped up in strips of linen, enclosed into papyrus and a plaited, often highly ornamental basket, before they were put into jars. The birds of prey were connected with Horus.

The list of the mummified birds of Egypt is (LORTET and GAILLARD 1905, MOREAU 1930 p. 75):

BIRD SPECIES: A. BIRDS OF PREY	No. of individuals studied from	
	Upper Egypt	Giza and Sakkara
1. *Milvus aegyptius* (Egyptian kite)	24	18
2. *Milvus milvus* (Red kite)	—	1
3. *Pernis apivorus* (Honey buzzard)	1	2
4. *Elanus caeruleus* (Black-winged kite)	4	—
5. *Buteo vulpinus* (Desert buzzard)	35+6	11+4
6. *Buteo ferox* (Long-legged buzzard)	15	—
7. *Circaetus gallicus* (Serpent eagle)	3	—
8. *Aquila heliacea* (Imperial eagle)	2	2
9. *Aquila clanga* (Spotted eagle)	26	1
10. *Hieraaetus pennatus* (Booted eagle)	1	3
11. *Haliaeetus albicillus* (White-tailed eagle)	1	—
12. *Falco babylonicus* (C. Asian Peregrine falcon)	13	3
13. *Falco peregrinoides* (Barbary falcon)	1	—
14. *Falco tanypterus* (Lanner falcon)	5	1
15. *Falco subbuteus* (Hobby)	1	2
16. *Falco cherrug* (Saker falcon)	1	1
17. *Falco naumanni* (Lesser kestrel)	2	3

18. *Falco tinnunculus* (Kestrel)	70	21
19. *Accipiter nisus* (Sparrow hawk)	37	15
20. *Circus aeruginosus* (Marsh harrier)	5	10
21. *Circus cyaneus* (Hen harrier)	5	1
22. *Circus pyargus* (Montagué's harrier)	1	—-
23. *Circus macrurus* (Pallid harrier)	1	1
24. *Melierax gabar* (Chanting goshawk)	4	1
25. *Pandion haliaetus* (Osprey)	—	2
26. *Torgos nubicus* (Sociable vulture)		
27. *Gyps fulvus* (Griffon vulture)		
28. *Neophron percnopterus* (Egyptian vulture)		
29. *Tyto alba* (Barn owl)	—	2
30. *Bubo ascalaphus* (Eagle owl)	—	1
31. *Otus scops* (Scops owl)	2	1
32. *Asio otus* (Long-eared owl)	1	—
33. *Asio flammeus* (Short-eared owl)	1	3

B. OTHER BIRDS

34. *Threskiornis aethiopica* (Sacred ibis)   very abundant, mainly at Sakkara
35. *Plegadis falcinellus* (Glossy ibis)   4
36. *Anser albifrons* (White-fronted goose)
37. *Anas crecca* (Teal)
38. *Anas querquedula* (Garganey).

Mummies of the crocodile (*Crocodilus niloticus*) abound, especially at Esne. Once only the mummy of an uraeus serpent or asp (*Naja haje*) was discovered. Among the material of embalmed fishes LORTET and GAILLARD found only those of *Lates niloticus*. They all came from Esne, the ancient Latopolis. Apart from the many adult fishes an amazing number of very young brood was found mummified. No doubt at other places similar cemeteries of oxyrhynchus and of bynni fish will be found.

LORTET and GAILLARD (1908, 1909), in later publications, have added many other mummified animals to their earlier list, such as serpents, jackals and foxes. They describe the necropolis of the Sared Baboon in the Wadi Gabanet in the hills of Thebes.

Important are also some contributions of GAILLARD (1934) to the prehistoric fauna of Egypt. From an old, but not exactly dated site at Sebil and Kom Ombo in Upper Egypt he mentions: *Hyaena crocuta spelaea, Equus asinus, E. caballus, Hippopotamus amphibius niger, Bos brachyceros, B. primigenius, Bubalus vignardi, Alcelaphus buselaphus, Gazella isabella.* Without an exact dating we are unable to discuss these finds. From the neolithicum of Toukh in Upper Egypt GAILLARD enumerates: *Canis familiaris, Sus scrofa cf. palustris, Bos brachycerus, Bubalus cf. caffer, Capra hircus mambrica, C. h. reversa, Ovis longipes palaeoaegypticus, Gazella isabella.* Most of the bones found are from domestic animals and, when the date will be fixed, will be of high importance for the history of the domestic animals in Egypt.

A small number of other animals was found in the crops of mummified birds of prey. They belong to the contemporaneous, not to the mummified fauna. Among these are: Two rodents (*Acomys cahirinus, Rattus alexandrinus*), some birds (*Cuculus canorus, Coracias garrulus, Hirundo rustica, Pterocles senegallus, Burhinus oedicnemus*) and a lizard (*Mabuia sp.*).

Mollusc shells from the excavations at Karnak, dating from the Ptolemaic period, were identified by A. LOCARD: *Murex brandaris* (1), *M. anguliferus* (5), *Fasciolaria trapezium* (1), *Strombus tricornis* (2), *Pterocera lambis* (5), *Cassis glauca* (1), *Cypraea pantherina* (1), *C. melanostoma* (1), *C. histrio* (1), *C. caput-serpentis* (1), *Meladomus boltenianus* (2), *Vivipara unicolor* (1), *Tridacna gigas* (8), *T. elongata* (1), *Pectunculus pectiniformis* (1), *Meleagrina margaretifera* (1), *Ostrea plicata* (6).

These shells are too few to consider them as having been food, especially as nobles and priests at least did not eat fish or molluscs in Egypt. But they are interesting from the point of view of provenance: Two species belong to the fresh water fauna of the Nile (*Meladomus, Vivipara*), all other are marine. Of these one only (*Murex brandaris*) is Mediterranean. The overwhelming majority belongs to the fauna of the Indian Ocean and of the Red Sea, only three species being wanting apparently today in the latter (*Cassis, Tridacna gigas, Ostrea*).

We have given before some examples of ancient Egyptian prescriptions. Other ingredients of animal provenance are the dung of various animals, from lizard and crocodile and flies to that of antelope, ass, dog and cat; blood of bat, dog; fat vulva, uterus, semen, testicles and milk of various animals. This type of prescriptions has survived the millennia. In the Syrian "Book of Medicine" we find them again in the medicines of the distinguished lecturer as well as in the appendix of native medicine. In the appendix this influence of magic, so conspicuous in Egyptian medicine, is still recognisable. And BUDGE (I : CXXXV) quotes a number of popular English folk-medicines from recent centuries (from CULPEPPER, *Last Legacy* p. 75 ff.), such as the droppings of a dog fattened with roast cummin seed, mixed with boiled earthworms against aches in the spine; ashes of hen-feathers for stopping bleeding; or toads, spiders, frogs or their spawn for the same effect. Jay against epilepsy, the liver of a mad dog as the best remedy for the biting of a mad dog, a dried owl for gout, hare blood against stones in the bladder, pigeon's dung against warts, earthworms against jaundice. Grease of an eel restores hearing in a short space; powder of a dead mouse against diabetes, etc. "The foot of a great living toad being cut off when the moon is void of course, and hastens to the conjunction of the sun, cures one of the King's evil, being hung about their necks.—The powder of earthworms, of mice dung, and a hare's tooth, put into the hole of a rotten tooth, it will drop out without any instrument." These examples are sufficient to restrain our first feeling of horror and nausea about the prescriptions of ancient medicine.

2. 33. ACTUAL FAUNAL CHANGES IN HISTORICAL TIMES

The same general thesis is maintained here about Egypt as that applied in this book to the fauna of Palestine, and elsewhere of that of Irak: no new elements have been added since late Mesolithic times, but the fauna has undergone continuous reduction and thinning from human dawn until our days. We do not suppose that any important fluctuations of temperature occurred since the mesolithic era. But even relatively small changes in the field of precipitations, slight increases of rain from 100 to 200 mm *per annum,* combined with a greater stability of annual and seasonal rain distribution, must have had far reaching consequences, changing wide areas and patches of desert into steppes or savannas, permitting passage and penetration of animals from the east, west and south.

The main changes can be summarised, as follows:

Extinct at the dawn of history became: some baboons, lion, *Lycaon pictus,* spotted hyena, giraffe, hartebeest, aurochs, fallow deer, shoe-bill, saddle stork, marabou.

Extinct at unknown phase of history or anyhow before the 18th century were: Ethiopian

hedgehog, civet-cat, *Gazella dama, G. soemmeringi,* chanting goshawk, hermit ibis, hippopotamus, crocodile.

Extinct since the beginning of the 19th century are: oryx, addax antelope, wild pig, ostrich
and sacred ibis.

Very rare and/or on the verge of extinction are at present: leopard, wild cat, Margerita's wild
cat, caracal, cheetah, BUXTON's coney, barbary wild sheep, ibex and many Ethiopian water
birds.

The about 100 species of identified birds from ancient Egypt, permit similar conclusions.
Unfortunately almost all passerine birds and many accipitres of the illustrations are useless
for identification. The rest are mainly waterbirds or those intimately connected with hygrophytic habitats. Against expectation the influence of the contraction of marshes, papyrus
swamps and reed thickets was surprisingly small, as far as the number of species, but not as
far as their abundance and breeding intensity are concerned. The sacred ibis has only recently
disappeared. Whilst still locally frequent 150 years ago, the last breeder was observed in
1876. More sensitive birds, such as shoe-bill and saddle stork, had disappeared in early
antiquity. The disappearance of the extended papyrus swamps in Lower Egypt has put an
end, not only to the ibis, but to all the rich fauna of water birds (see F. Hasselquist
1757). The Sudanese goshawk (*Melierasc gabar*) has also disappeared since long. The breeding
of geese, ducks, herons, cormorants, a.o. becomes more and more rare. MOREAU (1930
p. 73) hints at some changes in the relative abundance of some ducks: the shelduck being
now rarer, the shoveler commoner than in old times. Red-breasted goose and bean goose
must have been common winter visitors to ancient Egypt. The ostrich has disappeared only
within the past century.

HILZHEIMER, unfortunately, ascribes these faunal changes in the first place to climatic
fluctuations. This is certainly exaggerated: The main faunal characters were well established
in the predynastic period. The big animals, dependent on hygrophytic habitats, declined in
number with the desiccation of the Fayum swamps, the mangrove thickets of the lower Nile,
etc., to which the accumulative effect of human hunting must be added. The savanna animals
did find a very precarious subsistence in the dry steppe patches, swallowed successively by
the advancing desert. They were apparently finally driven to the margins of the hygrophytic
areas of the Nile where they could easily be killed in consequence of their concentration. The
fate of all other animals, disappearing in historical times, is not doubtful: direct and indirect
extermination by the "progress" of civilization.

We may add that the formation of local subspecies of birds since the formation of the
deltas of the Nile and of Irak, permits us to fix the minimal period required by nature for
this purpose at 5000 years. The delta of the Nile began to be formed about 10000 years ago,
when the Nile first reached the Mediterranean shores.

2.4. GRAECO-ROMAN ZOOLOGY ON THE FAUNA OF THE MIDDLE EAST

2. 41. ARISTOTLE

The peak of Greek natural history was reached with ARISTOTLE (384-322 B.C.), the father of natural history in general as well as of biology. His scientific personality and importance are much underestimated today and his biological works remain almost unread. We must deny ourselves here the discussion of his great achievements and restrict ourselves to his few remarks on animals of the Middle East. These are mostly based on second or third hand information and do not show the usual standard of ARISTOTLE's biological books.

Most of these remarks are quoted from the Natural History of Animals (*Historia animalium*: H.A.), a few from the Parts of Animals (*De partibus animalium*: P.A.). The most pertinent notes are contained in the chapter on animal geography: all molluscs of the Red Sea are of exceptional size. In Syria the sheep have tails of one ell's length and the goats have pending ears, one span long and four fingers wide, and reaching close to the soil. Cattle and camels have a mane on their shoulders. In Lycia the goats are shorn like sheep (probably a reference to an Angora goat-like type) ... Some animals are larger in Egypt than in Greece, as are cattle and sheep; others are smaller, such as dogs, wolves, hares, foxes, ravens and kites; crows, goats and others are of the same size in both countries. The reason of these differences is the abundance or scarcity of food. Wolves, kites and all carnivorous animals find poor food in Egypt where birds are smaller and rarer. Hares and other vegetarians are smaller because of the short season of fruits ... In Arabia lizards are over an ell long and also mice are bigger than our fieldmice. Their forelegs are one span long, the hindlegs one ell up to the first articulation (figures obviously corrupted; refers to the jerboa) .... No wild deer or wild goat occurs in Lybia. The snakes of that country are very big. Some travellers landed there and found the bones of many oxen, which had apparently been devoured by snakes. When they departed, some of these snakes followed their triremes and some of them succeeded in capsizing one of the ships .... In Europe lions are restricted to the area between the rivers Achelous and Nestus. And leopards are restricted to Asia, and do not occur in Europe. Asiatic animals usually are wilder, European ones more courageous (H.A. 8 : 27).

Two species of Ibis occur in Egypt: a white and a black one. The white species is spread all over Egypt, whilst at Pelusium—and only there—the black ibis lives (H.A. 9 : 19; The black ibis is the black hermit ibis (*Comatibis eremitia* L), which is extinct in Egypt now, whilst the white or sacred ibis (*Threskiornis aethiopicus* Lath.) is still abundant in Ethiopic Africa, but not in Egypt any more. Whilst common in the dynastic period, and still not uncommon in the days of Napoleon's expedition, it disappeared during the first half of the past century).

... The mungo of Egypt calls for help before attacking an asp; against the bites of the asp it smears itself with mud before the attack, in the following way: it first sprinkles itself with water and then wallows in the dust ... The Egyptian plover (*Pluvianus aegyptius* L.) flies into the opened mouth of the crocodile and cleans its teeth. Thus the plover finds its food, and the crocodile—noticing how it benefits him—never hurts the bird (H.A. 9 : 7).

... The wolves near Lake Maiotis co-operate with the fishermen by driving the fish into their nets; when, however, the fishermen do not share their catch with them, the wolves tear their nets, when those are on land for drying (H.A. 9 : 24) . . . . The hippopotamus of Egypt has a mane as a horse, cloven hoofs like cattle and a flat face. It has an astragalus-bone as have the other animals with cloven hoofs and half-hidden tusks, the tail of a pig and a voice like that of a horse. It is as big as a donkey. Its skin is so thick that lances are glanced off from it. Its inner organs are like those of the horse and the ass (H.A. 2 : 4).

The lioness of Syria brings forth young five times only: the first time five young and further every time one young less, until finally she is sterile. The young are very small and can scarcely run in their second month. The lion has a mane, which is wanting in the lioness. The lion changes only its four pointed eye-teeth, two above and two below, in the sixth month of its life (H.A. 6 : 28).

In Syria there still lives another hemionus (half-ass; refers to the onager) which is no cross-breed of horse and ass like the mule, but resembles it in every other respect. They excel in speed. These half-asses are fertile amongst themselves. In the time of Pharnakes, the father of Pharnabakus, some of them were brought to Phrygia, where they still exist; but only three, whereas there were ten before (H.A. 6 : 29).

The Egyptian mice have hairs as stiff as those of a hedgehog (the porcupine mouse *Acomys cahirinus*). Another mouse moves on two feet (the jerboa *Jaculus jaculus* L.; H.A. 6 : 30).

In Egypt and some other places the females give birth in the eighth month of pregnancy and in an easy way. Their children live and grow, in spite of their remaining only eight months in the mother's womb (H.A. 7 : 4) . . . The oryx has one horn and cloven hoofs (H.A. 2 : 2).

The winter agrees better with the wide- than with the long-tailed sheep, better with the short-haired than with the sheep with long wool, and worst with those with curled wool (H.A. 8 : 12).

Some birds migrate to far countries. The cranes thus migrate from the country of the Scythians to the swamps near the sources of the Nile. Also the quails migrate; they are fatter in autumn than in spring (H.A. 8 : 14).

The ostrich has some characters of a bird, some of a quadruped. It differs from the quadruped in being feathered; and from a bird in being unable to soar aloft, and in having feathers that resemble hair and are useless for flight. Again it agrees with quadrupeds in having upper eye-lashes which are the more richly provided with hairs, because the parts of the head and the upper part of the neck are bare; and it agrees with birds in being feathered in all the parts posterior to these. Further, it resembles a bird in being a biped, and a quadruped in having a cloven hoof; for it has hoofs and no toes. The explanation of these peculiarities is to be found in its bulk, which is that of a quadruped rather than that of a bird. For, speaking generally, a bird must necessarily be of very small size. For a body ot heavy bulk can be raised into the air only with difficulty (P.A. 4 : 14).

We end with the description of two more animals as given by Aristotle:

1. The chameleon. Of all the oviparous animals that live on land there is none so lean as the chameleon. For there is none that has so little blood. The explanation of this is to be found in the psychical temperament of the creature. For it is of a timid nature, as the frequent changes it undergoes in its outward aspect testify. But fear is a refrigeration, and results from deficiency of natural heat and scantiness of blood (P.A. 4 : 11) . . . The chameleon has the shape of a lizard, but the ribs join into the abdomen, as in the fishes; also the vertebrae have dorsal processes, as in the fishes. The tail is very long, with a thin end and

usually coiled up. Its body-position is higher than in the lizards, with which it agrees in the articulation of the feet. Every foot separates into two parts of opposite position, thus as the thumb of our hand towards the other fingers. Each of these toe-bundles separates into some toes: three inward and two outward on the forelegs, two inward and three outward on the hind-legs. Each of these toes has a short, curved claw. The body surface is rough, as in the crocodile. The eyes are in a groove; they are big-round and covered by a skin similar to the body skin with a small central opening, through which it sees; but it never closes this opening. It can turn the eyes in a circle into any wanted direction. When it inflates itself, it changes colour. Usually it is black, as a crocodile, grey as a lizard and dark-spotted as a leopard. The change of colour is over all the rump, the eyes and the tail. Its movements are excessively slow, as those of the tortoises. When it dies, it turns grey and retains this colour after death. The throat and the trachea are like those of the lizards. It has no flesh, except a little on the head, the cheeks and the beginning of the tail. Blood is found in them only in the region of the heart and in the eyes, above the heart and in the veins, but even there very little only. The brain is slightly above the eyes, with which it is connected. When we cut away the skin around the eye we find a shining body, similar to an iron ring. Almost throughout the entire rump some membranes extend which are harder and stronger than in most other animals (i.e. the lungs). When the chameleon is entirely cut open, it still continues to respire for a good time, although the heart contractions last for a shorter time, and it heavily pulls in not only the flanks, but the entire rump during expiration. A spleen is not distinctly present. It hides as do the lizards (H.A. 2 : 7). This description was apparently obtained from a correspondent in the Middle East.

2. The camel. Also the Arabian camel has a double udder and four tits, as has the cow (H.A. 2 : 3). The female camel lays down for copulation and is entirely enclosed by the male's body, whose head is turned forwards as in most quadrupeds. In this way they remain for a full day, seeking solitude for the act, where only the camelherd may follow them. The penis is so sinewy, that row-strings are made of it (H.A. 5 : 2) .... Its rutting season in Arabia is in the month of Maimektrion. It bears five months and brings forth one young only. Camels grow mature when three years old. The females come in new ardour only one year after having borne (H.A. 5 : 12) ... The camel bears ten months (cf. the preceding quotation! This shows clearly, either that not much value was given to actual numbers, or that the tradition of numbers was especially careless in the manuscripts) and brings forth one young only. At one year of age the young is separated from the flock. The camel lives more than fifty years. It gives birth in spring and produces milk until the next conception. Meat and milk are very sweet. The latter is usually diluted for consumption by two or three parts of water (H.A. 6 : 25) ... The camel prefers muddy and thick water for drinking (H.A. 8 : 10 ... Most camels live about thirty years, some much longer, even up to 100 years (H.A. 8 : 11). The male camels never copulate with their mother, and refuse to do so, when forced ... (H.A. 9 : 47) ... The female camel is also castrated when used as a war camel, in order to prevent pregnancy. Some peoples of Upper Asia keep about 3000 of them. They run better than Nisaean horses (H.A. 9 : 37).

Another collection: "On marvellous Things heard", often quoted as a work of Aristotle, is an amusing, but uncriticized collection of interesting anecdotes. We quote a few of them, which come from a member of the Peripatetic school after the death of the master:

8. They say that in Byzantium the hedgehogs can distinguish between the wind blowing from the north or from the south, and promptly change their holes; when the south wind blows, they make openings in the bottom, and when the north does so in the sides (cf. H.A. 9 : 6).

10. They say that in Syria there is always one leader of a herd of wild asses. When one of the younger animals wishes to mate with a female, the leader is enraged and pursues the young animal until he catches it, and then, stooping between its hindlegs, tears out its organs.
19. They say that in Lydia much honey is collected from trees.
23. In Thessaly they record that snakes are born alive in such quantities that if they were not eaten by storks the people would have to leave. Consequently they honour storks, and it is unlawful to kill them; if anyone does so, he is liable to the same penalties as a murderer.
25. In Cyprus they say that mice eat iron.
26. And they say that the Chalybes, in one of the islands lying above them, collect gold from many of these creatures. For this reason apparently they cut up the mice which they catch in mines.
27. It is said that when one goes from Susa to Media in the second stage there is a large quantity of scorpions. Consequently the king of the Persians, whenever he went through the district, stayed there three days, ordering all his men to hunt; and he gave a prize to the man who caught most.
72. Some say that in Babylonia certain fishes remain in holes which retain moisture when the river dries up; these come out to the threshing-floor to feed, and walk on their fins and wave their tails; when they are pursued they flee, and diving down stand to face the pursuer. For men will often approach, and even torment them. They have a head like a sea-frog, but the rest of their body is like a gudgeon, but they have gills like other fish (this possibly refers partly to a *Clarias*).

2. 42. PLINY

Cajus Plinius Secundus (23-79 A.D.) is the great compilator of Roman natural history. The 37 books of his *Historia naturalis* formed the background and main source for mediaeval zoology.

In his description of Syria we find the following notes: The Dead Sea does not receive the living body of any creature: bulls and camels swim and float aloft upon it. Hence the opinion that nothing there will go down and sink to the bottom (5 : 16). On the sea-coast of Phoenicia (near Dor = Tantura) a river runs called Crocodilon, whereupon stood a town in times past bearing that name (5 : 19).

Books 8 to 11 contain the zoology. Much of his material has been taken over from ARISTOTLE, yet many observations have been added: The lions of Europe between the rivers Achelous and Nestus, are much stronger than those from Africa or Syria (8 : 17). MENTOR, the Syracusian, happened to meet a lion, in Syria who behaving in a humbly manner, in token of its obedience and submission, seemed to tumble and wallow before him; he for very fear started back and began to flee, but the wild beast still followed him and was ready at every turn to present himself before him, licking the very tracks of his footsteps as he went, in a flattering manner, as if he would make love to him at last. Mentor was aware that the lion had a wound in his foot, and that it swelled in consequence of this; whereupon he gently plucked out the spill of wood that had got into it, and so eased the beast of his pain. This accident is, as a memorial, represented in a picture at Syracuse (8 : 21). Black lions are found in Syria only (8 : 23). Camels are bred in the Levant among other herds of big domestic animals (8 : 26). Around the Nile there breeds another serpent, the scincus, in form and proportion somewhat alike to the crocodile, but not so big as the mungo. Its flesh serves as a singular antidote and also to provoke the heat of lust in men (probably *Varanus niloticus*) (8 : 28). The beavers castrate themselves, when driven by hunters, as they very well know that they are chased for their genitals and the stone which the physicians call castoreum. Otherwise it is a dangerous beast. For verily he will bite down the trees growing by the river sides, as if they were cut by an axe. Where he once has bitten into a man, he never lets loose until he has knapped the bone to pieces, and has heard it crack. It is tailed like a fish, otherwise resembles the otter. Both these beasts live in the water, and have hair softer than the plumes of feathers (8 : 47). Deer pass the seas swimming in flocks and whole herds in a long row, each one resting its head upon the buttocks of its mate before him and this they do in rotation, so that the foremost retreats behind the hindmost, and this is usually seen by travellers between Cilicia and Cyprus (8 : 50). In Arabia the lizards are a cubit long (8 : 60). The cattle of Syria have no dewlaps at all hanging from their neck, but hunches standing up on their backs instead of that (8 : 70; reference to zebu). In Egypt a bull is worshipped as a god under the name of A(s)pis. This beast is marked as follows: with a white spot on his right side, like the horns of a crescent, and a knot under the tongue. After the a(s)pis has reached a certain age they drown him in a certain well..... (8 : 71). Clothes and coverings made from Arabian wool are the best of all (8 : 72). In Syria sheep have tails a cubit long, and they bear the most wool there (8 : 75). It is a wonderful thing to see that nature has not only brought forth diverse creatures in sundry countries; but, even in one region in the same climate, has denied some of them to live in every part of one and the same country. And in Lycia the wild goats, roebucks and does, never pass the mountains that border upon the Syrians, no more than the wild asses pass over the hills dividing Cappadocia from Cilicia (8 : 83). Some creatures do no harm to the inhabitants of a country, but kill all strangers. In Syria there are snakes, especially along the banks of the Euphrates, which will not touch the Syrians laying asleep along it. Even if a man leans upon them and is bitten by them, he will hot be hurted. But to men of all other nations whatsoever, they have the most spiteful inclinations: they will with great greediness eagerly attack them and kill them with extreme pain. Therefore the Syrians do not destroy them. In Latmos, a mountain of Caria, the scorpions will do no harm to strangers but they will sting the inhabitants to death (8 : 84).

Among the aquatic animals (Book 9) nothing of wider interest about fishes is recorded from this region: But all riches of the sea are nothing in comparison with the purple-shells and the pearl-shells. The richest merchandise of all and the most sovereign commodity throughhout the whole world are pearls. Most come from the Indian Ocean: but to find them we must search among the huge and terrible monsters of the sea. We must go over many seas and sail into remote countries to reach those parts where the sun is excessive and extreme. And when all this is done, we may still miss them. Even the Indians, looking for them among the islands, and doing all they can, are glad to find a very few only. The greatest number of them is to be found on the coasts of Taprobane (Ceylon) and Toidis, and in Perimula in India. But the most exquisite and perfect pearls are got about Arabia, within the Persian Gulf of the Red Sea. This shell-fish which is the mother of pearls, differs not much in the manner of breeding and generation from the oysters. For when the proper season approaches, they seem to yawn and gape and open wide. It is said that then they conceive a certain moist dew as seed, through which they swell and grow big ... And the fruit of these shell-fishes are the pearls, better or worse, greater or smaller, according to the quality and quantity of the dew which they received.... (9 : 54). The pearls from the Red Sea are the purest (9 : 56). It seems that there is more than one species of pearl-producing shell-fishes. For Juba reports that in Arabia there is a kind of scallop (*Pecten*), but thick and rough like a sea-urchin, which produces pearls within the flesh of the shell-fish (9 : 56).

Purple-shells ordinarily live seven years. They lay hidden for 30 days about the dog-days, as do the burrets. They meet in troups during the spring, and by rubbing the one against the other, they gather and yield a certain clammy substance and moisture like wax. But the purples have in the midst of their neck and jaws the beautiful colour, so much in request for dyeing fine cloth. It is nothing but a little thin liquor in a white vein, which makes that rich and bright colour of deep red purple roses. The rest of the fish yields nothing. Fishers try and take them alive, for when they die they throw up and shed that precious dye and juice together with their life. The Tyrians, when they light upon any great purples, take the flesh out of their shells to get the blood out of that vein. But they press and grind the smaller purples in certain mills, and so gather their rich liquid. The best Asiatic purple colour is got from Tyre... (9 : 60). But the Tyrians make their deep red purple by dipping the wool first in the liquor of the Pelagian purples only, whilst it is not thoroughly brought to the boiling-point, but when it is still green and unripe. Soon after they change it to another cauldron in which the colour of the buccinum is boiled only. Then the excellent dye is obtained which is as deep red as coagulated blood, looking blackish, but shows a bright and shining lustre in the light (9 : 62). Purple has been used in Rome at all times (9 : 63). The inundation of the Nile offers a miracle surpassing all others: As the river falls and returns to his channel there are found upon the mud young mice half made, proceeding from the generative powers of the water and the soil: part of their body is living already, the rest of it yet to be moulded from earth (9 : 84).

The phoenix bird of Arabia surpasses all other birds in colours. It is reported to be as big as an eagle. It is golden about the neck, the rest of it a deep purple red, the tail azure blue, intermingled with feathers of rose carnation colour. The head is adorned with a crest and pennant with tuft and plumes. Manilius says that it was never seen feeding. In Arabia it is held to be a sacred bird dedicated to the sun. It lives 660 years. When it grows old it builds himself a nest of twigs and branches of the Cinamon and Frankincense trees. And when it has filled this with sweet aromatic spices, gives up his life thereupon. From his bones and marrow at first a little worm breeds which becomes a pretty bird. It first carries the whole nest with the dead bird to the sun-city near Panchaea and lays it upon the altar there. MANILIUS affirms that the much spoken of great revolution of the year when the stars return to their first (starting)points agrees with the span of life of this bird. This year should begin at high noon, the very day when the sun enters the sign Aries. In 47 A.D. the phoenix flew into Egypt and was brought to Rome and shown to the people (10 : 2, refers to the Golden Pheasant of China, *Phasianus pictus,* cf. O. KELLER vol. II. p. 146). Yet ARISTOTLE denies that the ravens conceive by their mouth, no more than does the Egyptian ibis. They only have a wantonness for billing and kissing one another, as have the doves and pigeons (10 : 15). In Syria Comagena the grease of geese is put together with cinamon leaves into a brass pot, which is covered with much snow and they let it thus stay for use in the sweet ointment called Comagenum after this country (10 : 28).

PLINY also reports of swallows as carriers of information. CAECINA took swallows from the homes of his friends. When he won in a horse-race, he painted the colour of the winning horse on their breasts, and turned them loose, "knowing quite well that everyone would go home to the same nest from whence it came". Thus he informed his friends speedily about his good luck. And that once a besieged Roman garrison asked and obtained information through a swallow in a similar manner (10 : 34).—The Seleucid birds (=*Pastor roseus*) come and help the inhabitants of Mt. Casius in Syria against the locusts. When the locusts devastate their fields Iupiter sends these birds on the constant prayers and supplications of the population and they will destroy the locusts. Nobody knows from where they come or where they go, as they are only seen upon such occasions, when there is need of their help (10 : 39).—The Egyptians pray and invoke the ibis, when they are troubled and annoyed by serpents coming among them. Likewise the Eleans turn to their god Myiagros, to get rid of a multitude of flies which pester them so much that they breed a pestilence among them. When that idol is appeased, all the flies die (10 : 40).—In the Delta of the Nile near Heracla there is a mighty bank thrown up only by a continual number of swallow nests, piled one upon another for some hundred metres. This bank is so firm and strong that being opposed to the inundations of the Nile it is able to break the force of that river when it swells, and is itself invincible: a piece of work that no man is able to perform. Also in Egypt near Coptos there is an island consecrated to the goddess Isis, which the swallows fortify every year, for fear lest the Nile should break down its banks and corne over them. In early spring, during three nights, they bring straw, chaff and similar stuff to the cape of the island to strengthen its front. And during this time they work so hard, that some swallows die from this work. They go to this task every year, when the spring is about to come and they will not fail, no more than soldiers under military discipline going to service and war. A third sort of swallows hollow out the river-banks to nest within. The young birds of the river-swallow are a specific and effective remedy against the deadly disease of the throat and many other human diseases. They do not build at all, but when they see the Nile beginning to swell eventually to reach the height of their nest-openings, they are gone many days before (10 : 49).—In Arabia lives the Cinnamolgus, which builds its nest from twigs and branches of the cinnamon tree. When the inhabitants see that nest they bring it down by shooting arrows with lead head, in order to use the cinnamon (10 : 50).—Much alike the Purple Gallinule which seems to bite in the water as it drinks and to use its foot as a hand to reach it up to its bill, there is another wading bird, called *Himantopus*. It is smaller, but just as long-legged and stalking just as high. It lives in Egypt and goes on a foot with three toes. It mostly feeds on flies (10 : 64).—Doves lay eggs and hatch them ten times a year, some of them even eleven times and in Egypt there are found some that would not omit doing so even in mid-winter, in December (10 : 74).—There are some eggs that will become birds without the hen silling on them, by the work of nature only, as is seen from the incubation of eggs in dung-hills in Egypt (10 : 75).

A fourth kind of flies bigger than wasps and hornets called Bombyx, breeds in Assyria. They build their nests of earth and clay, fastening them to a rock or stone, just like salt. These nests are so hard that they can scarcely be pierced with the point of a spear. There is also wax in them and their cells and their larvae are bigger. They develop differently: out of a big worm with two feelers a caterpillar grows. Out of this first a Bombylius develops, then a Necydalis, which after six months turns into the Bombyx. Silkworms spin and weave webs like those of the spiders for the pleasure of our women, who therefrom make their fine silks (bombycina). A woman of Cos, Pamphila by name, first devised the weaving of these webs of silkworms (11 : 26; The first part refers to the Bombykion of ARISTOTLE, which clearly is a species of a *Chalicodoma*-bee, whilst the second part refers to the silkworm of Cos, the moth *Pachypasa otus*, to which the following quotation refers). In the island of Cos certain silkworms are born from the flowers, which are beaten down from cypresses by rain-showers, terebinths, ash and oak trees, and which take life through the vapour arising out of the earth. First they are like small and naked butterflies. Growing impatient of the cold, they soon cover themselves with hairs, and against the winter with thick clothes. With their rough feet they gather all the cotton of the leaves. Then they card it with their claws, extend it at full length and hang it between the branches, combed into a fine and thin textile. Then they enwrap themselves into it, to nestle within. Thus they are collected by man, put into earthen pots, kept warm there and fed with bran, until such time when they get their wings, and then the people go to their other work. The wool is left to get soft in some moisture, then spun into a small thread, with a spindle made of some reed. Even men are not ashamed to wear these silken robes, as they are light and thin. We have so much forgotten to wear an armour that even the normal clothes seem to us too heavy! But the Assyrian silk has so far been left for the women (11 : 27). The Assyrian silk refers to the true silk of the Chinese Silkworm *Bombyx mori* L. which was brought by caravans along the famous old silk-road of Central Asia to the Levant.

The locusts oviposit in autumn by thrusting into the soil the thorn or stick through which the eggs come. These eggs remain in the soil all winter. Late in the spring of the following year they send out small blackish and legless larvae which creep with their wings. In a rainy spring the eggs die, while many hatch out in dry springs. Some believe that they have two annual generations. Certainly the females die soon after oviposition, because a small worm develops in their throat and kills them. The males die at the same time . . . . They breed only in plains. Those of India are said to be three feet long and their legs to be used as saws, after being thoroughly dried. These locusts die in another way: the winds take them up by whole troups and they fall down into the sea or into lakes . . . They do not fly in the nights for cold, as some say. But they overlook that they often continue their flight over sea for some days without rest. When famine approaches, they seek food in far countries. Their coming is always hold to be a plague of the gods caused by their being heavily displeased. In that case they are bigger and make such a noise with their wings that men take them for strange birds. They shade and darken the very sun as they fly, like a great cloud. People fear that they should alight in their territory. Their strength is such that after long flights over sea they still traverse large countries of the continent. Where they settle they cover whole fields like a cloud. They devour everything, even the doors of houses. Many times they came in whole armies from Africa to Italy. Often the people of Rome sought help and remedies from the Sibylline books. In Cyrenaica there is a law to destroy them three times a year: first by destroying the eggs, then the hoppers and finally the adults. Neglect of this is punished like desertion. In the island of Lemnos a certain quantity of dead locusts is prescribed which everybody has to bring in to the officials appointed. They honour the jays, because they attack the locusts and destroy them. Military law is enforced in Syria to kill them. In many parts of the world this pest spreads. But in Parthia they are taken for good food. Their voice apparently comes from the back of the head. Where this joins the shoulders they are supposed to have teeth, which by grating one against the other provoke the chirping about the time of both equinoxes. Locusts copulate as all other copulating insects: the female carries the male and bends its body end upwards. Thus they continue for some time before separating. The females are smaller than the males (11 : 35). The biological observations at the beginning refer to the Moroccan locust, *Dociostaurus maroccanus* THNB., which causes damages in Italy until these days. The flights from Africa concern the Desert locust (*Schistocerca gregaria* FORSK.). In Cyprus a four-legged, winged big fly flies out of the very middle of the fire of the furnaces of copper, the Pyralis or Pyrausta. It dies as soon as it leaves the flames (11 : 42).

During his aedileship SCAURUS showed the bones of the seamonster to the people of Rome before which ANDROMEDA was thrown to be devoured. They were brought from Jaffa to Judaea and were forty feet long: the height of the ribs was greater than that of Indian elephants and the vertebrae a foot and a half thick (9 : 4. Refers to the bones of a whale).

Gall-apples of oaks are described: the best galls are those of Comagena, the oaks bear acorns one year, galls the other year. They are used for dyeing wool (16 : 9). The greatest wealth of the oak is the Coccus of the ilex-oak. At first this is like a mange on the shrubs of ilex aquifolia. The scraped grain is called Cusculium. The poor people of Spain collect it and pay with it half their tribute. The Coccus also grows in Galatia, Africa, Pisidia and Cilicia; the worst come from Sardinia (16 : 12). With regard to the Coccus dye from Galatia and Portugal: when it is of one year's age it makes but a weak tincture; but after four years the strength of it is gone, so that, either old or young, it is of no great value (9 : 65. The Coccus is a *Kermes*-scale-insect).

The ignorance of our physicians is the cause that all sponges are reduced to two kinds:
the Africans which are tough and firm, and the Rhodians which are softer. About Lycia
TROGUS writes that the softest sponges grow in the deep sea, in those places from where
other sponges had been plucked away before (31 : 47).

2. 43. STRABO

Perhaps none fulfils our request for a description of the animal in the landscape of
the Middle East better than STRABO of Amasia (66 B.C.-24 A.D.), who has visited and
travelled extensively throughout our regions. We therefore append the almost unabridged
account of his notes on animals from Anatolia to Arabia and partly from Egypt (Books 1
to 17 of the Geography).

There are large lakes in Armenia. The next one is the Van lake (Arsene, Thopitis).
Its waters contain nitre .. and are unfit for drinking. The Tigris passes through this lake
(*ex errore*!) ... with rapidity, whence it has its name, for the Medes call an arrow Tigris.
This river contains fish of various kinds, but the lake one kind only (11 : 14 : 8). In
Armenia there is also a mine of Sandyx, to which the name of the Armenian colour is given
(We quote this passage, as it may refer to the well-known Armenian cocheneal (*Margarodes
hameli* BR.) which is collected in Armenia from the root-collar of grasses.). This country is
not inferior to Media for breeding horses which, even equal the Nisaean horses of the kings
of Persia. The satrap of Armenia used to send annually 20000 foals to the Persian king at
the time of the Mithracian festival (11 : 14 : 9).

Next to the mouth of the Halys (Kizil Irmak) is a fertile plain ... It also affords pasture
for flocks of sheep which are covered with skins and produce a soft wool; very little of this
wool is found in Cappadocia and Pontus. There are also deer (zorkes) which are rare in
other parts (Red deer still abound in the mountain ranges along the Pontian coast of Anatolia;
(12 : 3 : 13). The plain near Amasia is well-watered and constantly covered with herbage, and
it is capable of affording food to herds of cattle as well as to horses. Wild animals of all
kinds, which resort here on account of the abundance of food, are frequently hunted
(12 : 15). The wild inhabitants of the mountains above Trapezunt live on the flesh of wild
animals and on the fruits of trees. They cut off three of Pompeys cohorts, as they were
passing through the mountains, by placing on their road vessels filled with maddening honey,
which is procured from the branches of trees. The men who had tasted the honey and lost
their senses were attacked and easily despatched (cf. BODENHEIMER, 1942; and XENOPHON,
Anabasis; 12 : 3 : 18). On the sea-coast there are natural advantages for the capture of the
pelamydes (*Thynnus*) ... The fishermen obtain their subsistence mainly from the capture
of pelamydes and dolphins. The dolphins pursue shoals of various fish, and grow fat on
them. They are easily taken, when they approach the land incautiously. They are caught with
a bait and cut into pieces; large quantities of the fat are used for all purposes (12 : 3 : 19).
Near Amasia is Cabeira with the palace of Mithridates, the park for keeping wild animals,
and the hunting ground in the neighbourhood (12 : 3 : 31). EUDOXUS says, without defining
the spot that fossil fish are found in Paphlagonia in dry ground, and also in marshy grounds
near the Isnik Göl (ASCANIUS; 12 : 3 : 42). The Tuz Göl (Tatta) is a natural salt-pan.
If birds touch the surface of the water with their wings, they immediately fall down in
consequence of the concentration of the salt upon them, and they are thus taken (12 : 5 : 4).
The mountain plains of Lycaonia are cold and bare, affording pasture only for wild asses.
Although the country is ill-supplied with water, it is surprisingly well adapted for feeding
sheep, but the wool is coarse. Some persons have acquired very great wealth by these flocks.

Amyntas had more than 300 flocks of sheep in these parts (12 : 6 : 1). Among the summits of the Taurus there is bred a worm in the trunk of the styrax tree, which eats through the timber to the surface, and throws out raspings like bran or saw-dust, a heap of which is collected at the root (Probably caterpillar of the leopard moth *Zeuzera pyrina* L. or of a bark-beetle.). Afterwards a liquid distils which readily concretes into a gum-like mass. It is used for incense. Many spots produce the olive and excellent vines, and afford abundant pasture for animals of all kinds (12 : 7 : 3). The country around Ladik (Laodicea) breeds excellent sheep, remarkable not only for the softness of their wool, in which they surpass the Milesian flocks, but also for their dark or raven colour. The Laodiceans derive a large revenue from them (12 : 8 : 16).

APELLICON, when attempting to restore the parts (of the books of the library of ARISTOTLE) which had been eaten and corroded by worms, made alterations in the original text, and published the books full of errors (13 : 1,54). The story about the Teucri (in Mysia) and the mice from which the name of Apollo Smintheus is derived (for mice are called sminthii) must be transferred to this place. Writers defend the derivation of titles from insignificant objects by examples of this kind. After the parnopes Hercules had a surname, and was worshipped as Hercules Cornopion (the Oetaeans call them cornopes), because he delivered them from locusts. So the Erythraeans near the river Melius worship Hercules Ipoctonus, because he destroyed the ipes or worms, which are injurious to vines (Probably the grape-berry moth *Polychrosis botrana*). For this pest is found everywhere except in the country of the Erythraeans (in Mysia). Among the Aeolians in Asia one of their months is called Pornopion, and a sacrifice is performed to Apollo Pornopion (13 : 1 : 64).

At the mouth of the Maeander is the Samson Dagh (Mycale), which abounds with animals of chase, and is covered with forests (14 : 1 : 12).

At Borsippa in Assyria bats of much larger size than those in other parts of the world abound. They are caught and salted for food (16 : 1 : 7). Bee-keeping was obviously well established at Strabo's time, for: they bury the body of the dead in honey, first besmearing it with wax. There are three communities which have no corn. They live in the marshes and subsist on fish (16 : 1 : 20). Near the Tigris lions also breed. There are fine pastures. It also furnishes the stone Gangitis, which drives away reptiles (16 : 1 : 24). The south of Mesopotamia at a distance from the mountains, is arid and bare. The Arabian Scenitae, there live a tribe of robbers and shepherds, who readily move from place to place, whenever pasture or booty begins to be exhausted (16 : 1 : 26). From the Euphrates town of Scenae to Syria it is a journey of 25 days. There are (on the road) owners of camels, who keep resting places, which are well supplied with water from cisterns or transported from a distance (16 : 1 : 27).

The name of the river Orontes was Typhon before. Typhon was a serpent which, being struck by lightning, endeavoured to make its escape, and sought refuge in the ground; it deeply furrowed the earth, and, as it moved along, formed the bed of the river; having descended underground, it caused a spring to break out, and from this Typhon the river had its name (16 : 2 : 7). At Apamea (Kulat-el-Mudik) the Orontes flows through wide-spread marshes and meadows of vast extent, affording pasture for cattle and horses. Seleucus Nicator kept 500 elephants there. It was formerly called Pella and a breed of horses was kept up there. In the royal stud, there were kept over 30.000 breeding mares and 300 stallions where colt-breakers were employed (16 : 2 : 10). POSIDONIUS reports that at Macras (near Beirut) a dead serpent was seen, which was nearly a plethrum long, and so bulky and thick that men on horseback on each side of its body could not see one another; the jaws when opened could take a man on horseback, and the scales of the skin were larger than a shield

(Obviously a sperm-whale, the 'scales of the skin' probably being the teeth (16 : 2 : 17). Tyre recovered from the siege of Alexander by skill in navigation and by the (export of) purple-dyed manufactures, the Tyrian purple being in highest estimation. The shell-fish from which it is procured is caught near the coast, and the Tyrians have other requisites for dyeing in great abundance. The great number of dyeing works renders the city unpleasant as a place of residence on account of the smell, but the superior skill of the people in practising this art is the source of its wealth (16 : 2 : 23). At Jaffa, according to some writers, Andromeda was exposed to the sea-monster (16 : 2 : 28). Between Acco and Caesarea lie Mt. Carmel and cities of which nothing but the name remained, such as Crocodilopolis (16 : 2 : 27). From Ascalon to Suez travelling is performed by camels, through a desert and sandy country, in the course of which snakes are found in great numbers (16 : 2 : 30). At Ashdod (Gadaris) is a lake of noxious water. If beasts drink it, they lose their hair, hoofs and horns. At Taricheae (on the Lake of Gennesareth) the lake supplies the best fish for curing (16 : 2 : 45). The Syrian desert is occupied by the Arabian Scenitae. They do not till the land at all, or only to a small extent, but they keep herds of cattle of all kinds, particularly of camels (16 : 3 : 1).

From Arabia Palestine and Syria are reached first by a barren and sandy track, with a few palms, acacias and tamarisks. Water is obtained by digging. It is inhabited by the camel-breeding Arabian Scenitae. Extreme southern Arabia, opposite to Aethiopia, is watered by summer showers, and is sown twice, like the land in India. Among other products there is in particular an abundant supply of honey; besides horses there are numerous herds of animals, asses and swine; also birds of every kind, except geese and the gallinaceous tribe (16 : 4 : 2). Near Kosseir are three islands: two of them covered with olive trees, the third less shaded but abounding with guinea-fowl (*Numida meleagris*; 16 : 4 : 5). Behind the bay is the island Ophiodes (Zamarkat), so named because it was once infested with serpents. It was cleared of the serpents by king PTOLEMY PHILADELPHUS, on account of the destruction caused by these noxious animals to the visitors of the island and on account of the topazes found there (16 : 4 : 6). After this the sea abounds with seadogs.... This is followed by the city Ptolemais near the hunting-grounds of the elephants, founded by EURYMEDES, who was sent by PHILADELPHUS to the hunting ground (16 : 4 : 7). These Upper Nile countries are the haunts of lions. The wild beasts are driven out of these places, at the time of the rising of the dog-star, by large gnats. Far in the interior lives a naked tribe, which generally shoots the animals from trees, sometimes from the ground. They have numerous herds of wild cattle among them, on the flesh of which they subsist, and further on that of other wild animals (16 : 4 : 9). Further southwards are the Cynamolgi with long hair and long beards, who keep a breed of very large dogs for hunting the Indian cattle (obviously big antelopes!) which come into their country from the neighbouring district, driven thither either by wild beasts or by scarcity of pasturage. The time of their incursion is from the summer solstice to the middle of winter. Above is the city Darada and a hunting ground for elephants. The district is inhabited by the elephant-eaters, who hunt them. When from the trees they discover a herd of elephants passing through the forest, they approach them stealthily and hamstring the hindmost stragglers from the herd. Some kill them with bows and arrows, dipped in serpent's gall. Others mark the trees against which the elephant is accustomed to rest, approach it on the opposite side and cut the trunk of the tree low down. When the animal comes and leans against it, the tree and the elephant fall down together. The elephant is unable to rise, because its legs are formed of one piece of bone which is inflexible; the hunters leap down from the trees, kill it, and cut it in pieces. The nomads call the hunters impure (16 : 4 : 10). Above them lives the small tribe of the ostrich-eaters.

With them live birds of the size of deer, unable to fly, but running with the swiftness of an ostrich. Some hunt them with bows and arrows, others under cover of the skins of dead ostriches. They hide the right hand in the neck of the skin, and move it as the birds move their necks. With the left hand they scatter grain from a bag suspended to the side; they thus entice the birds and drive them into pits, where the hunters kill them with cudgels. The skins are used both as clothes and as coverings for beds. The Simi are at war with this tribe; they use antelope horns as weapons (16 : 4 : 11). Their blacker neighbours rarely live beyond 40 years, as the flesh of their bodies is eaten up by worms. They feed on locusts which south-west and west winds, when blowing violently in spring, drive in crowds into the country. The inhabitants catch them by throwing into the ravines materials which cause a great deal of smoke, when gently set on fire. The locusts, as they fly across the smoke, are blinded and fall down. They are pounded with salt, made into cakes, and eaten as food (AGATHARCHIDES and DIODORUS SICULUS (III : 28) mean that the locust's feeding habit causes a kind of winged louse to originate in the interior of the body). Above them extensive pastures were abandoned in consequence of multitudes of scorpions and galeodid-spiders (tetragnathi), which formerly abounded to so large a degree as to occasion a complete desertion of the place long since by its inhabitants (16 : 4 : 12). Near the straits are many hunting grounds for elephants.... The fish-eaters collect fish during the ebbing of the tide, which they cast upon the rocks and dry in the sun. When they have well broiled them, the bones are piled in heaps, and the flesh trodden with the feet is made into cakes, which are again exposed to the sun, and used as food. In bad weather, when fish cannot be procured, the bones of which they have made heaps are pounded, made into cakes and eaten, but they suck the fresh bones. Some also live upon shell-fish when fattened, which is done by throwing them into holes and stagnant pools of the sea, where they are supplied with small fish, and used as food when other fish are scarce. They have various kinds of places for preserving and feeding fish, from whence they derive their supply (16 : 4 : 13). The turtle-eaters live under the cover of shells which are large enough to be used as boats (either turtle Cafa paces, shells of *Tridacna,* or whale bones). They throw their dead as food to the fish, the tide carrying them away. Follow three islands: that of turtles, of seals, and of hawks. Follow some elephant grounds. When pools of rain water are dried up, the elephants dig holes with their trunks and tusks to find water. Near the promontory of Pytholaus (? Zeila) are two very large lakes.... The Otheris, a fresh water lake, is inhabited by hippopotami and crocodiles. On the margin grows papyrus. The ibis is seen near this place (16 : 4 : 14).

The coast from Deire abounds with elephants and ant-lions. The later have reversed genitals, a golden coloured skin, but are barer than the Arabian lions. The leopards there are of great strength and courage. The rhinoceros is hardly smaller than the elephant: not in length (from head to tail) as that seen by Artemidorus at Alexandria, but, judging from the one I saw, (a span less) in height. It had the size of a bull, the colour of a grey elephant, was shaped almost like a wild boar, especially the fore-head, except the front, which bears a hooked horn harder than any bone. This it uses as a weapon, like the wild boar its tusks. It also has two hard welts, like the folds of serpents, encircling the body from the chin to the belly, one on the withers, the other on the loins. This is what I saw myself. ARTEMIDORUS adds that the rhinoceros is particularly inclined to contend with the elephant for a place of pasture, thrusting its forehead under the elephant's belly and ripping it up, unless prevented by the trunk and tusks of his adversary. Giraffes (camel-leopards), breeding there, do not resemble leopards, for their variegated skin is more like the streaked and spotted skin of the fallow deer. The hind-quarters are so very much lower than the foremost part, that it seems as if the animal sits upon its rump, which has the height of an ox; the fore-legs are as long as those of the camel. The neck rises high and straight up, but the head greatly exceeds that of the camel in height. In consequence of this want of proportion the speed of the animal is not so great, I think, although ARTEMIDORUS says that it surpasses any other animal in speed. It is however not a wild animal, but like a domesticated beast; for it shows no signs of a savage disposition. Artemidorus continues that the country also produces various monkeys: cebi (baboon, *Papio babuin*), cynocephali (the hamadryas, *Papio hamadryas*) and sphinxes (*Cercopithecus callitrichus*). They have a face like a lion, the rest of the body like that of a leopard, and are as large as a deer. There are wild bulls also, carnivorous, and much greater and swifter than ours, and red in colour. The spotted hyena (crocuttas) is, according to Artemidorus, the mixed progeny of a wolf and a dog. He also mentions serpents of 30 cubits length, which can master elephants and bulls. This is not exaggerated (16 : 4 : 15-16). The women of the nomadic Troglodytae wear shells around their necks, as a protection against fascination by witchcraft (= evil eye). They bury their dead beneath stones, place a ram's horn over them and go away. They travel by night; the male cattle have bells fastened to them, in order to drive away wild beasts by their sound. Later they also used torches and arrows for repelling them (16 : 4 : 17).

Close to Akaba is a plain, well-wooded and well-supplied with water; it abounds with all kinds of domestic stock, wild asses, wild camels, harts and hinds; also lions, leopards and wolves are frequently found (16 : 4 : 18). In the land of the Sabaeans are snakes of a dark-red colour, a span long, which jump up as high as a man's waist, and whose bite is incurable (16 : 4 : 19). A great part of the Nabataean country is fertile. The sheep have white fleeces, their oxen are large, but the country does not produce any horses. Camels serve as horses (16 : 4 : 26).

At Arsinoe (or Crocodilopolis, in Egypt) the inhabitants worship the crocodile, which is kept by himself in a lake. It is tame, gentle to the priests and is called Suchus. It is fed with bread, flesh and wine, which strangers, who visit it, always offer. Our host had brought with him a small cake. We found the crocodile lying on the edge of the lake. The priests went up to it, some of them opened its mouth, another put the cake into it, then meat and finally a fluid of honey and milk. The animal then leaped into the lake, and crossed to the other side. When another stranger arrived with his offerings, the priests took it, and running round the lake, caught the crocodile and fed it as before (Poor crocodile!; 17 : 1 : 38). Besides doing this crocodile-worshipping Arsinoe is the ichneumon-worshipping city of Hercules: hence the canal and the lake Moeris is full of these animals; for they venerate them and are careful not to do them harm; but the people of Hercules worship the ichneumon, which is most destructive both to crocodiles and asps. The ichneumons not only destroy the eggs of the latter, but even the snakes themselves. The ichneumons are protected by a covering of mud, in which they roll, and then dry themselves in the sun. They then seize the asps by the head or tail, and dragging them into the river, kill them in this way. They lie in wait for the crocodiles, when the latter are basking in the sun with their mouth open; they then drop into their jaws, and eating through their intestines and belly, come out of the dead body (17 : 1 : 39). Next follows Cynopolis, where they worship the dog Anubis and provide subsistence to dogs as sacred animals. On the other side of the river is Oxyrhynchus, where they worship the fish of this name (*Mormyrus oxyrhynchus*) and have a temple dedicated to it; but all other Egyptians worship this fish. For all Egyptians alike worship certain animals; three land animals: ox, dog and cat; two birds: hawk and ibis; two fishes: lepidotus (*Barbus bynni*) and oxyrhynchus. Other animals are worshipped locally: sheep at Sais and Thebes the latus (another Nile fish), at Latopolis, a wolf at Lycopolis, a hamadryas at Hermopolis, a baboon near Memphis, which looks like a satyr but otherwise is between bear and dog, coming from Ethiopia. The Thebans worship an eagle, the Leontopolitae a lion, the Mendesians a pair of goats, the Athribitae a shrew. They do not assign the same reasons, however, for this difference of worship (17 : 1 : 40). At Tentyra the crocodile is regarded as the most odious of all animals. The other Egyptians worship it in spite of its hostility towards the human race. But the people of Tentyra trace and destroy it in every way, just as other people have a natural antipathy to snakes. Yet they suffer no injury from the crocodiles, but dive and cross the river when no other person ventures to do so. When crocodiles were brought to Rome for exhibition, they were attended to by some Tentyrites. A reservoir was made for them with a platform along one of the sides, to let them bask when leaving the water. Their attendants went into the water, drew them in a net to a place where they might sun themselves and be on exhibition, and then dragged them back to the reservoir (17 : 1 : 44). Fish occur in large quantities in the Nile, of different kinds and peculiar in character. The best known are: oxyrhynchus [1]), lepidotus, latus, alabes, coracinus, choerus, phagrorius, silurus, citharus, thrissa, cestreus, lychnus, physa, bous, and a large fish which emits a fort of wailing sound (= cat-fish, *Clarias* sp.). The animals peculiar to Egypt are the ichneumon and the Egyptian asp, which have some properties which those in other places do not possess. There are two kinds of asps, one a span in length (? *Echis*) whose bite is more immediately mortal than that of the other; the other is six feet long. Among the birds, ibis, Egyptian hawk (and cat) are tamer than those elsewhere. The nycticorax (probably here: night-heron) is large as an eagle with us, and its cry is harsh, but in Egypt it is of the size of a jay, and its cry has a different note. The tamest animal, however, is the ibis; it resembles a stork in shape and size. There are two kinds, a white and a black one. Every street in Alexandria is full of them. In some respects they are useful, in others troublesome. They are useful, because they pick up all sorts of small animals and the offal thrown out of the butchers' and cooks' shops. They are troublesome, because they devour everything, are dirty, and are prevented with difficulty from polluting in every way what is clean and what is not given to them (17 : 2 : 4).

2. 44. CLAUDIUS AELIANUS AND ARTEMIDORUS OF DALDUS

2. 441. AELIAN

CLAUDIUS AELIANUS lived about 250 A.D. although born in Italy, he wrote in Greek. His 17 books 'On the nature of animals' (*Peri zoon idiotetos*) are a scrappy and gossipping collection of animal anecdotes, mostly from earlier writers, the rest from hearsay. Yet, in spite of this lack of originality and of real observations of his own, these books are an almost inexhaustible source of animal tales and legends of the late Roman period. AELIAN often refers to animals of the Middle East. Of these references we can give here a small selection only.

Mammals. 5 : 53. How the hippo feeds. The hippo is a creature of the Nile. When the fields are maturing and the corn turns yellow, it does not immediately feed. First it makes an estimate of its want from the field. Only then it enters the field and feeds, with its back always towards the river. When the peasants come to drive it away, it thus faces its enemies (cf. PLINY, *Hist. Nat.* 8 : 25 : 39).

5 : 56. On the Syrian deer. The Syrian deer lives on the highest mountains, such as the

---

[1]) *Mormyrus oxyrhynchus* L., *Cyprinus bynni* FORSK., *Lates niloticus* L., *Labeo niloticus* FORSK., *Tilapia nilotica* L., *Silurus ? schall* L., (?), (?), (?), a herring, *Mugil* sp., (?), *? Tetrodon*, (?)

Amanus, the Lebanon, the Carmel. (Follows: the swimming of the deer to Cyprus, which has the best pastures).

6 : 20. The wolf, the wildest of all animals. The Egyptians tell that they even devour one another. They form a circle and run one after the other, until one of them grows dizzy and falls down. This individual is immediately attacked, torn down and devoured by the other wolves. This they do only after an unsuccessful hunt.

6 : 22. On the spotted hyena. Great is the wile of the spotted hyena. It hides in the forests and listens when the wood-cutters call each other by their names and talk together. Then it imitates their voice and calls their names. The man called approaches, the hyena retires and calls again. The wood-cutter still follows the call. When he is far away from his comrades and alone, the hyena attacks, kills and devours him (cf. PLINY, *Hist. Nat.* 8 : 30 : 44, 45).

11 : 25. About the elephant of Ptolemy. Ptolemy II Philadelphus received a young elephant as a gift. It was educated in the Greek language and understood Greek. Until then it was believed that elephants only understand the Indian language.

Birds. 4 : 26. About hunting with predatory birds and with ravens. The Indians hunt hares and foxes without dogs. They catch young eagles, vultures or ravens and train them in the following way for the hunt: some meat is tried to a tame hare or fox, which is let loose. The birds are sent after them and are permitted to take this meat. They chase them with all their might in order to obtain the alluring reward. When they are well trained, they are sent after wild mountain hares and foxes. Hoping for their usual bait the birds follow them, catch them speedily, and retrieve them to their master, according to Ctesias. They then are given the intestines of the prey instead of their usual reward.

2 : 48. On the Egyptian ravens. The Egyptian raven of the Nile approaches the sailors in quest of some food. They are quiet when they obtain it. Yet when their quest is refused, they fly with the ship, rest on the sail-yard, feed on the tackle and tear the ropes.

Reptiles. 6 : 17. Story of the love of a dragon for a virgin. In the land of the Jews the inhabitants tell us that at the time of king Herodes a dragon loved a beautiful virgin. He visited her and slept with her as her lover. Yet the virgin had little confidence in her lover, in spite of his gentle and tender behaviour. Thus she stood away for a month, hoping that the dragon would forget her. The solitude, however, only made his passion increase. He came day after day and even by night and was very unhappy not to find her. When she returned, he embraced her with his rump and beat her legs tenderly with his tail, to show his anger.

16 : 39. On the dragon of Chios. A big dragon which was much feared because of its mighty hissing once lived in a densely wooded valley of Chios, near Mt. Plinnaeon. A fire destroyed the forest after a storm and burnt the dragon to death. The Chians came and found its giant bones and the enormous head.

Fishes. 2 : 17. On the Echineis. The echineis is a black fish, as long as a moderate eel. It is named after the habit to fasten itself to a ship in full run and with full sails. When it bites into the afterpart of the ship the latter is stopped, just as a wild horse when sharply bridled. In vain is the swelling of the sails, in vain the blowing of the wind! Depression overcomes the sailors.

10 : 43. On the fishes of the Nile. The plain fields to both sides of the Nile look like a large sea during the mid-summer inundation of the river. The Egyptians row along their fields, fishing where they have ploughed before. When the river turns back into his natural bed, the fishes are left without water in the mud and are collected by the peasants, as a sort of fish crop (cf. Diodorus 3 : 16).

Insects. 2 : 25. On ants. Ants appear in large numbers, single and in groups of two and three, on the threshing places in the threshing season, collecting the grains of barley and wheat, and returning with them to their nests. Some collect the grains, others carry the burden to the nest. They carefully avoid to be in the way of their heavily loaded comrades. When they have filled their store-rooms with these grains, they pierce every seed into its centre and eat this centre. The rest of the seed is sterile. These valiant economists do so in order to prevent that germination after the rainfalls destroys all their stores and leaves them exposed to hunger, after all their troubles.

4 : 46. About the beetles which are used for dyes. In India live certain vermilion animals as big as beetles. When they are first seen they have very long legs and are soft. They come into being on the trees which bear "electrum" and feed on the fruits of this tree. The Indians catch it, press it and dye clothes and other textiles in its sap. Such a cloth was given to the king of Persia. Its beauty was much greater than that of any dyes produced in Persia, as CTESIAS says. Even the much appreciated clothes of Sardinia are less shining and less bright. (This Indian vermilion dye is the oldest mention of the lac dye, produced by certain coccids: *Laccifer*).

2. 442. ARTEMIDORUS

As animal omina from dreams continue to be regarded as important until late into the Arabic tradition, to AD-DAMIRI for instance, we will quote a really authentic source, ARTEMIDORUS of Daldus in Lydia (about 150 A.D.). Apart from the dream-book (*Oneirocritica*) with which we are here concerned, he wrote an *Oronoskopeia,* an, unfortunately lost, book on bird omina, and a *Cheiroskopeia,* a cheiromantic book.

(4 : 56). You must also compare the peculiarities of the animals with those of men. Magnanimous, energetic and terrible animals, loving freedom, such as lion, tiger, leopard, elephant, lammergeyer, announce men of that character. And the impetuous, rough and unsociable boar and bear indicate similar men. The cowardly, rapid and vulgar deer, hare and dog associate us with vulgar men and deserters. Dull, lazy, wily species, such as the hyena, join us to dull and lazy subjects, even to poisoners. The menacing, giant and powerful dragon, basilisk and python announce powerful companions, but poisonous snakes, like asp, viper, horned viper with rich men and women. Animals, whose appearance is more menacing than their power, such as aesculapius' adder, toad, sand boa, indicate flatterers and very troublesome company. Small animals, such as spider, newt, lizard bring us in the company of petty and despicable men, yet still able to cause damage to us. Open aggressors as raven and wolf mean brigands and robbers; clandestine aggressors, such as kite and fox, waylayers. Polite scholars are announced by graceful and lovely paroquets, partridges, peacocks; writers, musicians and orators by lovely singers such as swallow, nightingale and wren; but swindlers and impostors by the imitating monkey, and the black bird. Spotted and dotted animals like the leopard indicate cunning, but also marked men. Beasts of burden or of transport, such as ass or draught-ox mean workers or subordinates; those which refuse the yoke, as bulls, mares and wild asses refer to obstinate and unruly people. The gregarious storks, cranes, starlings, jackdaws and doves symbolise social, good-natured company; jackdaws and starlings also announce storms; cranes and storks also enemies and robbers. The vultures, feeding on carrions, mean lazy, dull people or grave-diggers, undertakers, tanners or banned persons. Night birds, resting during day, as the owl, the crow, the night heron, characterise adulterers, thieves or people with a nightly profession. Those with a varied voice, such as raven, crow, etc. announce polyglots or polyhistors. Neighbours are indicated

by the sessile swallows and crag-martins, but they also indicate that slaves who ran away have taken the way home. Every animal with various meaning must be interpreted according to all of them. Thus a leopard means proudness of character, but indicates also a spotty character by its colouration, and the partridge for instance, refers to a graceful, but cunning man.

The second book of the *Oneirocritica* contains an analysis of all animals appearing in dreams. Hunting dogs indicate a profit from abroad, when ready to depart for the hunt, but lack of business when returning from it. Well-fed and friendly watchdogs mean safety of house and of business; when they are ill they announce sickness and loss of property; when wild and biting: attacks by cowardly rascals and severe losses. Strange dogs, when friendly, prophesy frauds by low men or women. White dogs mean open, black secret, foxy half open, and spotted dogs terrible attacks. Melitaean pet-dogs are the most beautiful thing in life. When they suffer, they symbolise grief and affliction (2 : 11). Sheep are always a favourable, goats always a bad omen. White ones of both are always more favourable than black sheep or goat. Obedient, strong and speedy asses are good omina, especially with regard to marriage and acquaintances. Mules are favourable for work, especially in the field, but announce fertility in marriage. Cattle are favourable, oxen mean trouble; a bull: danger. A tame and friendly lion means fortune and profit, a leopard a man or woman of low character, also danger for the eyes. The bear means a woman. Beyond Africa and India an elephant indicates danger and fear because of its colour and size. I knew a rich and healthy woman in Italy, who dreamed of how she was riding on an elephant and died soon afterwards. The wild ass announces a reckless enemy and someone of not noble character. The wolf symbolises a brutal, open enemy; the fox a secret one, usually a woman. Monkeys and lynx design rascals and swindlers, also diseases; the hyena a poisoner or a low man with unnatural instincts. Boars are always unfavourable. The deer is favourable for travels, but turns brave men into cowards (2 : 12).

A friendly dragon announces fortune, a wild one disaster; a snake a slow fever and an enemy. Vipers indicate rich women. Their attack and bite are favourable. When the housewife hides it on her bosom, it means adultery; when she shows fear, she will fall ill. Newts are like snakes, but indicate enemies dealing with shipping or with fishery. Aesculapius' snakes, big toads, horned vipers and chameleons are bad omina. Poisonous spiders, scorpions and centipedes indicate bad men (2 : 13). The various fishes and other marine animals indicate various troubles, as a rule, whilst pond fishes mean moderate fortune (2 : 14). Only the dolphin is a good omen when seen in the sea; outside it announces the death of a dear person (2 : 16).

Big birds are more advantageous to the rich, small ones to the poor. The falcon symbolises a royal and rich woman, proud of her beauty and her fine manners. The raven, because of its colour and of the frequent change of its voice, may be compared with the adulterer and the thief. Flocks of cranes and storks foreshadow robbers and enemies; in winter storms, and in summer drought. Single cranes are a good omen for travellers in connection with their return, because of their migrations. The stork announces many children because of the help which the young storks render to their parents. The swan symbolises a musician; to sick persons he means recovery, except when he sings, thus announcing death (2 : 20).

The swallow is said to announce the death of a youth, sufferings and deep mourning, as according to the legend this bird has risen from deep mourning. But in my experience the swallow does not foreshadow any misfortune, except when it suffers or changes its color. Its warbling is not a mourning song, but an encouragement to work. They are absent in winter when soil and sea lie fallow, but return in spring, when work begins. And they sing early in the morning to remind people of beginning their work. They are a good omen for work, actions and music, but especially for matrimony (2 : 56). Except to quail breeders, quails announce bad news from overseas, as the quails arrive from beyond the sea, and bad in so far, as they are eager to combat and give despondency. In friendship, matrimony and social life they foreshadow quarrels and disputes. To travellers they indicate ambush and robbery, as they themselves fall into the hands of hunters (3 : 5).

The crocodile is a pirate or a murderer, the cat an adulterer. It is a thief of birds, which are compared with women (3 : 11). The mungo and the weasel, because of their wild and untamable character, indicate rascals and plotters; the former men, the weasel women (3 : 12). The mouse is an inhabitant of our house and eats the same food. Many playing mice announce great pleasure and increase of servants. When something extraordinary will be seen, it will actually happen. The marten indicates a malicious woman, a lawsuit or death (3 : 28). A mole symbolises a man blinded by disaster and conviction for a hidden crime (3 : 64). All owls indicate stagnation of business and fearlessness. Only the barn owl is favourable to pregnant women, as it is viviparous and nourishes its young with the milk of its breasts. Owls are a bad omen for travellers. Owls nesting in a house announce that it will become desolate (3 : 65).

In all these interpretations the meaning of the dream depends upon the character of the animal seen. We have given this short survey, as until late in the middle ages interpretations of dreams were treated in many zoological books. And even ALDROVANDI and GESNER (16th century A.D.) still include them as special chapters in their great books on animals.

III. FROM THE NEOLITHICUM TO THE END OF THE IRON AGE (4500 to 3000 B.C.)

3.1. NEOLITHICUM AND CHALCOLITHICUM

3.11. THE NEOLITHICUM AND THE CHALCOLITHICUM IN PALESTINE

The neolithic period is properly defined as a stone age where improved stone implements are combined with the appearance of early pottery and with the absence of metal tools. Agriculture and husbandry were known, as we have seen, since the mesolithic Natufians. The classification of the Palestine Neolithicum has met with great difficulties, mainly because the trend of its development differs from that in the classical neolithic regions of Europe. A retarded mesolithic culture, the Tahounian, follows the Mesolithicum proper in Palestine. Thus we find neither polished stone implements nor pottery in the lowest strata of Jericho. A primitive pottery appears in Garstang's layer IX, but the stone implements show no improvement.

VINCENT postulates a slow, but continuous development from the Meso- to the Chalco-lithicum (also called Eneolithicum), without the intercalation of a typical neolithic culture. That is apparently correct, as all the European characters of a neolithic culture are missing. Yet there exists a period leading from the Meso- to the Chalcolithicum. And the erection of temples in dense settlements surpasses by far any development known from the Mesolithicum. We therefore agree with DE VAUX (1946) and apply the name Neolithicum to our local period, without inference of its detailed homology with that of the corresponding European neolithic civilization.

JEAN PERROT stresses recently, and we fully agree with him, that not the special tech-nique of implements is the most important point in fixing the dating of a period. We visualize since the dawn of agriculture and animal husbandry in the Mesolithicum, the Neo-lithicum as the progressive development of agriculture and animal husbandry which have however still strongly supplemented by food gathering and by hunting for the full satisfaction of food requirements, until in the Chalcolithicum agriculture and animal husbandry are able to satisfy all the food needs of the human society. Yet this development of agriculture is only a concomitant, if perhaps even the central one, of many other parallel developments, all part of a living civilization. The strata, the contents, the extents and the provenience of these civilizations are slowly revealed before as entities before our eyes. These entities of living civilizations are the object of prehistoric research and nomenclature, not the nature of the locally produced implements, which are not only variable in time and space, but often are produced by the same men. Thus J. PERROT established on the dunes of Israel, that early and late palaeolithic flint-implements were contemporaneous and produced by the members of the same civilization together with typically neolithic implements. This is a certain proof, that not a few tools by themselves can be used for reliable dating of a civilization.

Recent discoveries of M. STEKELIS at Kilwa and the Um 'Usbah cave of Mt. Carmel show that the Neolithicum of Palestine, in this definition, is of more general distribution and of a longer duration than has been realised hitherto. GARSTANG's neolithic strata at Jericho (about 5000 B.C.) belong to a late stage of the Neolithicum. Neolithic civilisations were widely spread over Palestine and Transjordan throughout the sixth millennium B.C., with their beginning perhaps at a still earlier date.

A pre-ceramic Neolithicum at Jericho has been well characterised by the excavations of GARSTANG (1940). Its beginnings are not later than 5000 B.C. A definite temple-building existed, where numerous votive figurines out of clay and mud were found, of human beings, of phallic character, and—most interesting for us—a great percentage of domestic animals, such as cows, goats, sheep, pigs and dogs. GARSTANG compares these discoveries with certain excavations from Tepe Gawra and Brak in Mesopotamia. "We probably do not err in supposing that the original neolithic settlers who domesticated animals and introduced agriculture were devotees of the moon god, the shepherd's friend. Sheep pens are actually mentioned in connection with the cult in a Babylonian hymn to the moon god Shin" (1940 p. 51):

Oh Shin, watchman of the temple thou hast been made
......., guardian angel of the temple
Thou hast gathered the oxen, bringest back the sheep
....
To the ewes and lambs thou (givest)
Sheep of the pens therein thou......
God of the new light art thou; ....
To the leading goats (?) the kids thou (givest)
With the kids and she-goats the oxen (thou makest to lie down) together
God of the new light art thou; ....
.... cows and oxen among the sheep (thou pasturest?).

(Transl. by Prof. LANGDON, Babyl. Liturgies p. 1).

These temples do not contain any evidence of burnt sacrifices. All the fabricated flint tools were evidently designed for domestic, pastoral and agricultural purposes, such as sheep skinning and shearing, sewing of skins, ploughing.

ALBRIGHT (1940 p. 95) and STEKELIS (1935) characterise the "megalithic culture" as the last great manifestation of the Old World stone age. Their great burial monuments, called dolmens or menhars, flourished widely in the Middle East during the neolithic and chalcolithic periods. They first appear in the hills and highlands of Palestine, Trans-Jordan, Syria etc. about 5000 B.C. "There can be no doubt that they belonged to pastoral peoples, who herded cattle, sheep and goats, and who may have been members of many different races, since there is not a scrap of tangible evidence for the often inferred "megalithic race". In the absence of sculpture and carvings and on account of the poorness of offerings in the tombs little can be said about their culture (STEKELIS 1935), except that they laid great stress on burials, which does not *eo ipso* involve highly developed ideas about life hereafter.

The late penetration of the coastal plain by a non-Semitic people in the early fourth millennium is visualised by TOLKOWSKY (1924). These people, a short-set race, who had already learned the art of manufacturing flint tools and arms by chopping off splinters from natural stone, and of forming rough pottery for domestic uses out of clay, had arrived in western Palestine some thousands years before from beyond the Jordan. "For dwellings, they had first elected the innumerable caves which are to be found in the limestone hills that fringe the maritime plain along its eastern boundary". The north part of this plain, the Sharon, was bordered in the south by the Yarkon River, which takes its rise east of Petah Tikva and flows into the sea at Tel Aviv. It was covered with fairly dense oak forests, the haunt of the aurochs, the fallow deer and the red dear, the bear, and the lion. The southern or Philistian plain was open country with herds of gazelles. Here the hunter settled down. The forests furnished wood for the first small fishing craft, which made it possible to collect fish from the sea. Fish bones were pierced and served as ornaments. More commonly the empty shells of marine and fluviatile molluscs, such as *Mactra, Cardium, Murex, Leguminaia,* etc., all still present on the beaches of Palestine today, were stringed and served as ornaments. Many such pierced shells have been found in the oldest sites. Even today similar strings of the shells of *Melanopsis turrita* are sold as ornaments at Tiberias and near Baghdad.

From long before the Ghassulian these shells were traded to the inland cities, where heaps of them have been found in the excavations of Gezer and elsewhere, which possibly have plaid the rôle of small money at some period, just as the Cauri shell still does in many parts of Africa.

3. 12. THE CHALCOLITHIC AGE IN PALESTINE (TELEILAT GHASSUL)

The chalcolithic, ceramolithic or eneolithic age lasted in Palestine from about 4500 to about 3000 B.C. The early beginnings of the art of pottery in the late Neolithicum develop into a common industry, which from now onwards is one of the main guides of the archaeologist for the dating of his objects. Every period has its own shapes of jars and its own patterns of ornamentation. At the same time flint is rapidly replaced by copper as the main material for tools and weapons. All Middle East settlements of that period are situated in large valleys or in low plains where water conditions made irrigation possible. This era begins in the fifth millennium B.C. with the so-called Halafian culture in the north of the fertile crescent. In the circular temples, or tholoi, animal figurines of the type and of the species just mentioned from early Jericho are found in abundance. Only the dove, later so closely associated with Astarte-Ishtar, the mother-goddess, is added. "It was in the Halafian age, well before 4000 B.C., that the highest stage in early decorative art was reached by basket-makers and rug-weavers. The intricate polychrome geometric and floral—not animal—designs with which the Halafians decorated the inside of shallow bowls and platters have not been surpassed in beauty. In the roughly contemporanean Ghassulian of Palestine it serves to adorn fresco paintings." (ALBRIGHT 1940 p. 98).

The Ghassulian culture in Palestine was a highly developed settlement culture. The house-shaped ossuary, discovered by SUKENIK near Hedera, shows advanced conceptions of life hereafter. Religion had reached a high standard of material expression.

To the fourth millennium B.C. belong the wonderful excavations of the Biblical Pontific Institute of Jerusalem at Teleilat Ghassul (A. MALLON, R. KOEPPEL, R. NEUVILLE 1934 and 1940). These excavations opened the understanding of the entire chalcolithic period in Palestine, traces of which since have been found in many other places, such as Beisan, Megiddo, Jericho, Afuleh, recently in the Negeb, and elsewhere. Teleilat Ghassul near Jericho but on the other side of the Jordan, has given its name to this old civilization. It was a town at the period mentioned. Many skeletons of infants in jars from the town area point to the possibility of infant sacrifices beneath newly built houses, such as existed at a later period of Canaan, at Gezer for instance. Enormous jars served as stores. Burned wood and fine ashes testify the presence of hearths. Woven textiles were found and things that have been taken for olive kernels.

Among the many objects of art connected with animals we start with the clay figurines. These are similar to those from Jericho, but represent mainly dogs. A few have been interpreted as goats. The dog is apparently a dingo-like paria. A few primitive animal drawings (dark-red on mud-red) are found among the geometric ornaments of some jars. Among these we recognised an ostrich (without head) and a gazelle followed by a dog. Among the ornamental reliefs on the ceramic we find some plastic snakes, the rump spotted with round holes, such as were still popular in later Canaanite pottery. Most of the ornaments were made by putting the end of a finger into the wet clay. Some of them have been interpreted as impressions made by snail shells. Their shape makes this very improbable. Some specimens of this pottery show a very primitive type of animal decoration: the outlines of some animals are roughly and primitively drawn by a limited number of pointlike impressions (pointillation); mainly of domestic animals, among which we think to recognise an ass. One jar is described as being bird-shaped. We doubt this interpretation, as the ends neither resemble a tail nor a head, as is the case in all later bird-jars.

The bone objects for domestic and ornamental purposes are no less varied than those from the upper layers of Mt. Carmel. They are apparently mostly made out of gazelle bones. A most interesting point is the discovery of many small ornamental objects of mother-of-pearl. Fortunately quite a heap of unworked shells were found in the lowest layers of the excavations. The big shells for the production of mother-of-pearl belong to two species: the relatively thin and wide-elliptic large shells of *Leguminaia saulcyi* BOURG., and the thick-shelled heavy, much narrower and slightly shorter shells of *Unio grelloisi* BOURG. They both are fresh water shells, the former of which is found today in the rivers Yarkon and Rubin, north and south of Jaffa, the latter still being abundant all through the Jordan system. We have no reason to assume that their distribution was different in those days. In addition, the excavations revealed a number of the following marine shells: *Cardium edule* L., *Mactra corallina* L., *Pectunculus glycimeris* L., and a few shells of *Columbella rustica* L. and of *Cypraea sp.* Now, all these shells are marine and could not have been found nearer than on the southern coast of Palestine, between Jaffa and Gaza. The *Cardium* and *Mactra* shells all have a small hole pierced close to the hinge, showing that they were stringed to necklaces. These shells definitely establish trade relations or temporary migrations between Teleilat Ghassul and the shore. The following parallel may be of interest: Among the treasures carried by a desert tribe of Central Australia was a pearl oyster-shell, which was worn by the eldest as a sporran. Now this shell could only have come from the coast, a distance of nearly 500 miles, and must have been passed from hand to hand, and from tribe to tribe. (D. W. CARNEGIE, Spinifex and Sand. London. 1898, p. 243 f.). Still another shell was found in considerate numbers in the town, the smooth-skinned *Melanopsis praemorsa cf. buccinoidea* OL., which may have lived in the watering-places of domestic stock as well as in any spring close to the settlement. The shells are all unpierced and so did not serve ornamental purposes. The species is still extremely abundant in all fresh waters of the Jordan Valley.

Some of the ceramics show very definite patterns on their lower side. In some cases this pattern was obviously produced by pressing the lower side whilst still wet, against a plaited mat. Yet one piece caught our eyes, which seems to reproduce the hexagonal cells of a honey-comb. Apart from the much greater size of these hexagons, however, such an impression should have given a positive relief, but not one copying the comb-structure. We therefore reject the conclusion that combs obtained by hunting wild bees have been used for the production of these remarkable ornamental structure.

The biggest surprise however was the discovery of a number of painted walls, unfortunately in a rather bad condition of preservation. All three of the major pictures interest us in connection with animals. The first, a picture representing persons, is still of very doubtful interpretation. At the extreme left a few rays indicate the presence of a giant star, possibly representing the sun. A small black man, or rather his torso, turns, his back to the star, toward five pairs of legs, facing towards the sun. These usually interpreted as being the legs of five men, representing bigger men such as negroes and men of cream-colour. Yet Father VINCENT has given a lively reconstruction of a very different interpretation: the negro stands in a worshipping position before a bull of enormous size. The remaining three pairs of legs are neglected. Fig. 23 shows this vivid picture. We think that the poor condition of the picture does not permit a definite decision. It is to be hoped that similar contemporaneous paintings may solve this problem in the future.

The second picture is that of a bird. Apart from the fragments of some faces or masks a fairly likely reconstruction of a bird has been made out of one leg, the end of the tail and the small head and bill. The colour is black in a cream-coloured background. Considering that at least the colours black, white and red were at the disposal of the artist, this mono-chromy of the bird picture is surprising. The figure is 40 cm long. The head is similar in shape to a pigeon's head, to which bird however the size does not fit. We feel unable to identify this bird.

The last picture is that of a giant star. In the left upper corner we find two animals, which have been described by MALLON as follows. Two dragons are found at the extreme height, at the right a winged monster with strongly curved body. The wing contains a white crescent and is similar to a butterfly wing. The head is phantastic with a yawning mouth, with two eyes one behind the other along the head, as the artist did not know the technique of perspective. On the upper side of the head we find two horns and two ears, again one behind the other, and, perhaps under the head, some teeth. The left dragon with recurved horns, small ears and eyes, all drawn one behind the other, is mutilated. Our interpretation of this image differs considerably from this description. The left animal is certainly not a dragon. Its shape, the yellow colour and the black horns characterise it easily as a gazelle. The red-coloured animal facing it at its right certainly is meant to be some carnivore, which strongly suggests a fox. The triangle at its back, which was interpreted as wings, is almost certainly an independent ornament. By pure accident it came into touch with the animal's back. If it would have been intended to be a wing, it must have also appeared paired. At the lower quarter at the right a waterfowl with reds legs, beak and neck is depicted. It is much to be regretted that these earliest colour pictures of Palestine animals have come to us in such a mutilated condition. R. EISLER (1949 p. 104) interprets this star picture as a highly complicated astral compass card, such as was still used by the Arabs, and the many designs are interpreted as various constellations, such as capricorn, sagittarius, ursus major, etc. We are unable at present to take up any position regarding this interpretation which would fill us with great awe, if really the priests of a small provincial town would have been able to develop such intrinsic knowledge of astronomy.

In a small tumulus near Teleilat Ghassul dating from the transition period of the early to the middle bronze (2100 to 1900 B.C.) M. STEKELIS (1948) discovered a tomb with a human skeleton, wearing a necklace of beads made from broken pieces of ostrich egg-shell. Other parts of the beads are made from red quartz, sandstone and the shells of *Pectunculus sp.* and *Nassa arcularia*.

In the last years, JEAN PERROT has greatly enlarged our knowledge of the chalco-lithicum of Palestine, by his repeated excavations of a subterraneous settlement near Bersheba (3500 to 3000 B.C.). The most important discovery are the bones of domestic horses from that settlement. This changes our earlier view on the age of the domestic horse. The armenoid population of chalcolithic Bersheba had obviously brought the horse with it from N.E.Asia Anterior or from western Central Asia. We are wanting however so far further proof that these domestic horses were definitely established in Palestine since the 3rd millennium B.C. The earlier opinion that the Hyksos brought early in the 2nd mill. B.C. the horse from Elam may still be correct in so far, as it leads to the permanent establishment of the horse in the Middle East.

Further important discoveries are elephant tusks and ivory amulets. We await with great impatience the determination if this ivory came from the Syrian, or—as we are inclined to assume—from the African elephant. This will be an important guide for the extent of commercial and cultural relations of that period. Mussels for the production of mother-of-pearls have been identified by O. HAAS-Chicago as *Aspatharia cf. nilotica* LAM. which also hints to African contacts.

3.2. PHOENICIA AND SYRIA IN THE SECOND MILLENNIUM B.C.

3. 21. UGARIT AND ITS CULTURE

The ancient history of the Syrian coast has been much elucidated by the excavations at Ras Shamra, the capital of Ugarit (a few miles north of the present Lattakiya; C. SCHAEFFER 1939). This territory was under permanent human occupation since the Lower Palaeolithicum. Strong cultural bonds existed between Ras Shamra and Upper Mesopotamia since at least the late Neolithicum in the 5th millennium B.C. Certain contacts also existed with Palestine (Jericho, cf. GARSTANG). The painted pottery of the fourth millennium B.C. shows "the same astonishing technical and artistic skill by which the Cretan civilisation established its reputation a thousand years later" (SCHAEFFER p. 3). These discoveries led to a revision of the opinion that the Minoan culture was mainly influenced by pre- and protodynastic Egypt instead of by Western Asia. Mesopotamian influences dominate until the fall of the Akkadian empire early in the third millennium B.C. Then the cultural level dropped and the country was heavily involved into all the imperialistic tensions and wars of the great powers neighbouring the "fertile crescent". There Ras Shamra played an important rôle as one of the biggest harbours and staple towns and thrived again by the international trade with the Middle Kingdom of Egypt as well as with Crete. Under THUTMOSE III Ras Shamra was organised as one of the most important bases for military operations in N. Syria and beyond. Hurrite and Mitannian influence in art in the second millennium is shown by a very fine ceremonial axe with gold socket, on which two lion heads and a boar appear (SCHAEFFER pl. VI, 2). Contemporaneous bilingual lexica include, apart from the Sumero-Akkadian h a r- r a = ḫubullu, one in Sumero-Hurrite-like languages. E. THUREAU-DANGIN (1931) translated parts of it which contain nautical ("fishing-boats") and agricultural (irrigation channels of various types, heaps of wheat, of sesame, of dates) series of words. During the period of the Egypto-Mitannian alliance AMENHOTEP III passed Ugarit in order to hunt lions in the Mitanni country. All these foreign influences created a characteristic mixed style of art in Ugarit. This mixture of Mycenaean, Egyptian and N. Syrian style is well expressed in the beautiful hunting scenes of lions, wild bulls and gazelles on a golden cup of the 15th century B.C., to which period most of the following objects and texts also belong. Small art objects sometimes show animals (ointment boxes in duck shape, weights in the form of a bull or a lion). The bull weight is of special interest, as the bull combines a straight back with very short horns, both characters of advanced domestication. The glorious history of Ugarit ends in the 12th century B.C., mainly in consequence of invasions of the "sea peoples".

A famous Ugarit king in the middle of the second millennium was NIMGED, probably of Hurrite or Mitanni origin. His reign may even have extended far into Palestine. In the wide steppes of the northern Syrian desert king NIMGED, in accordance with Mitannian traditions, hunted from a chariot. One of these hunts is represented on an outstanding piece of art, a gold bowl from Ras Shamra. SCHAEFFER (1939 p. 33) describes this bowl: "the King is depicted standing in his chariot, shooting an arrow at an antelope which gracefully leaps away in front of him (The goat beard however characterises it even in the absence of the horns as a wild goat or ibex, the presence of which in the steppe is unrealistic, S. B.), preceded by a majestic wild bull which covers the retreat of a cow and its calf. It was a very special kind of spot, and the following method was used: on arrival at the place when the animals had been started by dogs, of which one is seen following his master's chariot, the horses were given a free rein to chase the game. The reins were tied to the pole of the chariot and wound round the hunter's waist, so that he could hold his balance better, and both hands were free for handling his bow. At the end of the chase the royal stallions were victorious and the exhausted quarry could be easily dispatched. It was in fact a kind of coursing hunt, in which the beasts were killed at bay. Sometimes it happened, as shown on the bowl, that a cornered bull charged the chariot. The sport must have called for a great deal of coolness and skill. It is obvious that one could only indulge in it on fairly open level ground, as is, for instance, the steppe-land on the confines of the desert, where gazelles and wild bulls lived." Four more ibexes (or goats) are represented in the centre. Another animal, possibly a lioness takes to flight with the wild cow. The scene is well composed and very lively in movement.

In the harbour town of Ras Shamra heaps of *Murex*-shells, crushed to pieces for the extraction of purple dye, indicate the early presence of factories of purple dye. The purple colour is still vivid on some pottery fragments found in the ruins of these factories, after having been buried in the ground for over 3000 years. A tablet, recently found. notes that three loads of wood are to be dyed purple (SCHAEFFER p. 38).

In this connection the following Nuzi (Kirkuk)-text from the 15th/14th century B.C. is of the highest importance (PFEIFFER and SPEISER 1936 p. 121): "Ili-ittiya, the merchant, took one woman of the palace for five talents of copper. And on the arrival of his caravan, for the five talents of copper (the equivalent) in cedar, cypress, tamarisk, and myrtle wood, in x and in y, in blue and red purple wool, and in rouge extracted from worms Ili-ittiya shall produce and in the palace to Taya deliver. (Seal of Ili-ittiya, the merchant)."

The names for the purples are *ugni* and *kinnahi*. Three further texts regarding purple are quoted by SPEISER, from which it becomes clear that *takiltu* of the Phoenicians (the *thkheleth* of the Hebrews) is equivalent to *uqnu*, all meaning blue purple. *Kinahu* is a variety of *tabarru*, the red purple. SPEISER (*loc. cit.*) and MEISLER (1946 p. 7) have pointed out that Canaan, the *Kyn'nw* of the ancient Egyptian conquerors, embracing *sensu latiore* all Palestine and Syria as well as Phoenicia, is derived from this word *kinehu*, after this most important produce of its shores, just as the Greek name Phoenicia is a derivation of the Greek word for purple (phoenix).

Of no less interest is the "rouge extracted from worms" (*huruhurati sha tulti*), which were imported by the same Phoenician merchant into N. Irak. This is doubtless the oldest mention, discovered so far, of the crimson dye (the *tholaath shani* or *karmil* of the Bible: *Kermes* spp.). After that this crimson is mentioned in the Bible in the days of Solomon, again as coming from Phoenicia. Whilst the purple was sold as dyed wool, the crimson was sold, as in the Mediterranean regions until the Middle Ages, as a paste made the larvae recently hatched by the female insect. Only some years ago the common crimson scale insect of the Lebanon has been described by the writer from oaks (BODENHEIMER 1926: as *Kermes biblicus*). A treatise on the treatment and training of horses shows complicated traditions and a high standard of horse-keeping in the royal stables. A warrant of arrest is preserved against a riding-master who absconded from the royal palace with three horses.

The cults and the religious literature from Ras Shamra show an intimate relationship to that of the Old Testament. We are here interested in the connection of this cult and of these legends with the agricultural year. Fertility rites for the fields, the orchards and the domestic animals with libations were performed in certain places by pots of the rhyton type, often in the form of animal heads or of a hedgehog. The goddess of fertility is sometimes accompanied by two snakes. SCHAEFFER (p. 43) suggests that possibly this association is still vaguely recalled in the story of EVA, the mother of the human race, and the snake in Genesis. The same author (p. 60) points out that the supremacy of El in the Canaanite Olympus Parnassus clearly indicates a tendency toward monotheism. El usually took the form of a bull. The legend of the union of this bull with Asherat, the mother of the gods, reminds us of the legend of Zeus and Europe. El brings blessings upon this earth which strikingly resemble the land of "milk and honey" of the Old Testament: "The skies shall rain down fat, and the valleys shall become meadows" or "Now the earth shall grow fat from the rain of heaven, streams of honey shall gush in the valleys". Baal, the son of El, had the strength of a bull, striking and destroying his enemies with his horns (cf. 1 Kings 20 : 10). When figured in human shape, the bull-horns are affixed to his helmet. The serpent Lotan is mentioned, "swift and crooked", with seven heads (cf. Psalm 74 : 14). Lotan is an abridged form of the biblical Leviathan. Snakes with two heads (teratological abnormalities) occur occasionally in nature. One such deformed specimen of *Natrix tesselatus* was recently found in Trans-Jordan.

Baal represents the rains and his son Aliyan the waters of the ground. Baal and Aliyan rule during the cool and rainy season. Every year "Baal descends into the womb of the earth, when the olive and the fruits on the trees are exposed to the sun". Aliyan still remains to watch over the fertility of the domestic stock and is then killed by Mot, the summer god and the god of the harvest. His virgin sister Anat goes to search him, finds his body on Mt. Akra, buries him and sacrifices him a hecatomb of 420 beasts, described as 70 wild bulls, 70 oxen, 70 sheep, 70 (?) deer, 70 gazelles and 70 wild asses. Anat now looks for Mot and kills him in a terrible fight. "She scatters his flesh in the field to be eaten by the birds". This killing of Mot is at the end of the harvest and of the scorching summer. She brings Aliyan back to life and Baal returns, initiating the revival of the vegetation (C. VIROLLEAUD 1931).

A few animals are mentioned in these texts: Aliyan is accompanied by wild beasts, 7 *hlm* and 8 wild boars, perhaps symbolising the storms and thunderstorms of the spring. A lamb is sacrificed to El. A "devastating dog for the lamb" may refer to a wolf, if it does not mean a "dog of the devastated country". "The field ruled by the murderous lion turns into a hunting field." Connected with Mot are the "birds of heaven and the fishes of the sea". It is less probable that this refers to the migrations of these animals, than to the main seasons of hunting and sea-fishing. "The strength of Baal will strike Mot like that of wild bulls. His strength will bite Mot like the beasts of Basan. His strength will attack Mot like galloping horses."

The ass as the main beast of burden is mentioned in another song of Aliyan (W. F. ALBRIGHT, JPOS. 14. 1934 p. 120).

A first vocabulary of the Ugarit language of about 900 words (GORDON 1940) contains the following animal names (including a few animal products):

Ugarit word	Gordon's translation	Remarks
ibr	bull	
'hp	horse ailment	
ayl	deer	Perhaps stag
aylt	gazelle	Perhaps hind
imr	lamb	
anhr	dolphin	
anuh	kid	
irby	locust	

argeman	purple	
arh	cow	
atn	she-ass	
btn	serpent	
gmr	a ferocious animal	
da 'iy	bird	
dg	fish	
khlm	a ferocious animal	
khnzr	swine	
khprt	ewe	
khrgb	father of eagles	
khsn	grasshopper	Perhaps locust hoppers
ykhmur	deer	Perhaps roe-deer or fallow deer
klb	dog	
ubit	lioness	No name for the male lion!
ltn	a mythic snake	The Hebrew leviathan
ll	lamb, kid	
nbt	honey	
nshr	eagle	Perhaps vulture
ssw	horse	
'gl	calf, heifer	
'srm	birds	
phl	jack-ass	
prt	young cow, heifer	
zin	sheep and goats	
zml	mother of eagles	
rum	buffalo	Wild cattle, aurochs
rimt	coral	
tnn	dragon	Hebrew: tanin, today crocodile
twr, tr	bull	

The interest of this short list of animals lies in the great number of animals recorded which, however, beside domestic animals, contains only few generalised names. The incompleteness of the list is well characterised, for instance, by the absence of a name for the male lion.

3. 22. THE TELL HALAF

Following this sketch of old animal art and lore in Phoenicia, we now pass to one about ancient N. Syria. The most amazing material results from the excavations at Tell Halaf, one of the many low, rounded hills stretching along both sides of the Turko-Syrian border (M. VON OPPENHEIM, 1931). It lies close to Ras el-Ein on the river Chabur. OPPEN-HEIM assumes that at least the orthostats from his excavations go back to the third millennium B.C., in spite of inscriptions referring to king KAPARA, who lived in the 11th century B.C. His dynasty was destroyed around 1100 B.C. by TIGLAT-PILESER I. Yet he assumes that KAPARA simply put his name on older works and that his inscriptions simply refer to the building of the temple, but not to the manufacture of the sculptures. In view of the use of camels, horses and other animals on these monuments we are definitely interested in the correct dating of these works of art. We understand that the 12th or 11th century B.C. is at present accepted as the probable date of the smaller orthostats by most archaeologists. The people of that region were the western Subaraeans, now called Hurrites, whose monuments stretch from Tell Halaf, Tell Ahmar, Hama, Karkemish, Senjirli to Marash.

The big basalt monuments of Tell Halaf are archaic but vivid in character and show affinities to the Sumerian sculptures. From the latter a great number of mixed creatures and of phantastic animals are borrowed, such as bull-man, man-lion-bird-bull, winged sphinx, winged lion, winged bull, griffons and lion-griffons, men with four and women with six wings (cf. ISAIAH 6 : 2), horned lion with wings and hind-legs and tail of an eagle, fish-man, bird with human head and with a scorpion tail, men with two lion heads, and others. This abundance in phantastic creatures shows the wealth of this people in animal legends. The abundance of very naturalistic animal representations bears witness that at least in the ruling classes hunting game was a very important past-time.

On the eastern front of the great temple of Tell Halaf we find reliefs of the hunt of bull and fallow deer. The hunting archer may represent the king. The size of these reliefs is 1.4 × 2.0 m. The wild bull, as on many ancient monuments, has one ear only on the side turned to the spectator, one horn rising from the other side (not from "the mid of the head"). In all animals the eyes were grooves filled with white limestone inlaid with black stone pupils. The counterpart, the hunting scene of the fallow deer, shows the same composition, except that the head is turned and both antlers are fully drawn. Between these two reliefs we find one showing a striding, short-maned lion. An ibex and a hunting dog also appear. Big sculptures (3 m long) of a lion, a bull and a lioness are bearing three giant gods on their back in the main entrance to the temple. These have smaller reliefs on the sides of their bases: a deer with ten-tined antlers being devoured by a lion, a lioness suckling its cub, a gazelle hunt. Flying or squatting eagles often appear as symbols of the sun. One eagle appears as a giant statue (1.8 m high). The head and beak are unproportionally greater than the rump.

The 187 small orthostats (182 *in situ*) are reliefs along the basic row of the temple walls. Their size is about 70 × 50 cm and 20 cm thick, partly made of black basalt, others of limestone dyed with ochre. Horses with riders and horses on chariots are often represented, the latter with men hunting lions or bulls. In one of these scenes the lion bites into a horse's belly. The horses have a short cut mane and medium-sized heads. Without additional proof we cannot share OPPENHEIM's view (p. 139) that the horse was native in Upper Mesopotamia at that period and that is was locally domesticated. The wild animals, which he confesses himself unable to distinguish into wild asses and horses, are almost certainly all onagers. Pl. VII shows that the Syrian onager has actually a very horse-like appearance. OPPENHEIM records that onagers lived in the close neighbourhood of Tell Halaf until the last perished in the extremely hard winter 1910/11. One orthostat only depicts a camel, ridden by a man, characterised by OPPENHEIM as a noble, holding in one hand a stick, a bridle in his other. The picture reminds us of the scene of JACOB's flight before Laban (Genesis 31 : 19 ff.).

One hunter on foot (apparently Gilgamesh) thrusts his sword into a standing lion, which bites into the hunter's other arm. A small archer, almost on the back of another lion, illustrates the artist's struggle with perspective and arrangement. Other hunting objects show an ?eagle, a big ungulate and a giant goose. Lions appear in eleven of the orthostats, always in another position. The leopard occurs twice. We first were inclined to take it for a cheetah because of an apparent collar, with which identification, however, the big head is in contradiction. Comparison shows that similar neck-furrows occur in other animals also. They are a peculiarity of the artist's style. Reliefs of the aurochs are common. Those in basalt have only one horn in profile, those in limestone two, in the same position. This difference is obviously a consequence of the material. It seems therefore doubtful if really the figuration of two species of wild cattle was intended: viz. aurochs and bison, one slender with a long, narrow head, the other plump with a strong, smaller head (OPPENHEIM p. 142). A more intensive study of all orthostats will be needed to settle this point. Gilgamesh appears holding a lion's skin in his hand.

The deer was usually the fallow deer (antlers with 6 to 8 tines). Yet finds in the neighbourhood also shown the red deer. The fallow deer is often connected with a wild pistacchio tree, characterising it as an animal of the mountain forests. Ibex and gazelles are easily distinguished by the shape of their horns and by the presence or absence of the goat beard. A closer study of the orthostats will probably show that the ibex-group embraces both, the ibex and the wild goat, so common in the neighbouring mountain ranges. Wild boars occur twice, once also a domestic pig, the later in a scene, not as a "monograph". Orthostat 63 K shows an elephant, unfortunately in bad condition of preservation. A long-eared hare and a ?beaver occur in empty spaces on two orthostats of deer. The latter identification may be correct, as beavers lived in historical times in the Chabur river as well as near Antiochia. Unfortunately we have not seen this orthostat.

Among the birds we find two ostriches. In one of these reliefs the empty space is filled with another bird, which OPPENHEIM takes for a hawk. It strongly suggests however a rooster, especially if the roughness above the head represents a comb, or more probably a rock-partridge. Other birds of the collection are houbara, wild goose, flying duck and heron. Animal fights are a usual topic, most of them very vivid in figuration. In a number of fights between bulls and lions the former are often victorious. Lions often attack ungulates. One especially beautiful orthostat shows a lion biting through the throat of a stag. On another a lion carries a lamb.

Two other orthostats show a ship or a boat on a river with three fishes of the *Varicorhinus*-type in the water. The other represents a sitting man holding a fishing rod.

Two exceptionally large orthostats show an animal orchestra, a motive not unusual in the ancient Middle East. OPPENHEIM (p. 158) describes the larger one: "The animals are vividly represented, without overlapping. A lion sits at the left hand edge on a rock in human position, playing the harp with his right paw. Towards the lion strides a big ass on its hindlegs, its mouth half open. Also the other animals run on their hindlegs or jump towards the lion. The ass is followed by a bear (with long tail!), holding a large cymbal in his paws and by a gazelle bearing a bowl. In a lower row a dog strides behind the ass, apparently holding its tail, a pig with cymbal or drum, another bear with a stick over its shoulders holding two jars in this way, another small animal and a monkey. Four more animals are vertically arranged between the lion and the ass: a jumping dog, a wild cat, a wolf or dog and below a fox with long bushy tail, all playing instruments. They are apparently dancing to the lion's play and they may be drunk. The ass, in his excitement, drops seven pieces of excrements." The second, less well-preserved orthostat is similar. OPPENHEIM suggests that this animal orchestra illustrates an old Subaraean legend, possibly a solstice festival.

Some more orthostats, now in the Museum of Aleppo, show a man fighting a ?gazelle, a man with a fly-fan, a ?gazelle with two men, an ungulate with lynx or wild cat, and a flutist with a bird, interpreted as being a bird-catcher.

The small finds of Tell Halaf include weights in duck-shape, terracotta figurines: heads of bulls (OPPENHEIM pl. 56,8 is more probably a donkey), of snakes and birds, some rider figurines. On the small ivory objects a deer, a lion and a monkey are depicted. On the ceramics we find drawings of horses, bulls, ibex, sheep and various birds.

The small National Museum of Aleppo, a real gem for the connoisseur, comprises a number of additional objects from N. Syria. The finds from Tell Ahmar include a fragment of a striding bull (8th century B.C.), a bull forming the base for a Hittite god (11th century B.C.), and a vase with two serpents (ab. 1400 B.C.). Most unusual is a coloured hunting scene from the palace of Tiglat-Pileser III. It shows the king ready to shoot from his chariot another arrow at an opposing lion wounded already by three arrows. A rider on horse-back follows the king, probably as a security measure. Two empty chariots follow, presumably for the transport of the killed lions, the body of one dead lion laying behind the king's chariot.

The base of a (missing) god at Qastel Junduq (12th century B.C.?) shows a stag instead of a bull. The deer often replaces the bull in the mountains as the symbol of the great god.

At Arslan Tash we find a bull as base of a (missing) god (8th century B.C.), massive sculptures of striding lions and a lion's head and rider's orthostat. Of special interest are a number of ivory plaques from a bed of King Hazael of Damascus (850 B.C.), which are almost contemporaneous with the Samaria ivories. They were originally covered by a thin layer of gold, the eyes being filled by some white material. Most beautiful is the plaque with a feeding red stag with ten-tined antlers and that of a cow suckling its calf. A lion's head probably covered a corner of the bed. Two rams of Amon are on another of these ivories. These plaques are characterised by showing Aegean, Assyrian and Egyptian influences (ROTROU 1932 p. 79 ff.).

Other objects of interest include a big massive bronze head of a sheep from Qatna (15th century B.C.) and various duck-shaped weights. The latter are from basalt, in various sizes, each weighing a part or a multiple of a mina (= 404-505 gram).

An interesting apotropaic tablet from Arslan Tash (about 700 B.C.) containing a Hebrew incantation against demons, the stranglers of the night, was recently translated by H. TORC-ZYNER (1946 p. III). It belonged to one of the exiles of the northern kingdom after the fall of Samaria and throws light upon the current Israelite superstitions before the fall of the kingdom. The front-side depicts a winged sphinx and one of the rare pictures of a wolf. The latter apparently devours a man, actually, as will soon be seen, a demon (pl. XXIII). We reproduce here part of the interesting inscription:

Incantation to Ssm:	............Thou hast made for us a covenant of eternity, which thou hast made for us, (thou) and every god and "chief" and "officer", all our holy ones, by conjuration of heaven and earth above, by conjuration of Baal below the earth, by a conjuration ....
The she-wolf to Hwrn:	Put, Hwrn, six (demons) into my mouth, and seven (will devour) my rival-wife, and eight (she who also is) the wife of my holy husband.
The conjurer to the She-stranglers of the night:	
The gods to the conjurer:	To the She-demons in a dark chamber: Go away horror, horror of my night. With olive-oil thou are washen, it went away....

3.3. THE EGYPTIAN DOMINANCE IN THE SECOND MILLENNIUM B.C.

3.31. THE EARLY DYNASTIES UP TO THE HYKSOS PERIOD THE NOVEL OF SINUHE

Interrelations between Egypt and Palestine/Syria are very old. Egyptian art objects at Byblos, the ancient name of Tripolis, which was for a very long time the main Syrian trade and later military port of Egypt in Syria, date back to early in the fourth millennium B.C., the predynastic period of Egypt (WAINWRAIGHT 1934). King ATHOTIS of the first dynasty (about 3500 B.C.) is the first Egyptian ruler announcing to have smitten the Asiatics. Many are the reports on fighting and mining in the Sinai peninsula during the following centuries. A seal cylinder and Egyptian alabaster work from the end of the first dynasty have been found in the plain of Sharon (ROWE 1936).

About 3100 B.C. King SENEFERU sent ships to Syria to obtain logs of cedar wood. Similar reports of cedar wood from the slopes of the Lebanon continue to be mentioned for over 2000 years. Many such statements are found, for instance, in the documents from the rule of THUTMOSE III. The "Valley of the Cedar", referring to the Lebanon, is even mentioned in some old Egyptian legends and tales. A scene in the Lebanon showing actual wood-cutting from the rule of Seti I (about 1325 B.C.) is reproduced by GRESSMANN (1909 II p. 128). A scarab from the 18th dynasty found at Jericho probably illustrates a cedar tree (ROWE 1936 p. 149 no. 623).

Under the rule of Sahura (fifth dynasty, about 2965 B.C.) ships came from Palestine/Syria laden with jars of olive oil (baq). Olive oil from Palestine certainly was introduced since the 4th dynasty and it remained a staple product of trade between both countries for many centuries. Syrian bears and other animals are shown in reliefs of the mortuary temple of Sahura. All this shows that Canaan was a fairly rich country about 3000 B.C.

WENI, a general of PEPI I fought the "sand-dwellers" of Canaan. Asiatics invaded the delta of Egypt at the end of the 6th dynasty (since 2631 B.C.). Egyptian domination in Canaan declined, until in 2375 it was restored with the rise of the 11th dynasty.

One of the oldest Palestinian documents in Egyptian tombs was found in the tomb of Khnumhetep II, prince administrator under pharao SENUSERT II of the XVIIth dynasty, at Beni Hassan. The time is approximately 1900 B.C., almost during the life of father Abraham. On one of the walls of this tomb, reproduced by NEWBERRY (1893, pl. XXX and XXXI) officers and members of the household of Khnumhetep are shown together with a party of foreigners from western Asia which bring agricultural and other produce either as a present or for trade or in order to obtain a permit for trading. These bearded foreigners appear in the third row of the wall-painting, headed by the royal scribe Neferhotep, who holds in his hands a papyrus roll with the following inscription: "The year six under the majesty of Horus, the guide of the two lands, the King of Upper and Lower Egypt, SENUSERT II, the number of Aamu brought by the son of the ha-prince Khnumhetep, on account of the mesdemt, Aamu of Shu, number amounting to 37." The scribe is followed by Kheti, "the superintendant of the huntsmen", and behind him the party of foreigners headed by Abeshah, the hak-prince of the desert. Above this row is an inscription: "arrival bringing koḥl which

37 Aamu bring to him". The Aamu are regarded as identical with the Amorites. The eye-paint kohl or collyrium was found by R. F. BURTON (I 1879 p. 66) in the Wadi el Mukhbir in the coastal area of Midian. A similar material from the Sinai, still used by the Arabs as kohl, proved to be iron, not antimony. The beasts of burden were grey-coloured asses. These were also the usual beasts of burden of the ancient Egyptians, who explored North-Arabia with their aid in the time of Rameses III for instance. The Sheikh Abeshah leads an ibex, the following man a gazelle.

The real beauty of the Egyptian tomb paintings is usually not realised by the layman. Fig. 30 gives an uncoloured reproduction of the sheikh ABESHAH with the ibex. The asses are beautifully reproduced by DAVIES (1936). On plate IX of DAVIES' work (our plate XIV) we find a detail scene of the same tomb "birds in an acacia tree". This detail forms part of a large scene in which the prince Khnumhetep, accompanied by his son and his treasurer, pull in a clap-net full of birds over a pool in the marshes. He is seated and hidden by a screen of reeds, which is pierced with peep-holes at intervals. An angle of the net (top at right) enclosing two of the trapped ducks and the left edge of the water are in the picture. The acacia tree (*Acacia arabica*) with birds is balanced by another to the right of the clap-net, reproduced in colours by GRIFFITH (1905 IV frontispiece). This tree is still common today in every Egyptian village. "The sweet-scented little yellow flower bells being distributed amongst the delicate pale-green foliage, decoratively arranged around the brownish stems. The pale-yellow midrib of the leaf adds to the light effect of the whole." The birds perching on the branches also show a fair resemblance to nature. The hoopoe (*Upupa epops major*) is common in Egypt today, but its tail is square and not forked as in the picture, and the crest is erect only in flight. The bird with (unnaturally!) spread wings and the one above it are both Nubian shrikes (*Lanius nubicus*). Next below follows the red-backed shrike (*Lanius collurio*), and standing under the tree on the right is a red-start (*Phoenicurus phoenicurus*), only with blue substituted for grey. The red-start is rare in Egypt, also in its ancient paintings. At the bottom on the right we observe still unsnared ducks swimming among the water-plants. As a whole this detail is an extraordinary piece of composition and delicacy and understanding of nature even of the most minute characters. Under King SENUSERT III of the same 12th dynasty battles were fought in Palestine. Cattle from Canaan is depicted in the tomb of Djehewty-hetep at El Bersheh, with a herdsman saying: "Utterance of . . . . The cattle of Syria during the counting(?). Ye (once) trod the sand (of the desert), ye now (in Egypt) walk on the herbage" (ROWE 1936, NEWBERRY 1893). The cattle by its shape may well represent the present Beruti-race, yet the horns are more slender and longer in the illustrations. This is an archaic character in cattle.

From 1800 to 1600 B.C. we find the Hyksos or shepherd kings of Asiatic origin ruling N. Egypt and Canaan from Avaris (= Raamses) in the delta. These Hyksos brought the horse to Canaan as well as to Egypt in that period. AHMOSE I, the first king of the famous 18th dynasty, performed the liberation of Egypt about 1580 B.C. This ruler started a long series of victorious expeditions to Palestine, Syria and the Upper Euphrates under AMENHETEP I, THUTMOSE I, THUTMOSE II, Queen HATSHEPSUT and especially under THUTMOSE III. The "Valley of the Cedar", Retenu and Sinai were often mentioned in Egyptian popular poetry. We may mention here the famous autobiographic novel of SINUHE, who lived under AMENEMHET I (about 1890 B.C.), the first preserved manuscript of which goes back to about 1780 B.C.

SINUHE, a high official of the crown-prince Sesostris, takes flight from Egypt during political troubles. At the eastern border he first meets with some bedawi, who pastured cattle and received him kindly. Later he comes to Byblos and from there to Palestine, where

NENSHI, the son of AMU, is kind to him. He marries him off to his eldest daughter and settles him in the good land Yaa. "There were figs in it and vines, and it had more wine than water. Plentiful was its honey, abundant its oil, and all fruits were on its trees. There was barley in it and wheat, and countless cattle of all kinds. Great too was that which accrued to me by reason of the love bestowed upon me. He made me ruler of a tribe of the best of his country. Bread was made for me for my daily fare, wine for my daily drink, cooked meat and roast fowl, over and above the wild game of the desert; for that men hunted for me and laid it before me, besides the spoils of my hounds. And many . . . . were made for me, and milk prepared in every way." Obviously a country of "milk and honey"! He led the army of the country against the invading bedawi. "I plundered their cattle and carried off their people and took away their food." There came a mighty man from Retenu who challenged him. And Sinuhe accepted the challenge and killed him, taking all his cattle. Finally Sinuhe returned to Egypt where he was well received. (ERMANN 1927).

One of the many snake charms of ancient Egypt (from the pyramids of Sakkarah, about 2400 B.C., from PRITCHARD 1950 p. 326) runs: "words to be spoken: 'Back with you, hidden snake! Hide thyself! You shall not make King Unis see you! Back with you, hidden snake! Hide thyself! You shall not come to the place King Unis is, lest he tell your name against you: Nemi, the son of Nemit. The servant of the Ennead fell into the Nile.' Turn about, turn about! O monster, lie down!".

From the same source we borrow an Egyptian dream interpretation (from a hieratic papyrus; PRITCHARD 1950 p. 495): If a man sees himself in a dream, and he sees a large cat, that is a good omen; it means a large harvest will come; but when he sees himself catching birds, that is a bad omen, as it means taking away his property.

3. 32. THE ASIATIC EXPANSION OF THE XVIIITH DYNASTY

The great Asiatic expansion of Egypt took place in the XVIIIth dynasty, which reigned from 1550 to 1400 B.C. The great conqueror was THUTMOSE III, who conducted more than ten campaigns into the north of Syria and into Northeastern Irak. This period began with a campaign in 1533 B.C., when THUTMOSE crossed the Sinai with his army and was kindly received by the king of Gaza. He immediately continued his march, which led to the decisive victory at Megiddo a few weeks later. The fight cannot have been very hard, as the casualties of the conquered comprised only a few dozen killed and 340 taken prisoner. Yet the booty was enormous: 2041 mares, 191 young horses, 924 chariots, 1919 oxen, 2000 goats, 296 bulls, 20500 sheep and many precious objects.

Long lists of tributes and of booty from Retenu appear from now on regularly in the documents of this ruler, as preserved on steles and on temple walls in Thebes and elsewhere. The long lists of these tributes really suggest that Palestine-Retenu must have been a fairly rich country at that period. However, the conclusion that all the objects were products of the country must not be drawn. We quote a few of the registered tributes, restricting ourselves mainly to animals: in the 24th year of his reign THUTMOSE obtained bulls, oxen, sheep and goats, 1718 vessels of wine, vessels of honey, ivory and precious wood. In the 25th year the pharaoh brought many plants and shrubs from Retenu (up to Aleppo) into Egypt to introduce and acclimatise them there. We will have to discuss later their illustrations in the temple of Amon Ra at Thebes. In the 30th year 200 prisoners, 40 chariots and 188 mares are mentioned after a campaign to Kadesh. In the 32th year his campaigns led THUTMOSE to the Euphrates where he hunted and slew 120 elephants in one hunt. In the 34th year mares and asses were obtained from the Lebanon, and an exceptionally large and rich tribute from

Retenu. In the 38th year large flocks and herds are mentioned among the tribute of Retenu. During another campaign, in the 42nd year of his reign the king of Kadesh let loose a mare and sent it to the Egyptian stallions. THUTMOSE was ready on a stallion to attack. All stallions became excited at once and were on the point of breaking loose. The situation was saved by AMEN-EM-HEB, the great general of THUTMOSE, who ran towards the mare and ripped her open with his sword, cut off her tail, and presented it to the king.

D. PATON (1918) has published some of the texts concerning the tributes of Retenu to THUTMOSE III. He mentions quantities of grain, i.e. barley and unwinnowed wheat and resin, green ben-nutal oil and wines, and fruits, and all the luscious things of the land. They were transmitted to the treasury. In another year the tribute of the chiefs of Retenu was 30 horses, chariots wrought with silver and gold, decorated with paintings, 90 man-servants, 40 maid-servants, gold, dbn, qdt, long-horned and dehorned cattle, sacrificial bulls and asses.

In still another year we find among the tribute of Retenu: five first rate and five pollard oxen, 45 bulls, 749 small rams, therebinth resin, 823 jars of hooney, ivory and carob wood. Canaan must really have been a country of milk and honey!

This tribute is very lively illustrated by a caravan which lays the tribute of Retenu before the Pharaoh, on the tomb of one of the great governors of the Pharaoh. We refer to Rekhmara, once prefect in Retenu, who ended his days as prefect of Thebes, where we also find his tomb. Here we find tribute brought from Retenu by 15 men with light-coloured skin, walnut-coloured eyes, blond or red beards, clothed in long white robes with blue and red borders, straight, without . . . . The hair is partly treated with fat, partly brushed and bound by a white ribbon. These Asiatics bring gold vessels, bronze, pottery, etc. They also bring a war chariot, two horses, a Syrian bear, an elephant and ivory. It is obvious from figs 31, A. that the proportions of size are entirely neglected. Yet here we have doubtless representations of the Syrian bear and of domestic horses from Palestine at a very early date. The representation of the elephant, one of the few pictures of the Euphrates elephant which has survived to our days, strongly supports the earlier assumption that it was an Indian elephant. Among other characters Hamy points to the relatively short ears and to the relatively short tusks. In addition, one of the Retenu men carries ivory. The appearance of the elephant may be illustrated by the following story.

A stele of THUTMOSE III has lately been found in Nubia. Among its clamours declamations of the heroic deeds of the pharaoh we find the following description of this elephant hunt (YEIVIN 1934 p. 199): "Now, another occasion of victory, which Re ordained for me. He repeated for me a great deed of valour at the lake of Niyy. He caused me to meet troops of elephants; My Majesty fought them, namely a herd of 120 elephants. Never had the like been done by (any) king since (the time of the) Gods, who received the White Crown. I have narrated these (things) without boasting on account of them, without there being a lie in (my recital). I have achieved this according to that which ordained for me my father Amon-Re, Lord of Karnak." On this same stele another, highly interesting version of the battle and siege of Megiddo is given. The lake Niyy was always located on the Upper Euphrates and Habur, where TIGLATH-PILESER I hunted elephants in 1110 B.C., 350 years later.

The whole episode has been given a highly dramatic and political interpretation by YEIVIN (1934 p. 224): "Would it be too bold to suggest a political move behind this hunting expedition? One can almost visualize the king of Naharen (Mitanni), harassed in his retreat by the pursuing Egyptians, reaching Niya, and, before evacuating it, suggesting that the notables of the town persuade THUTMOSE to remain a few days in the neighbourhood to relieve the retreating Mitannian army from the constant pressure of the pursuers. The district is well-known for its big game. The monarch of Egypt allows himself to be persuaded that "that contemptible foe of Naharen" is such a negligible enemy that the pursuit of his fleeing army need not be allowed to interfere with the truly royal sport. He consents to stop some days for a hunting expedition. He is guided to the watering place of the elephants at a lake near by. Was there a plot to assassinate THUTMOSE "by accident"? Certainly the Egyptians knew nothing about the hunting of elephants. Had they known anything about it the king would never have allowed himself to be caught "in the water between two rock-walls".

We can now reconstruct the little episode of the hunt. The native guides bring THUTMOSE and his retinue to the lake, the watering-place which is the rendezvous of all game in the neighbourhood. The shores of the lake are a little precipitous, and the beasts either used a small dry water-course or a trodden out, narrow pathway running down to the lake. Here would be an excellent place to ambush any game returning after drinking. When the guides were told to arrange for the annihilation of the king and his retinue they would lead them into the miniature canyon instead of ambushing the beasts above and shooting arrows or throwing lances at them as they passed. The unsuspecting Egyptians probably went down into the gorge, thus cutting off the retreat of the elephants. Then the herd appeared, led by a large bull-elephant, which attacked the hunters blocking the passage with THUTMOSE at their head. At the first sign of trouble the native guides no doubt fled hurriedly leaving the king to his fate. His fate would have been certain had it not been for the timely intervention of general Amen-em-heb, who has told us: "then, the large (bull)-elephant, which was among them attacked His Majesty. I cut off his hand (= trunk)—he being alive in front of his Majesty, while I was standing in the water between two rocks. With the death of the leader the rest of the herd could be easily dealt with. If there was a plot to assassinate THUTMOSE, and the evidence rather suggests it, it was frustrated."

Dr. B. MAISLER kindly informed us about another stele of THUTMOSE III, which may put a new interpretation on the location of Niya. This new stele, as most others, is in strictly geographical and time sequence with the actions and events. The king proceeds from Retenu to Shemsh Itom, crosses the Orontes river on boats. Then he turns southward and reaches NAYA, from where he continues to Ugarit (Lattakiyeh). The presence of elephants in the swamps around Antiochia would not surprise the zoogeographer, as the swamps and woods from the Upper Euphrates to Antiochia were certainly once a continuous habitat, which only subsequently was divided into different areas. If THUTMOSE really killed 120 elephants in one hunt, there is little wonder that this animal soon died out in this small, isolated refuge of his.

The new stele, a translation of which was kindly given to me by Dr. B. MAISLER, contains another interesting note on hunting (lines 11 and 12). From Kadesh the King proceeded to hunt on the (*Rsbjw*) in the woods, where many deer stags, hares, (*moswt*) and onagers were killed.

The general AMEN-EM-HEB, whom we just mentioned, has left many very vivid paintings on the walls of his tomb at Shekh abd al Kurna, telling many an event gone through together with the "King of South and North", of whom he was a greatly trusted and intimate friend. "I behold an excellent deed which the Pharaoh did in Ni. He hunted 120 elephants for their tusks. I engaged the largest among them, which had attacked His Majesty, and I cut off his trunk ("hand"), while he was alive in the presence of His Majesty, whilst I stood in the water between two rocks. Then my master rewarded me with gold and changes of clothing."

We have mentioned the plants which THUTMOSE brought from Retenu to Egypt, in order to introduce them into his country. A full report on these collections are contained on the walls of the temple of Amon Ra, built by THUTMOSE III at Karnak near Thebes. The room is easy to find by the four papyrus shaped columns which remained intact (pl. XIII). The whole upper part of the walls of this room, often called 'the Botanical Garden', is removed and lost. It might have contained valuable documents there remain the decorations of the lower parts of the walls. Here one sees "the plants which His Majesty has found in the land of Retenu. All the plants which grow, all the flowers which are in the land of the Gods and which His Majesty has discovered there, whilst he went out to subject all these countries, obedient to his father Ammon who has put them beneath his shoes." 265 figures of plants and of parts of plants are preserved. Schweinfurth, who studied them, concludes: Some are exact illustrations, others are approximately correct drawings done from an inexact memory, others again are pure imagination, based on names and perhaps insufficient oral descriptions only. Pomegranate, which just was introduced about this time to Egypt, *Arum, Dracunculus, Calechoe* and *Iris* are recognizable with vertainty, *Dipscaus, Chrysanthemum* and *Convolvulus,* sycamore figs, dates, citron, melon, alraune (*Mandragora*), grapevine, and *Nymphaea caerulea* with much less certainty. All these drawings were made "in order" that THUTMOSE III be able "to put them before his father Ammon, in his great temple, so that they be remembered in eternity."

Apart from these plants a number of animals: 25 species of birds, two of mammals, one snake and locusts are represented. And on these animals, consisting the oldest zoological atlas from Palestine and one of the oldest zoological atlases in general, we have to dwell for a moment. WRESZINSKY has beautifully reproduced these plants and animals on plate 26 to 32 of the second volume of this great 'Atlas towards the cultural history of Ancient Egypt' (1924) and they are followed in plate 33 by a monumental display of the total tribute of Retenu. The mammals comprise two types of cattle, one polled and one with horns, and female gazelle. The birds are manifold and in general of unusual exactitude in execution. As the material is so ample there can be no doubt about the species or at least the genus of the greater part. It is remarkable that they have much better succeeded in figuration than the plants. All these birds, except a few duplications and a few very defective specimens, are reproduced in figure 32, and beneath this figure the identifications have been given. HILZHEIMER has attempted in WRESZINSKY's atlas to identify the species. In most cases we can fall in with him. Yet a few changes have been necessary. During this revision I enjoyed the aid of Dr. W. MOSES, Tel Aviv. Attitude and figuration of these birds are far superior to those represented in Hellenistic and Byzantine mosaics in our regions. The padding duck, the flying dove, the resting African darter and many others are wonderfully living reproductions of life observed in nature. The other animals are the asp or Uraeus snake and a pair of copulating locusts. It is hard to understand that this monument of THUTMOSE, well-known to archaeologists and published in easily accessible publications, hitherto escaped the attention of the zoologists interested in the fauna and faunal history of this country. All species of wild animals represented in the Karnak temple are still present in Palestine. Most important are the representations of the domestic cattle, as they prove the presence of a cattle of the modern Beiruti race at this remote past, before the penetration of the Jews into Canaan. The presence of the locusts may possibly indicate a heavy locust outbreak in Retenu during THUTMOSE's reign. But this is only a surmise.

In the period of THUTMOSE III also falls the foundation of the famous temple of Beithshan, where cult objects in the form of the heads of bulls and elephants were discovered (ROWE 1930). Also the successors of this great king ruled with strong hand in the Middle East of Asia. Reports on expeditions, tributes and commercial relations continue to be registered.

Towards the end of the 19th dynasty there rises another powerful king, RAMESES II (1300-1234), who made expeditions into Retenu and Kadesh (ERMAN 1930). From this later period of the 19th dynasty a number of literary documents of various kinds have been preserved, which contain points of interest for us. Thus there exists a series of advices for schoolboys to become officials combined with warnings against the other professions. In the warning against becoming a husbandman we read: "Dost thou not bethink thee how it fareth with the husbandman, when the harvest is registered? The worm hath taken half of the corn, the hippopotamus hat devoured the rest. The mice abound in the field, and the locust hath descended. The cattle devour, and the sparrows steal. Woe to the husbandman! . . . . ." (ERMAN 1927). Or about the soldier: "Come, let me tell you how he goeth to Syria, and how he marches over mountains. His bread and his water are borne upon his shoulder like the load of an ass; they make his neck as . . . . . as that of an ass, and the joints of his back are bowed. His drink is stinking water. He falleth out only to keep watch. When he reacheth the enemy, he is like a trapped bird, and he has no strength in his limbs. If he cometh back home to Egypt, he is like wood that the worm eateth. He is sick and becometh bedridden. He is brought back upon the ass; his clothes are stolen, and his servant has run away . . . ." (ERMAN 1927) "The soldier, when he goeth up to Retenu hath no staff and no sandals. He knoweth not whether he be dead or alive, by reason of the fierce lions." Many products from Retenu are enumerated in the long list of the proper equipment for the king's voyage of this period (ERMAN 1927).

To this same period belongs a literary controversy between an ancient Egyptian high official Amenemope, who assumed the heroic title Mahir, and the ironical author of the letters, another official, named Hori. We learn many geographical and other details of Retenu from this document, from which we quote a few lines: "Hast thou not trodden the road to Meger (presumably part of the Lebanon), where the sky is dark by day, and which is overgrown with pines (?) and oaks, and with cedars that reach heaven? There are more lions there than panthers and hyenas(?), and it is girt about with bedawi on (every) side... They say that another city lieth in the sea, whose name is Tyre, the port. Water is taken unto it in boats, and it is richer in fish than in sand......" (ERMAN 1927).

Bedawi tribes of the eastern frontier were permitted at this period to pass into the Wadi Tamilat to use it as a pasture. An Egyptian frontier officer reports for instance: "We have finished causing the bedawi tribes of Edom to pass the fortress of Merenptah, belonging to Theku, towards the pools of Pithom, in order to feed their flocks" (PEET 1924 p. 65). We may mention that the successor of RAMESES II, MERNEPHTAH I, erected the famous stele in the fifth year of his rule (1230 B.C.), on which among other victories in Canaan Israel is first mentioned as an inhabitant of the country: "Israel is desolated and has no seed". Under the rule of SETI II, the last king of the glorious 19th dynasty, also the last Egyptian king who strongly reigned over Retenu, an officer stationed in a frontier post of S. Palestine complains bitterly: "I spend the day gazing at what is in the sky, as though(?) I were catching birds. Mine eye glanceth furtively at the road, longing to go up to Palestine. I pass the night under trees that bear no fruit to eat. Where are their dates? They have none, they bear not. The gnat is there in the twilight, and the zewet-gnat at noon, ... and it sucketh at every vein." The gnats are mosquitoes and eventually sandflies, the zewet-gnats most probably horse-flies (*Tabanidae*) or bloodsucking flies like *Lyperosia*. "There are 200 large dogs here and 300 wolf-hounds, 500 in all, which stand ready every day at the door of the house whenever I go out, because they smelt the seber(?), when the jar was opened. However(?), have I not got the little wolf-hound of Teherhu, a royal scribe, here in the house? And he delivereth me from them. At every hour, whensoever I sally forth, he is with me as guide upon the road. As soon as he barketh, I run to undo(?) the bolt. Isheb is the name of a wolf-hound, red, with a long tail. He goeth by night into the stalls of the cattle. He beginneth with the largest first, for he maketh no distinction whatsoever, when he is fierce. God will deliver whom He will (from) this fire, which is here and which has no compassion. A scribe is here with me; the disease hath developed in his eye, and the worm gnaweth at his tooth. I cannot leave him destitute, when my company goeth forward" (ERMAN 1927). These dogs are probably two types of Levantine paria-dogs. Yet the wolf-hounds may also be jackals, the Isheb a wolf.

An abundance of scarab seals are found in many places of Palestine. They have been published with much care by A. ROWE (1936): Certainly most of these scarabs have been imported from Egypt, but a certain percentage was of local manufacture, of which provenance the clumsiness of many hieroglyphs bears witness. Almost all these Palestine scarabs—and scarabs can be very exactly dated by the cut of head, elytra, etc., as well as by the types of hieroglyphs, signs and illustrations used on the proper, the flat or lower side of the seal— belong to the period from the 12th dynasty (about 2200 B.C.) to the 26th dynasty (about 525 B.C.). Most of them, coming from all the archaeological excavations on sites from this era, belong to the Hyksos, the 18th and the 19th dynasties. The greater part are scarab seals proper, a few other seals and amulets.

Many animals appear as hieroglyphs, such as falcon, uraeus-snake, bee or hornet, scarabaeus, a.o. Common are also composed and mythological animals, such as sphinx, griffin, ape of Thoth, the Seth animal, the hippopotamus goddess, etc. All these have been left out of our index. The main animal is the lion (ROWE's catalogue No. 64, 69-71, 183, 313-324, 482, 510, 575, 586-589, 732-736, 814, 851, 852, 889, 893-899, SO. 35, S. 47, S. 54, S. 83, S. 86, S. 106, A. 33-37).

Common is also the ibex. ROWE offers always wild goat or ibex as an alternative. This alternative does, however, not exist, as no wild goats have lived in historical times either in Palestine or in Egypt. The animal can only be the ibex, in spite of the absence of the typical goat beard. All strongly curved, heavy horns belong to the ibex-type, those with less curved horns are gazelles (No. 69, 307, 308, 310-312, 320, 637, 842, 889, SO. HH 1, SO. 8, SO. 20, SO. 25, SO. 27, SO. 29-34, SO. 36, S. 95, S. 105). Other animals on the Palestine scarabs are:

gazelle: ?872, SO. 9, SO. 21;

bull: 483, 527, 722, SO. 28, S. 29, S. 91
  (often distinctly humped, but no zebu)
horse: 667, 668, 812, 843, SO. 18, SO. 26, SO. 39, S. 82;
  (often with rider or with chariot)
ram: 695-697, A. 43;
cat: S. 49, A 38-39 (as amulet);
dog: 813, S. 15 (and on a few hunting scenes).
duck: 576, 584, S. 45, S. 52, S. 53;
vulture: 66, 68, 324, S. 39;
ibis: 524;
flying falcon: S. 88, A. 44;

hippopotamus: 309, A 32, A 33;
  SO. 17
monkey: S. 71, S. 110, A 28-31;
  (mainly as amulets)
giraffe: S. 36; (once only)

hedgehog: S. 94;
hare: A 42;

goose: 771, 854, S. 26, S. 40, S. 90;
ostrich: 53, SO. 13, SO. 16;

frog: S. 51; S. 70; A 45;

lizards: SE. VB. 8;
crocodile: 71, 184, 306, 318, 319, 586, 590, 737, 814,
   850, S. 54, S. 86;
fish: 597 (*Tilapia* type), S. 31, S. 69, S. 69A;

Scorpions (738, 739, S. 25, S. 94A) are the emblem of the goddess Serket. They are mainly worn as apotropaia protecting the bearer from stings. On S. 25 the symbol of "good luck" is found at the side of the scorpion.

Most interesting are a few hunting seals. First we mention the lion hunting seal from the temple of Amenhetep III (18th dynasty) at Tell éd Duweir. It is a big scarab in limestone with light green glaze. Its text runs as follows:

Live the Horus, the mighty bull, rising in truth;
Two Ladies, Establisher of laws, quieter of
Upper and Lower Egypt; Horus of Gold, Great in strength, smiter of the Asiatics;
King of Upper and Lower Egypt, Rah-neb-Maat; Son of Ra, Amenophis ruler of
                                                 Thebes; granted
Life, (and) the royal wife Tiy, may she live! Statement of lions
Brought (down) by his majesty in his own shooting, beginning
From year one unto year ten: Lions
Fierce, one hundred and two (ROWE 1936 p. 127).

Some other lion hunt seals of the same king are preserved. Most of these lions have certainly been hunted in Egypt (see WIEDEMANN), but some of them may well have been killed in Palestine and Syria.

Pl xv (298) shows a man hiding behind a big shield of basket work, apparently in the process of stalking game behind it (cf. also W. M. F. PETRIE, buttons and design scarabs 1925 p. 27).

Another scarab (ROWE's no. 813) shows a man shooting arrows at an animal, with a dog at the bottom of the seal. On no. SO. 19 we see a man holding an ibex, faced by a horse. Three horned animals are hunted by a man on horseback (S 98). Most interesting is a lion with blood pouring out of its mouth, with a sphinx and an ibex above him (S 2). We reproduce it here as a parallel to the bleeding ibex from one of the old Kilwa rock-carvings.

The locust seal from Megiddo is discussed elsewhere. Other important local seals from the iron age of Palestine include some lion seals, that of Shema, the servant of Jerobeam, being the best known. Important is also the rooster seal from Tell Nisbeh near Jerusalem, which also is discussed elsewhere.

3.4. A SURVEY OF CONDITIONS IN CANAAN DURING THE BRONZE AND IRON AGES (3000 to 300 B.C.)

The Semitic-speaking Canaanites are found in Palestine since the beginnings of the bronze age. We do not know if they were organised in larger units and kingdoms before the early half of the third millennium B.C. Then early cultural influences from Egypt disappear under the force of the Amorite penetrations from the East. Possibly the breaking up of Canaan into a huge number of small city-kingdoms was the consequence of this Amorite conquest, similar to the splitting up of Greek territories after the Achaian conquest. These Amorite invasions strengthened the cultural ties with Mesopotamia. This eastern influence was very strong in all Semitic-speaking peoples of the Middle East, long before the appearance of the Hebrews with their migratory background of Ur and of Padan Aram, and before the Assyrian imperialistic expansions reached the shores of the Mediterranean. The early Egyptian influences are quite conspicuous in certain southern or military towns, such as Geser, Beisan, Megiddo, Ai, Byblos, etc. Of a purely cultural origin are the penetrations of Hittites, Mitanni and Hurrites. The Hyksos, invading Egypt through Palestine, brought horses and chariots with them. The Egyptian domination of Canaan during the XVIIIth and XIXthe dynasties has just been described.

A relatively poor civilisation of a provincial character ruled in this country during the third millennium B.C. But commerce with foreign cultural centres flourished at times. A slow accumulation of modest riches of the princes began on the solid background of agriculture and husbandry, such as described in the Egyptian novel of SINUHE. The early lists of tribute from Retenu to the Egyptian kings still unfold these accumulated riches before our eyes. But the greed of the Egyptian rulers speedily put an end to these temporary comforts and wealth of the local princes. The population was probably mixed with the Canaanites representing mainly the town people and the fellaheens, the Amorites, the nobles and the bedawi of those periods. Domestic stock was limited to sheep, goat, cattle and to asses as the only beasts of riding and of caravans. The Amorite type of life is still well characterised by Genesis (25 : 27): And Esau was a cunning hunter, a man of the fields, and Jacob was a quiet man, dwelling in tents.

Permanent settlements were first concentrated, as we have seen, in the fifth and fourth millennia B.C. in the Jordan Valley, later on followed by settling in the coastal plains and some scattered and loose occupation of the wooded mountains. From N. Syria and from Mesopotamia the early settlers of the Jordan Valley had brought with them the knowledge of primitive irrigation from running water courses. Until the beginning of the second millennium B.C. human settlements and cultivation were far too limited to change the landscape of Canaan. Careless cultivation of clearings brought about the first loss of agricultural soil, the beginning of a pitiless erosion of the soil, beginning only during the later Bronze period, perhaps in connection with the Philistine invasions (cf. A. REIFENBERG 1950). TAYLOR (1946 p. 6) describes the progress of soil deterioration as follows: "The Israelite invasion caused a certain amount of deforestation in the hill and border regions, with probable breakdown of terraces. The improvement of agriculture in the plains during the early Iron age led to increased forest clearing, followed by soil erosion. The extensive building activity in the time of Solomon probably started rash clearing and new erosion in the hills and possibly sand encroachment along the coast. The devastation under the Assyrian conquest (586 B.C.) led to the desolation of land and to the breaking down of terraced land. The subsequent wars between Assyria and Egypt increased this process, whilst in some places rejuvenation of the scrub and macqui worked in a preserving direction. In the Roman period a great recovery must have taken place, as is illustrated by the description of Palestine by FLAVIUS JOSEPHUS. This period ended with the destruction of Jerusalem and the revolution of BAR KOCHBA. The discussions of the Mishnah point to a certain recovery as does the flourishing of cities under Byzantine rule. Early pilgrim reports and study of soil levels confirm that there prevailed in Palestine well-balanced soil conditions and good agricultural practices from very early times, going on during Roman and Byzantine times up to the Moslem conquest, and perhaps somewhat later. Then came the great increase of the number of goats, the Bedawi invasion and Moslem civil war, when the terraces broke down and vaste quantities of earth were washed down from the hills and were spread by the wadis over the plains. The depth of the Roman or Byzantine bridges below the present ground level shows the enormous amount of 2.000.000.000 to 4.000.000.000 cubic metres of soil washed off the western side of the Central Range. This is enough good soil to make 4 to 8 million dunams of good farm land.''

The tendency to soil erosion is, of course, of primary importance as the background of the changes of the landscape and of its animal life. TAYLOR's survey is in fair agreement with the life of the patriarchal age in Canaan, as seen by ALBRIGHT (1933 p. 130): "In Genesis the Patriarchs are portrayed as seminomadic, i.e. as devoting themselves partly to sheep-raising and cattle-breeding, and partly to agriculture. They are, moreover, represented as wandering slowly about the country, but with definite bases, to which they invariably return. They always wander about the hill-country or to the extreme north of the Negeb, never in the coastal plains or in the desert. In the Middle and late Bronze ages the hill-country was still sparsely peopled, and almost the entire sedentary population occupied the coastal plains, Esdraelon and the Jordan Valley. The plains and broad valleys were dotted with towns, as shown by the innumerable mounds which remain to mark them. Settlement in these regions was considerably denser than it was in the Iron Age, or than it is today. A century ago the plains and the Jordan Valley were largely occupied by the Arab (= bedawi), while the sedentary population (outside of Gaza, Jaffa, Acre, etc.) was almost entirely in the hill-country, a curious reversal of conditions of the Bronze Age. The mountains of Palestine were then heavily forested on the watershed ridge and the western slopes, so that little space was left for agriculture. Moreover, cisterns had not then come into general use, so that there were no settlements except where there were good springs. Between the fortified towns of the hills there was ample room for seminomadic tribes, which have left abundant traces.''

ALBRIGHT completes his picture of the patriarchs (1942 p. 96 ff.), as follows: "There has been so much misapprehension of the function of nomadism in the formative stage of Israel that a clear statement of the situation, as we may reconstruct it with the aid of archaeology and human ecology, is badly needed. In the 13th century B.C. the domestication of the camel had not yet progressed to a point where it could have any decisive effect upon nomadism; no traces of domestic camels have been yet discovered in any contemporary record or excavation. It is not until the 11th century that camel-riding nomads first appear in our documentary sources. It is quite possible that pressure from camel-riding nomads may partly explain why the Israelites invaded Canaan just when they did, but it is certain that the Israelites themselves were not camel-nomads, but ass-nomads. In other words, the nomadic Hebrews cannot be compared exactly to any modern Arab society, whether bedawi, or semi-nomadic Arab, or travelling tinkers, such as the Sleib.''

The true bedawi cover great distances on camel-back. They live in summer in parts of the desert where the shepherd could not possibly exist, and they live in an almost complete symbiosis with the camel, from which they derive almost their entire subsistence. Asses, sheep and goats depend upon pasturage and water. With regard to the caravan asses this dependency however must not be exaggerated.

The semi-nomadic Arab still lives in tents, but he owns sheep, goats, asses and camels, and raises crops of cereals and sometimes of vegetables. He had a more narrow and circumscribed territory than the bedu. They engage in intertribal warfare, but not in long razzias. With the aid of his camels he can supplement his crops by caravan trade or by transport. Thus the Hebrews in the Patriarchal age migrated in regular seasonal movements between the Negeb and the hills of Central-Palestine.

The Sleib or Gipsy Nawars, the artisans and musicians of the desert, the women being often diviners, follow the regular trade routes with ass caravans. ALBRIGHT (l.c. p. 98) points out that the Kenites of the Bible lived in a similar way, and that they held a recognised place in early Israelite society.

The ancient Semitic pantheon in its origins was strongly influenced by and connected with the basic natural phenomena of the agricultural cycle, which we described from the sources of Ugarit. The old Phoenician lore about the origin of the world and of the gods, according to the description of PHILO of Byblos (born during the reign of CLAUDIUS), has been discussed by CLEMEN (1939). Historical traditions have left little traces of the oldest father of the gods, to be compared with the Greek Uranos. In the traditional Phoenico-Canaanite pantheon, El is the oldest father of the gods, dethroned by his son Baal. Yet he still lives in a far distant region in Mesopotamia, and the local gods still travel to visit him for occasional consultations.

Baal, the vegetation deity, Haddad the storm god, Dagon the grain god are personifications of the same god who is so often impersonated as a bull. We may only mention an old terra cotta figurine from Ascalon (VINCENT 1907 p. 169) or another one from Rihab in Transjordan (SCHUMACHER 1899). The golden calf of the Bible and the Baal statues of the Ephraimite tradition of the northern kingdom illustrate the strong survival of this symbolism. The goddess Anath is clad in a leopard skin. Kadesh stands upon a lion or leopard, often with one or two large serpents in her left hand. Astarte, Asthoret or Hathor, appearing in a four-horsed chariot on the battle-field, is often connected with serpents, and still more common with doves. A recent interpretation by ROWE (1941) is discussed with the excavations of Beth-shan. The gazelle was apparently another animal of Astarte (COOK 1930 p. 109), notably at Beth-shan. And a gazelle-goddess, a wild huntress from the Lebanon, was early known in Egypt.

The fish goddess Atergatis, mentioned by LUCIAN, and represented by small bronze figurines from Tell Zahariya (BLISS and MACALISTER 1901 p. 148 ff.) has a female breast and a head with a fish tail. She also appears on Graeco-Roman coins of Ascalon and Hierapolis. From the coins of that period much can be learned in general about animals connected with local deities. For further information on the Phoenico-Canaanite pantheon the reader is referred to VINCENT (1907), S. A. COOK (A 930) and W. F. ALBRIGHT (1940, 1942).

The cult places and rituals of ancient Canaan have been competently described by VINCENT (1907) and by WATZINGER (1933).

In an Egyptian text of the 13th century B.C. Anath and Astarte are called "the great goddesses who conceive but do not bear" i.e. the goddesses who are perennially fruitful without ever loosing virginity. They are both: mother-goddesses and divine courtisans (ALBRIGHT 1942 p. 75). This explains the often diverging texts about the virgin sister and the mistress of Aliyan. Aliyan again is not only the son, but the personification of Baal, whilst Mot is the personification of Death. In the Ugarit epos Moth stands for the dry, unfertile season. ALBRIGHT (1940 p. 176 ff.) further makes the following annotations about Anath: Another dominant characteristic was her savagery. A favourite type of representation shows the naked goddess astride of a galloping horse and brandishing a weapon in her right hand. Her favourite animals were the lion, because of its ferocity, the dove, because of its reputed fecundity, and the serpent, possibly because of its annual rejuvenation by moulting and its reputed immortality. A cult stand of the 12th century from Beisan shows a relief of the naked goddess holding two doves in her arms as she sits with legs apart to show her sex; below her are two male deities with arms interlocked in a struggle (?) with a dove at the feet of one of them; towards them from below creeps a serpent and from one side advances a lion. ALBRIGHT correctly regards this relief as an epitome of the myth of the pre-Israelite Canaanite religion of Palestine. The same author (1942 p. 79 ff.) remarks that the Canaanite god Resheph has the vulture and gazelle as his symbols, whilst Koshar, the originator of poetry, is also the inventor of all fishing appliances as well as of shipping, and the first iron-blacksmith.

It should also be noted from another tablet of Ras Shamra that the ass is definitely designed as the main beast of burden (W. F. ALBRIGHT, J.P.O.S. 14 1934 p. 120).

About the dragons and monsters, the Yam (Sea), Tannin, Leviathan (Lotan) and the seven-headed dragon-snake Shayat see ALBRIGHT (1942 p. 90).

Animals are rare on the pottery of the early bronze. Geometrical and ornamental patterns prevail in Canaan. In the free spaces between the main pattern there appear animals in the middle bronze age. These animal figures are well collected in the unpublished Corpus of Palestine Pottery of the late C. S. FISHER (Amer. School Archaeol., Jerusalem). Relatively few of these animals can be identified. The poor results of our attempt may be seen from pl. 139, 2: sandpiper or gadwit at the left, curlew at the right, possibly both herons, or fig. 3: oyster-catcher by shape, stork by attitude. The fish are hopeless: fins and shape change without apparent constancy or relation to definite species. Dolphins, tunny, and possibly mackerels, Caranxids, Triglids are recognisable. We identified: pl. 139, 9-14 crow or raven, 15 and 26 ? stork, 16-18 rock partridge, 19, 21 pigeon, 22, 23 Egyptian vulture, 25 ? flying duck, 27 flamingo, 28 bulbul, 30 peacock (? anachronism), pl. 140, 4 tunny, 5 shark, 20, 21 cattle, 26 goat. On the vase of Tell ed Duweir gazelles also appear.

W. A. HEURTLEY (1938 p. 21 ff.) has followed the development of two styles at Megiddo, development from a simple monochrome introduction of figures into the free spaces of the pattern to bichrome animals sometimes in groups of two, such as the bird hacking into the back of a fish. This motive has been explained as mythological, but may well represent the osprey hunting fish from the sea. An originally itinerant artist of the 16th century B.C. finally settled at Tell el-Ajjul, but exported his vases throughout Palestine and to Syria and Cyprus. HEURTLEY does not "know any parallel in earlier or contemporaneous vase-painting in this part of the world, except Minoan, to the carefully observed details in the work of the Tell el-Ajjul painter, or even in Minoan, in spite of its far more life-like drawing, to the character which he gives to his animals." The birds of the earlier style are drawn in outline, the interior filled with dots or stripes. The beak is just the prolongation of the upper line of the head downwards. In the latter style the body is solidly filled or at least its centre. These red and black paintings are beautiful to look at. Sometimes in birds the feathers are even indicated. But we do not believe that even this artist, the master of the animal paintings on pottery in the middle bronze, has aimed at representing specific birds or fish (fig. 33).

In the ceramics of the early iron age red and black designs appear: geometrical ornaments mixed with Mycenaean motives. The birds are of linear drawing, the body filled with
red colour (12th century). The invading Philistines retained this style, whilst in general
the ceramic style of the iron age degenerates and animals are wanting.

At the beginnings of the iron age the invasion and settlement of the Philistines and
of the Zakkari into large parts of the coastal plains took place. They were people coming by
ship, sailing boats without rowers from the North probably from Crete. They came with iron
weapons and added new forms and designs to pottery. Thus an ornamental swan-frieze on
their beer-mugs was quite characteristic. The unsettled political situation of Canaan towards
the beginning of the Hebrew conquest has been graphically brought forward by GARSTANG
(Joshua, Judges 1931). Egyptian influences were strong during the early Iron age. Ointment
boxes of faience or bronze in the shape of ducks, doves, crouching monkeys, lions, etc. were
still imported from Egypt, but part of them are undoubtedly local manufacture in Egyptian
style. Alabaster vessels were partly only produced in Egypt, and as the analysis of the stone
has proven, usually made locally. Ivory work of high artistic value and with regard to motives
and style under strong Mesopotamian and Egyptian influences, prospered in the 9th century
in Palestine and Syria. Some were worked as ivory inlay, sometimes in the form of birds,
others in high or low relief, sometimes with inlay of stones and sometimes covered by a thin
layer of gold. Common animal motives are lions, lions fighting bulls, pasturing deers, etc.
Strong Egyptian influence is demonstrated by the great number of imported scarab-seals,
the Mesopotamian cylindrical seals being much less common. Even the locally made scaraboid
seals often followed the Egyptian models. A few exceptionally beautiful seals are the lion
seal (of jaspis) of Shema, the servant of Rehobeam and the famous locust seal from Megiddo,
and the rooster seal from Tell el-Nasbeh. Israelite seals of ibex, riders, etc. are listed in
ROWE's catalogue (1936). Some beautiful specimens are in the Palestine Museum and in
the private collection of R. JONAS, both in Jerusalem. Phoenician influences dominated the
structure of Solomon's temple, as pointed out by the text of the Bible (I Kings). Not only
the material, but also many of the vessels of the temple were made after Phoenician models,
such as the molten sea, which stood upon 12 bulls or the ten brass bases on wheels with
their lions, oxen and cherubim. Later Assyrian and Persian influences grew stronger, until
ALEXANDER's conquests fused Palestine with the Hellenistic world, together with the entire
Middle East. The animal representations of the Iron age are discussed with the excavations.
Animal pictures on pottery grow rare and become rougher and degenerate in style. Certain
pottery cult vessels with plastic serpents, lions, doves, are also treated in the places where
they were excavated. Stamps with names of kings and sometimes with scarab beetles or with
birds (derived from the Assyrian winged sun) are found on many wine and oil amphoras
of the Israelite period. Characteristic for that period is also the multitude of small animal
figurines (bulls, horses with and without riders, dogs, sheep, goat, donkey, birds, etc.) which
were apparently devoted to domestic cults, and which became childrens' toys at a late date only.

3.5. ANIMALS IN THE EXCAVATIONS OF THE BRONZE AND IRON AGES IN PALESTINE

The Ghassulian culture of the fourth millennium B.C. was apparently widely spread over the Middle East. McCOWN (1943 p. 64) regards the Palestine Ghassulians as immigrants from Syria, basing this assumption on the intimate cultural relations between the stratum V of Ras Shamra and Teleilat el-Ghassul. The history of the Teleilat el-Ghassul settlements ends at the beginning of the Bronze age.

A more continual evolution was discovered in the excavations of Jericho, which cover the period from the end of the Mesolithicum (layer XVIII) to the Israelite invasion at about 1400 B.C. We mentioned before the shrine from about 5000 B.C. with its votive clay figurines of domestic animals. The later Canaanite, Hyksos and Egyptian strata revealed nothing extraordinary with regard to animals.

We now proceed with a selection of some Palestinian excavations for a more detailed description of their animal finds, such as Gezer and Tell Beit Mirsim, whilst from other sites only some more remarkable finds connected with animals will be discussed.

We begin with the amazing, almost single-handed effort of R. S. MACALISTER, who excavated from 1902 to 1908 Tell Jeser, the ancient Gezer (about 30 km S.E. of Jaffa). The dating of this early monumental work had to undergo some changes in view of later discoveries, but the essential results remain classic.

3. 51. THE EXCAVATIONS OF GEZER

Among the earlier excavators R. A. S. MACALISTER deserves great commendation who directed the excavations of the Palestine Exploration Fund at Gezer from 1902 to 1909 (MACALISTER 1912 3. 4). Animal bones and animal objects were carefully collected from the early Canaanite to the Byzantine strata. Whilst a few objects have been discovered from the Ghassulian, no settlement of that period has yet been discovered. MACALISTER distinguished the following strata:

Pre-Semitic, 3000-2000 B.C.
I. Semitic, 2000-1800   (Early iron age).
II. Semitic, 1800-1400   (Middle iron age).
III. Semitic, 1400-1000 ⎱
IV. Semitic, 1000- 550 ⎰ (Middle iron age).
Hellenistic, 550-100 B.C. (including a transient Persian period).

Animal figurines were rare in the Pre-Semitic period, becoming abundant in the Semitic periods III and IV, being uncommon again in Hellenistic times. They are often of infantile style, and usually solid. Hollow figures were used as jugs, with a hole in the back for pouring in liquid, the nose of the animal being a spout for pouring it out. Some of them were lamps, the wick passing through the spouted mouth. Larger ones were water-vessels.

The technical details are adequately described by MACALISTER (II p. 2 ff.), as follows: The eyes usually were pellets stuck into the head during all periods. Holes prodded with the end of a stick, ridges, dots and strokes, concentric circles also are used to represent the eyes. Mouth and nostrils are generally designed by two perforations and a slit, whilst in the hollow vessels they coalesce into a circular spout-hole. The head is looking forward in practically all animal figurines. As a rule the ears stand out prominently, in addition to the horns of the cattle. The legs are very simple bars. The knees are sometimes indicated by attached pellets. The figurines from the earliest period have mainly prodded eyes and the two pairs of legs are fused. Their rump is rather short. In the Persian and early Hellenistic period the rump is very long and flat with four straight legs. The material is always similar to that of contemporaneous pottery.

Domestic animals prevail, of course, among the animal remains of Gezer. Of these cattle is the most important species. A considerable number of cattle bones was found in all strata and about 3/4 of the recognisable figurines represent cattle. This predominance is due to the religious and ritual importance of this species. MACALISTER (II p. 4) could discern a peculiar race of cattle for each period, which was just as characteristic for each layer as the corresponding types of pottery. Fig. 35, 1-5 shows the typical horns for five periods: the horns of cattle in the Pre-Semitic and I. Semitic layer are fairly long, smooth and curved. They are, however, considerably shorter than those of the wild aurochs, the result of a long period of previous domestication. The horns are longer and larger in the II. Semitic period than in any other layer, and often show longitudinal grooves on the surface. They are smaller and spirally grooved in the III., almost without exception reduced to short conical knobs in the IV. Semitic period. Those of the Hellenistic age are similar to the last mentioned but more curved. With débris of Egyptian objects of the XVIIIth dynasty the torso of a zebu-like humped cattle (fig. 35, 6) was found. Fig. 35, 8 (pl. 124, 4) shows a cow with a ridge over the eyes. MACALISTER interprets this as a board hung on the horns of savage cattle. Similarly in fig. 39, 9 a leather cap is put over the animal's horns. Fig. 35, 10 shows a yoke on the neck, similar to that used today for putting cattle to the plough.

Next in abundance are sheep and goat at Gezer. Cooked and worked or unworked bones of sheep and goats are almost as common as those of cattle, but figurines of them are much rarer, probably because of their lower religious importance. Fig. 35, 22 shows a ram's head, that of a sheep and of a goat. Fig. 35, 25 represents a limestone slab with the graffito of a man with two goats. Sheep bones were sometimes used for making handles of knives.

Fig. 35, 27 (pl. 125, 27) is perhaps the rude figurine of a donkey with a lump on its back. This is probably a bale of merchandise, as a camel's hump would badly fit this figurine. But merchandise was usually carried swung over the donkey's back in panners or in saddle-bags, just as today. These panniers were separately stuck into the figurine, and are often lost, leaving the tenon-holes empty. Also pitchers were added on each side. Fig. 35, 17 shows a band with studded ornaments round the upper part of the head of a donkey.

Camel bones are common from at least the second Semitic period onwards. Considering the importance of this statement, a new identification of these bones is desirable. But the camel head (fig. 35, 28) is reported as also belonging "probably to the II. Semitic period". Small bronze pendants (fig. 35, 29) in camel form from Byzantine tombs were apparently worn as amulets or as ornaments.

Horses are rare before the Hellenistic age, but models of horse's heads with trappings were found from the III. Semitic period onwards. This is in agreement with our later information. For guidance a thong was put round the animal's mouth, with additional side-straps passing round his ears. The harness was ornamented with metal bosses. The reins were apparently attached to the thong on the snout (fig. 35, 13-16). On another figurine they are attached to a metal-studded collar on the animal's neck. No indication of saddling was found. This does however not prove that the horses were ridden bareback. The riders sat well forward, close to the neck (fig. 35, 19) of the animal. Yet occasionally they were sitting further back, similar to the position in which asses are ridden today in Palestine. Here a reference may be made to the famous riding statue from Ta'annak. Interesting is another figure of a rider (fig. 38, 1) from a little limestone cylinder. The horse was harnessed with reins and apparently a rope was bound round its nose, with a headstall between the eyes and ears. The mane was, sometimes at least, closely cropped. The rider held the reins in one hand. Another big animal (head and neck absent) with a curled tail follows the horse, possibly a dog in wrong perspective. A bronze horse bit was found in the III. Semitic layer.

Neither horse, camel nor donkey were used as draught-animals at Gezer. The streets of the town were also unfit for traffic of chariots. Pig figurines are rare. Boar tusks were common amulets. An alabaster figurine of Egyptian origin (35, 26) may possibly represent a man carrying a pig. Pig bones are rather rare. MACALISTER, however, discovered a number of pig bones, concentrated and not scattered, in the Pre-Semitic layer of a cave near the Place of Sacrifice. He (II p. 379) regards these bones as the relics of a sacrifice, and takes it as proof for the earlier sacred character of the pig with the Semites. For our deviating opinion we refer to p. 216.

The dog, "no doubt a half-wild paria as in modern Palestine", was common. His bones were used for making prickets and other tools. No dog figurine is preserved (perhaps in a long-mouthed head pl. 124, 6), but two complete dog skeletons were found in the cemeteries of the I. Semitic and of the Byzantine period, in the burial caves, where they probably fed on the corpses. No cat bones were found, but a few cat pendants of Egyptian origin (fig. 35, 12) were.

Domestic fowl does not occur till the Hellenistic period, from which some bones are available. Ducks, duck-, geese-, swan-heads, etc. are preserved (fig. 36, 2 and 3).

Wild mammal bones found in fair quantities in almost every stratum at Gezer belong to bear, hyena, wolf, jackal, gazelle, porcupine, badger, hare, rat, jerboa and mouse. Stag-antler tines were used as hafts of knives. The tooth of a hippopotamus was found in a large reservoir. A hippo's head in clay, possibly under Egyptian influence—as certainly was an ape's head—was also excavated. Also leopard teeth were found in a cistern. Ivory was in fair use at Gezer. Fig. 36, 10 possibly represents a crude elephant. A bronze model of a stag (fig. 36, 11) and a crude ibex on a potsherd are other finds. Lion figurines were found in the Hellenistic strata only.

Birds are not well defined usually. Ducks, geese and swans have been mentioned. To these dove and crane, perhaps rock-partridge and flamingo have to be added. A potsherd graffito from the III. Semitic stratum (fig. 36, 1) probably represents an ostrich. Fragments of painted ostrich egg-shells were found in the remains of II. Semitic interments.

The brass asp from the high place (fig. 37, 1), which was found in a pit near the High Place, makes MACALISTER think that the enclosure where the serpent was found, may have been a pit for keeping live serpents, preserved by the priests for charming and for tricks. More probably is that it was a votive model, made after the model of the brass serpent of Moses (cf. also II Kings 18 : 4). Fragments of plastic, and snakes on pottery grooved as usual were repeatedly found (fig. 36, 14 and 15). Pieces of tortoise shells are rather frequent, whilst no products made from them were found.

Large numbers of bones of tunny and other fish are properly interpreted as being imported food. Fig. 37, 16 and 17 shows two probable fish-hooks and a small fish pendant.

Many shells, mainly of *Pectunculus, Murex, Leguminaia* and *Buliminus,* were used as ornaments from the oldest layers onwards. Many oyster-shells were found near the High Place, elsewhere a small *Tridacna* shell (from the Red Sea), also a fragment of a cuttle-bone, and others were found. Polished tube fragments of *?Serpula* served apparently as amulets. Beads cut from polished shells are common. Cut shell fragments were also used as inlays. Apart from some unpolished pieces of red coral a few polished and pierced ones were amulets against the evil eye in the Hellenistic age. Large piles of snail shells and of cockle-shells from the same period indicate the middens, the refuse heaps of eaten snails. No such heaps were found in any pre-Hellenistic stratum.

Two doubtful identifications of arthropods have been made by MACALISTER. Fig. 36, 19 is interpreted as a millipede. We doubt very much if any animal was meant by this graffito from a cave wall. Fig. 36, 21 (ptm.) from a bowl of the III. Semitic period is interpreted as a spider, but we think it much more resembles a woodlouse or a species of *Lithobius* or *Scutigera* (*Myriapoda*).

Animals and their use at Gezer. MACALISTER (fig. 37, 22) made a reconstruction of some flint-knives arranged in the place of the extracted teeth of the jaw of a big mammal to serve as sickle. For this purpose the bone has to be worked on the place of insertion of the knives, before it is ready for handling. Bone-needles are common, usually flat and perforated at the broader end. Unperforated strips of bone were used for pricking holes into skins. Both are common in all layers. Small pins and needles were kept in cases made of the hollow shankbone of cranes and birds of similar size (fig. 37, 3). Ivory pins and ivory buttons are also common in all strata.

Necklaces and pendants from marine shells, mainly of *Pectunculus* and *Phasianella,* are common. Large piles of small shells, pierced by art or by nature at the hinge, occurred throughout the excavations from time to time, where the meat of the shell-fish was probably eaten. Corals, flat circular discs of pearls, chips of oyster-shells, etc. were used as beads in the early periods. The strings of beads were suspended from perforated plates of bone or stone (fig. 37, 6) with one perforation for each string. Small bells were ornaments or charms. Zechariah (14 : 20): In that day shall there be upon the bells of the horses, may indicate a similar early use at Gezer. Combs of bone or ivory are rare and late.

As ALBRIGHT (1933 p. 98) pointed out, toys did not come into general use until the Iron age, the period of the Israelite occupation. All earlier figurines are of a religious or magic character. The animal figurines of the later Semitic periods were probably children's toys in many cases. For playing with clay models of animals MACALISTER (II 305) refers to the sparrow-story in the apocryphal Gospel of the Infancy. Also shells were used as toys. For games, apart from pebbles, polished astragalus-bones of sheep were used.

Local seals from the III. and IV. Semitic periods show a number of rough animal figures. We will not go into the great number of seals, amulets and tablets of Egyptian and Mesopotamian origin, especially from the III. Semitic period onwards. We only refer to fig. 37, 9, a Mesopotamian clay tablet with animals from the zodiac.

For details of the Place of Sacrifice, the altar and the High Place in general we refer to the details of MACALISTER's description (II p. 378 ff.). On votive altars of the Hellenistic period in various places a number of animal figures occurs (fig. 37, 17 and 18), such as a primitive gazelle, a stag and his hind, a lion in fight with a man, a man stalking an animal, a lion attacking a donkey, etc.

Apart from the Egyptian amulets, the oldest amulets are of bone. Fig. 37, 7 shows the metacarpal bone of a goat. Spindle whorls from the sawn off and perforated head of human lemurs are common amulets through all the Semitic layers, with one perforated human patella serving a similar purpose. Also boar tusks, with joined basis to form a crescent and united by a silver band or ring (once in gold) or full silver imitations were common amulets in all Semitic periods (fig. 37, 10). We still have to mention a number of graffiti drawings carved into the walls of some of the caves. All these drawings (the best of which are reproduced in fig. 36, 18-21, are rather infantile and crude. They have been incorrectly regarded by MACALISTER (II pl. 46-48, and 1921 p. 14) as neolithic. There is no doubt any more, in the light of later archaeological experience, that these drawings belong to a late historical period, not going back before the Hellenistic age and perhaps even later. The troglodytes of Gezer were primitive, but not early men.

3. 52. TELL BEIT MIRSIM AND TELL TA'ANNEK

A very good general introduction into the history and results of the most important excavations, brought up to date, has been given by C. C. McCOWN (1943), to which book the reader is referred for a general and more detailed description of the general historical background.

Tell Beit Mirsim (about 25 km S.W. of Hebron), probably the ancient Kiriath Sepher, dates back to the early Bronze age (about 2300 B.C.). The material results of the excavations (1926 to 1932) were not very spectacular, but the wide experience of W. F. ALBRIGHT, the leader of the expedition, made them a remarkable corner stone in the history of Palestine excavations.

It may be of interest to mention ALBRIGHT's estimate of the population of Tell Beit Mirsim, as a general indication to the size of contemporaneous towns; at the time of the divided kingdom there existed about 300 houses with 2500 to 5000 inhabitants.

Kiriath-sepher (Tell Beit Mirsim) in the southern coastal plain with its eleven layers was excavated in 1926-1932 by the American School of Archaeology. Its culture lasted from the early Bronze to the early Iron II. For its description we follow the masterly view of the excavator W. F. ALBRIGHT (1933). The forests of the once wooded hills of the western slopes of Judaea were destroyed at 2200 B.C. The forests and high macqui had disappeared and the first Amorite town was built on eroded soil, on the bare rocks. Nothing in the lower strata awakes our special interest.

Early Bronze or Hyksos Age (about 1700 B.C.). In the levels E and D a large house was discovered with entrance through a large court with a rounded, plastered trough for feeding animals. The gate was wide enough to admit a chariot. No such arrangements are found in the houses of the older, pre-Hyksos levels (such as G, about 1800 B.C.). Inside this house a flat relief stele (30 × 60 cm) of the serpent goddess was found, of which other representations have been reported from Beth-shemesh and from Athlith. "The divinity of Tell Beit Mirsim appears as a draped figure. The entire upper part of the figure is lost. Fortunately, the serpent is completely preserved; it is a large snake, which comes out of the earth between her ankles, coils around her legs, while its head is seen between her thighs. In the Astarte plaque from Beth-shemesh we have a typical courtesan (*qedeshah*), with both arms upraised, holding long-stemmed flowers, while a serpent crawls down over her naked body, from her left shoulder, its head reaching her left hip. The larger, Hellenistic clay goddess from Athlit shows the naked goddess, with a serpent crawling up her right thigh." (ALBRIGHT 1933 p. 88). The serpents are, of course, not pythons, but refer to the general type of snakes, such as the common species of *Coluber*. In all cases the serpent's head is directed towards the vulva of the goddess, thus indicating its fertilizing character, with the goddess bringing forth vegetation, as symbolised by the flowers which she holds. Similar serpent goddesses are known from ancient Egypt, Mesopotamia and Syria.

The Late Bronze Age (level C; up to 1250 B.C.*).* Here a stone lion and a stone table of offerings with three lions in relief around the rim were excavated. The crude, laying, 60 cm long lion of limestone with its curled tail is the oldest lion figurine from Palestine, followed by the larger lion of Karnaim in Bashan (GRESSMANN no. 399). The table of offerings is 30 cm in diameter. The artistically exceedingly crude, but, as ALBRIGHT (1933 p. 94) points out, entirely local, products of an old, provincial Canaanite art, are ultimately derived from Egyptian prototypes. The lion is too small to have formed one of a pair of apotropaic guardians of the temple portal. ALBRIGHT therefore assumes that the lions have flanked the pedestal or throne, or may either have stood in front of it, or, as is common in Syrian art, the goddess may have stood on the lion.

The Early Israelite Occupation (Level B; 1200-950). This layer revealed a fragment of a small vase with the torso of a hollow figurine of a nude female with prominent breasts, pressing a dove with outstretched wings to her bosom. Similar figurines of Aphrodite are well-known from the Greek islands, but of a much later date (7th-5th centuries). From Cyprus and Phoenicia such statuettes are known also from the bronze age. The dove is, of course, a sacred bird to Astarte-Aphrodite, and—as ALBRIGHT (1933 p. 111) points out— exceedingly popular in the Syrian Iron age, possibly under Philistine influence. To the latest objects from that period the painted outline of a dragon on a large potsherd belongs, with hind-quarters and tail being broken off. "The dragon has an elongated body, the legs and feet of a fowl, and a bird's head. The head is turned so that the animal looks back over its shoulder, two plumes falling over its bill, while a peculiar crest in the shape of a duck-bill protrudes from the back of the head. It has analogies both with the Babylonian mushkhusshu, a crested serpent with four legs (forelegs leonine, hindlegs aquiline), and with the Egyptian sefer, a quadruped with a bird's head, two wings and a long tail. The crest suggests the former; the bird's head resembles the latter. Another illustration of Israelite or Canaanite art of this age is a scarab-seal in red marble, showing a man between two ostriches, which he grasps by the neck" (ALBRIGHT 1933 p. 112). This last motive is widely spread in Mesopotamia and Egypt.

The Period of the Jewish Monarchy (910-588 B.C.; *level A).* This is the highest level, as the Byzantine town was built in the neighbourhood at Khirbet Beit Mirsim. No domestic stock was kept in the town at that period. It was kept outside the walls. Farming and manufacturing and dyeing woollen goods were the main occupations. ALBRIGHT (1933 p. 119) has described the dyeing installations in detail. The wine and oil delivered in payment of the taxes were put into standard jars, which were stamped with an official seal. Many of these seals contain a four-winged scarabaeus.

The excavations of STARKEY at Lachish (Tell ed-Duweir), where the famous correspondence from the days preceding the fall of Jerusalem was found brought to light a few animal objects only (TUFNELL, INGE and HARDING 1940), such as a fine red jar with goats. trees, a stag, a lion and a bird as decoration (1940 frontispiece) from about 1205 B.C., some ivory carvings (pl. 17-19), glass and glaze pendants (pl. 21), scarabs (32-33) and pottery (pl. 28, 55-62). Similar objects were found by E. GRANT at Ain Shems, the ancient Beth Shemesh (1929: p. 97, 143, 167, 213; 1931: pl. 11 and 19; 1938: pl. 48, and 51).

Tell Ta'annek, the Biblical Taanakh, near Jenin was founded about 2000 B.C. and is listed among the Palestinian towns plundered by THUTMOSE III. The excavations by SELLIN (1904, 1905) yielded a number of animal seals, animals on pottery, primitive bone instruments, animals on lamps and a few animal figurines. One of these (1904, fig. 103) is listed as a wolf's head, but the determination remains doubtful. Of special interest are two objects, which we will describe in some detail (fig. 38).

SELLIN excavated besides two Canaanite Astarte figurines, a damaged hollow figurine of an animal with rider (17 cm long, 10 cm high), having two holes in its back which was either a lamp or a ritual vessel. The animal is, as usual, not definitely characterised. But Sellin's interpretation as a camel has much in its favour, whilst nothing contradicts it: first, the proportion in the size of the rider to that of the animal indicates a rather big animal. Secondly, the rider is sitting on the extreme hind part of the animal's back. This is the usual position of the rider in camel figurines of the Hellenistic period. Thirdly, there is the indication of a hump on the animal's back before the rider, which is perhaps less distinct as it should be. But the entire back of the animal is covered by a rug, which tends to hide the hump.

The other object is an incense altar (90 cm high, 30 cm broad, growing narrower towards the top, which is dated by SELLIN to 700 B.C., soon after the destruction of the Northern Kingdom. It is full of mythological reliefs, which we are unable to interpret properly at present. It belonged to a private house. Sellin connects it with the portable stoves mentioned in Genesis (15 : 17), Isaiah (31 : 9) and in the inscription of MESHA of Moab (lines 12 and 17). Two handles, one at each side have the form of ram's horns. The front wall, besides three windows, shows a holy tree flanked by two ibexes. The right wall shows three figurines with human heads, a plump animal rump, and wings (sphinxes or cherubim). Between them two lions rest, the forepaws resting on the heads of the sphinx beneath them. The heads of all these figurines project over the front wall. The left wall shows the same five figures, and in addition the relief of a small boy, choking a snake with opened mouth which stands erect before him.

3. 53. THE TELLS ALONG THE WADI GHUZZEH

FLINDERS PETRIE, the master and teacher of an entire generation of Egyptologists, turned his interest at the evening of his fruitful life to some mounds in Southern Palestine, along the Wadi Ghuzzeh. This wadi stretches almost from the Dead Sea to the south of Gaza, the ancient southern frontier of civilisation, and was fortified by small fortresses guarding the passage from Egypt to the coastal plain as well as to the Judaean mountains. These excavations, most of them preliminary work only, lasted from 1926 to 1936.

The Tell Jemmah, the ancient Gerar, proved to be an important Hyksos centre. The following remark of McCOWN (1943 p. 122) will make it clear that almost every ancient tell of Palestine contains a similar abundance of objects as those from Gezer described by us to some detail: "Only a careful study of the 72 fine plates of photographs and drawings in PETRIE's Gerar can give some conception of the richness and fullness of life in these ancient civilisations. Scarabs, seals; jewelry of rings, earrings, bracelets, pectorals, beads and pins; weapons of flint, copper, bronze, and iron: including spearheads, arrowheads, knives, and swords; ivory and bone work; kitchen and other household utensils, and tools; agricultural implements; figurines, divine, human and animal; and a tremendous mass of pottery of all sorts and ages—such a list poorly suggests something of what was found on a site which Sir FLINDERS regarded as worth only a single season of excavation."

The second hill was Tell el Far'ah, regarded by PETRIE as the ancient Beth-Pelet, whilst ALBRIGHT identifies it with Sharuhen, an important Hyksos centre. Among the remarkable finds was a bronze figurine of a rampant bear, holding faggots on his shoulders. The bear was unfortunately not connected with any of the tombs and could not be properly dated. In the residency of the XIXth dynasty, within the fortress, the ivory-band of a box with Egyptian motive and landscape (geese catch of the Nile, pasturing bulls) was found, representing, among others some fish and geese, as well as some birds in Cretan style, but regarded by PETRIE as Syrian workmanship (PETRIE 1930 pl. 43 and 55). Some remarkable potsherds with animal motives were contained in the cemetery of the XIX and XXth dynasties. A figure (cf. MACDONALD, STARKEY, HARDING 1932 pl. 58) shows the frieze of a jar where a series of birds and serpents faces a series of gazelles with serpents, with a roaring lion between them. Another jar shows gazelles (note the absence of the goat beard) feeding on a tree, and some fish.

Most important were the excavations at Tell Ajjul, about eight km south of modern Gaza. This ancient Gaza covered a considerable area: about four times as large as the Jerusalem of David and twice as large as that of Megiddo. PETRIE assumes that this ancient Gaza was abandoned by its inhabitants because of the heavy malaria, originating from the environments of the lower Wadi Ghuzzeh. This area is still rather malarious today. The shift to the site of modern Gaza is ascribed by him to the end of the late bronze period. The excavations revealed the usual stock of tools, figurines, jars, weapons, etc. Yet they show one rather unusual feature. In the Hyksos period—we recall that the Hyksos brought, or at least spread, the domestic horse over the Middle East—men, horses and sometimes donkeys were found buried within the same tombs. Apart from these horse burials, we find evidence there of sacrifices of horses and even of hippophagy.

FLINDERS PETRIE (1932 p. 14, pl. L) describes, how the foundation of the later Hyksos palace IV was signalised by digging a pit in the walls of palace III. Into this pit a horse was thrown after removal of the shoulders for eating, and the left thigh. On the new ground level, about 1060 B.C., there were the scattered bones of two other horses which had been eaten. Such a sacrifice would be impossible to Egyptians, and this stamps it as the Hyksos level. Another field of bones was found some way beyond the outer end of a long tunnel. The remarkable collection of bones contains some incomplete human skeletons together with the bones and skulls of ass, gazelle, horse and oxen. A number of such tombs are described in detail in the four volumes of PETRIE's Gaza (1931-1934). 1931 pl. IX. shows a burial with asses. In tomb no. 101 four asses were sacrificed and placed at a rather higher level than the human burial. A leg of an ass was disseevered. A fine horse burial had only one leg in situ, three legs had been removed, the hindlegs by chopping away the sides of the pelvis. Was there a regular habit to remove some of the legs?

Among the other finds of Gaza we mention some horse-bits of bronze, one of them with a circular cheek piece, a late Hyksos burial had elaborate strings of ostrich shell beads forming a chest-ornament.

The archaeological exploration of the Negeb, the Roman Idumaea, is still in its infancy. This is regrettable, as important results may be expected from the Palaeolithicum down to the patriarchal age, when the Hebrews roamed over the Negeb, and again from the Hellenistic and Byzantine periods.

3. 54. BETH-SHAN

Beth-shan, Scythopolis or Beisan, a mound on the river Jalud with a great necropolis on the opposite northern bank of the river, was an old and important fortress of Central Palestine. It was excavated from 1921 to 1933 by C. S. FISHER, A. ROWE and G. M. FITZGERALD.

The oldest strata showing settlements above the virgin soil are dating back to about

3750 B.C., i.e. to about the stratum VIII of Jericho only. Permanent stable settlements of considerable extent exist since the late bronze age. Beth-shan was occupied, as was the whole neighbouring district, by the Hyksos-invaders. Since THUTMOSE III, the builder of the Asiatic empire of Egypt (about 1475 B.C.), the town was for centuries a most important military stronghold of Egypt. The large temples of THUTMOSE III, RAMESES III, and others are proud witnesses of that period. Yet even at this period foreign influence was not absent. A good illustration for such influence is the beautiful lion-dog panel on the main gate of the temple of THUTMOSE, which definitely has a Mitanni or an Assyro-Babylonian background (pl. XX).

ROWE (1930 p. 16) describes it as follows: The upper register depicts a lion fighting with a dog. On the shoulder of the lion is a tuft of hair somewhat resembling a star. The star itself is usually an indication of a superior being and is seen on various lion-reliefs from Palestine, such as from Samaria or Tell el Mutesellim. The lion of this relief evidently represents Nergal, the god of plague and death. The dog guarded the temple against the penetration of this lion, who brings death and destruction with him. The dog resembles in ROWE's opinion the hunting dogs of ASSURBANIPAL at Niniveh. The Assyrians had the habit to bury figures of dogs beneath the thresholds of their houses, so that the spirits of the dogs could repulse any evil spirits, who may try to penetrate into the houses. The lower register shows the majestic lion of Nergal, as he is attacked by a dog, biting into his back. Thus the upper register apparently shows the apotropaic action of the mythic dog of the gods, preventing the lion-Nergal to enter the temple, the lower one illustrates the expulsion of the lion by the same dog. Many visitors raise another interpretation of the stele, namely it representing two phases of a sexual play between lion and lioness. Yet almost the only arguments in this respect are the similar figuration of the legs and the identical size of both animals. The interpretation proposed by ROWE should be accepted on the ground of many analogies in Assyrian art. Also the head and face of the dog can scarcely be interpreted as feline.

A number of other discoveries within the same temple permit a vivid reconstruction of the ritual of the sacrifices (ROWE 1930 p. 13, ALBRIGHT 1933). Just to the south of the inner shrine of the Makal sanctuary, ROWE found a room containing an altar of sacrifice. On the top of the altar is an L-shaped channel (20 cm deep and wide), through which the blood of the sacrificed animal was carried away from the altar. In the channel of the altar is a hole for the wooden peg to which the animal was tethered before the function. Against the south side of the altar the two horns of a bull, which had been sacrificed on the altar, were found lying. In the court yard just to the west of the altar steps the collar bone of a bull was found, presumably of the same individual, of about three years age, together with a bronze dagger, employed in the sacrifice (cf. I Sam. 1 : 24-25). Thus ALBRIGHT gives us a vivid picture of the last sacrifice offered in Makal's temple within the temple complex of THUTMOSE III, before the citadel of Beth-shan was destroyed by somebody we do not know. In the same court yard the socket of a pole was found upon which the carcasses of the sacred animals were suspended after the sacrifice. Near the collar-bone and the bronze dagger a heavy bronze pendant of a lion jumping on a bull was found. Apparently this pendant was hung around the neck of the animal, whilst it was shown to the people before the sacrifice.

Beth-shan was rebuilt in Hellenistic times (third century B.C.). Among its churches some have revealed splendid mosaic floors with animal motives from the Byzantine period, which will be discussed later, together with the beautiful contemporaneous animal mosaics from churches and synagogues at Gerasa and at Medeba in Transjordan.

The excavations of Beth-shan are of special interest in connection with the many ritual objects ornamented with serpents. It is often, and apparently rightly, assumed that the name Beth-shan itself means "house of the serpent", and that shan be connected with Shanan, the Semitic name of an old Sumerian serpent-deity. Many plaques with serpents (14th century B.C.) are doubtless indigenous. Upon a bowl an undulating serpent is depicted, and a a pottery model of a serpent has female breasts and a cup below for collecting the (or for ritual offering of) milk (COOK 1930 p. 38; ROWE pl. 45A. 4).

But the most interesting objects are a number of hollow vessels or incense shrines with snakes (pl. XXI). There is a three storey shrine with a seated goddess (with two doves?) on the top storey; two males or gods are fighting on the middle storey, together with a dove and a lion (or lioness); below a snake moves with its head towards the dove of the central storey (ROWE pl. 56 A. 3). ROWE supposes that the serpent is connected with Tammuz, the doves with Ashthoret. He suggests that the god at the left of the central storey be actually Tammuz. The serpent's head almost touches its feet. Also the hollow cylinders with snakes are connected by ROWE to sacred rites associated with agriculture, especially with the well-known "gardens of Adonis". These consisted of pottery vessels or baskets filled with earth in which wheat, vegetables and flowers were placed and watered. Originally they were a sympathetic magic for the promotion of growth and the renewal of vegetation *). This agrees with Isaiah (17 : 10): Therefore shalt thou plant pleasant plants and shalt set it with strange slips . . . . ROWE connects the slit in the cylinders with female genitals and fertility. "The dove inside the aperture would perhaps represent the allegoric birth of Ashtoret as dove from the underworld, bringing with her Tammuz, the serpent: the revival and ripening of the vegetation after its winter decay. Doves and serpents were commonly associated with Astarte, but although no direct evidence is forthcoming that the serpent was ever connected with Tammuz, the hypothesis seems not improbable. The serpent on the cylinders certainly seems to be a benevolent and not a malevolent one" (ROWE 1941 p. 53). The serpent is also one of the animals connected with the Egyptian god Seth (ROWE 1928 p. 89).

Snakes are common in other ancient traditions, and not all of them are connected with a serpent cult of this type. The most important snake traditions may be briefly surveyed as follows:

Snakes belong to the oldest ornaments on pottery. They first appear at the pottery of Teleilat Ghassul. Snakes are common on certain types of Canaanite ritual vessels, as well as in connection with certain gods in Egypt and in Mesopotamia. In Ugarit they are connected with the goddess. At Tell Beth Mirsim we find a snake crawling over the leg of the goddess. ALBRIGHT explains the snake head pointing to the vulva of this and other representations as a symbol of fertilisation. Snakes are also common on pottery vessels for the domestic cult during the bronze and iron ages.

We recall the episode of the brass snake in Numbers 21 : 6-9, the view of which saved from death those who were bitten by the fiery serpents, sent by God in punishment. This episode is recalled in II Kings 18 : 4, where HEZEKIAH removed the high places, and broke the images, and cut down the groves, and broke in pieces the brass serpent that MOSES had made: for unto those days the children of Israel did burn incense to it: and they called it Nehushtan. In this connection two archaeological finds are of special interest. MACALISTER (1903 fig. 13) found in the fosse of offerings of the high place at Gezer a brass snake among other votive objects. He dates it to the 15th century B.C. From its swollen neck it is obvious that this snake is an asp. In the collection of Mr. R. JONAH at Jerusalem is an iron

---

*) See also BAUMGARTEN, 1940.

snake, here and there coiled vertically, which was found in the valley of Ayalon. It almost certainly belongs to the Israelite period. The serpent's neck is not swollen. But nevertheless it may represent an asp or one of the common non-poisonous snakes, such as *Coluber asianus*. Similar snakes, but straight moving in slight lateral waves, are found at Susa (Morgan in Vincent 1907 p. 175 f. 121). Another common type of snakes is found on cylindrical jars with windows and often with two handles. Those incense vessels with plastic snakes crawling over the surface of the jar are common, at Beth-shan, at Megiddo, at Shechem (12th century B.C.). These were cult vessels in temples as well as for domestic cult. At the same period there appear clay-houses with many windows, in which gods, men or birds were sitting, whilst snakes crawl about the outer walls, where also lion reliefs are found. WATZINGER (1933 p. 70) connects these houses with the Ishtar cult.

These snakes are often regarded as relics of a local snake-cult. VINCENT thinks that the snakes were only attributes of pernicious forces, which should be favourably influenced (1907 p. 176). Also SELLIN regards the snake-figurines of Ta'annek (16th century B.C.) as protective amulets in houses. We agree with this opinion. ALBRIGHT's opinion just quoted also regards the serpents as attributes of the goddess Astarte only.

ALBRIGHT (1942 p. 189) also discusses, in connection with BÖHL's discovery at Shechem of a 16th century B.C. plaque (BÖHL, ZDPV 1938 p. 1, pl. I), the probability that the thick fringe of the robe of the goddess is sometimes a stylized serpent.

3. 55. MEGIDDO AND KING SOLOMON

The excavations of the Oriental Institute of Chicago at Megiddo, a monumental undertaking of wide aims and performed with the most modern methods, is, after 14 years of work (1925 to 1939) under the direction of FISHER, GUY and LOUD, only half-way its projected scope. The occupation of the town lasted from the Neolithicum until about 450 B.C., when the neighbouring town of Lejjun took its place.

Most interesting is the identification of its animal remains throughout the ages of occupation (BATE, 1939 p. 209; 1946 no. 26, p. 4). Miss BATE gives their stratification as follows:

Neolithicum:	small, ox, sheep and/or goat, gazelle, pig;
Chalcolithicum:	small *Equus,* small ox, sheep and/or goat, gazelle, pig, dog (or jackal), lion, bear;
Chalcolithicum to early Bronze:	small *Equus,* small ox, mamber goat, large horned sheep, pig, dog (or jackal);
Middle and Late Bronze:	small *Equus,* small ox, sheep and/or goat, pig;
Pre-Roman:	small ox.

The bones of a small *Equus sp.* are quite common in some tombs. They belong either to an animal of the *hemionus*-group or to a true ass. Nothing points to domestication. In one tomb (T 903) some limb bones possibly belong to a true horse.

The cattle was certainly domesticated, as no wild cattle of small stature is known from the Middle East. In contrast to the experience at Gezer, there was apparently at Megiddo one race of domestic cattle only from the Neolithic to the Pre-Roman strata: a small sized race, apparently with short horns and similar to *Bos longifrons*. Miss BATE points out that in the absence of a small domestic ox in the Mesolithic deposits of Palestine, this race was probably introduced by Neolithic immigrants into the country.

The very abundant bones of goats and sheep are usually too fragmentary for identification. But one twisted horn belongs doubtless to the local mamber goat, which originated apparently in Syria. Old records of this goat are available from Ur and Kish (Antiquity 1937 p. 226 pl. V), in Egypt from Neolithic to Hellenistic times (GAILLARD 1934 p. 78; LORTET and GAILLARD 1903 p. 106). The remains of "millions of animals" were discovered by Sir MARK SYKES near Hebemieh in the Jebel Druze forming a hill of lava-cemented bones, three acres in extent and over three metres high. Miss BATE determined these bones as belonging to the same race as the mamber goat of Megiddo. The bones must have been accumulated before the lava flow, which therefore must have taken place rather recently. It is too early to interpret this bone-hill as a kitchen midden or as big sacrificial mound. The date as well as the object of this accumulation, remain still obscure.

It may even be a big herd killed by the volcanic eruption. Only a few of the Megiddo bones can be definitely ascribed to a large sheep. The ventral side of a spiral horn core is gently rounded, not keeled as in the recent *Ovis vignei*. It differs from the horn cores of wild sheep, but resembles those from a late deposit at Badari. Miss Bate assumes therefore that it belongs to a domestic race (fig. 40).

Pig remains occur in almost all layers. The small size of the bones suggests a domestic race.

Skull fragments of *Canis sp.*, from a skull of jackal-size, probably belong to a domestic dog. The apparent shortening of the skull and of the mandible point in this direction; but further material is needed.

The distal end of a humerus is the only remains of a lion in a chalcolithic tomb (T 903). In the same tomb a single imperfect humerus of a large Syrian bear was found.

A few animals appear on Chalcolithic pottery (ENGBERG and SHIPTON 1934). The scratched figures of a stag, an ibex and a ?baboon are recognisable on some potsherds. Some stylized animals appear as impressions of cylindrical seals on some pottery jars (fig. 43).

The central importance of Megiddo in the Egyptian conquest of the XIXth dynasty has been mentioned before. An interesting locust seal found at Megiddo will be discussed later (STAPLES 1932). The most conspicuous finds of the Egyptian period are the ivory carvings from a palace, probably collected by an art-loving governor. Their manufacture is dated by LOUD (1939) from about 1325 to 1160 B.C. Ivory was an old object of international trade of the Phoenicians, the Canaanites and of the peoples of the Aegeis (GALLING 1937 p. 142). Study of the Samaria ivory by experts has revealed from its granular structure that the rough material were tusks of the African, not of the local Indian elephant (CRAWFOOT). The Syrian elephant was not abundant enough any more in historical times to be the object of an important trade and ivory manufacture. In spite of all foreign influences, Egyptian as well as Mesopotamian, with regard to motives, there is no question about their being locally manufactured. The tusks were imported via Arabia from Abyssinia.

Fig. 41 gives a good impression of the beauty and wealth of the Megiddo ivory works.

Among the most important results of the excavations of the Solomonic palace (about 950 B.C.) was the discovery of extensive horse stables. Trading of horses and chariots was doubtless an important business of Solomon. Albright (1942 p. 135) even thinks that he held a practical monopoly of this trade through his domination of the normal trade routes. These stables are described by Watzinger (1936) and by McCowN (1943 p. 179) as follows: The stables "were built on a standardized plan and stretch out in regular rows and sections on both sides of the great central street. On each side of a hard lime passageway are rows of stalls set face to face and paved with cobblestones. At the head of each stall was a stone manger and on each side of it a stone pillar which served both as tie post and a support for the roof. In a corner of the pillar toward the passage is a hole for the tie rope. Usually the stalls are in groups of twenty-four each, thus making twelve chariots the size of a squadron. In the north stables were ten such ones and two stables with room for thirty horses each. On the south side of the mound were five more stables, each for thirty horses. Here there was also a great court or parade ground. Altogether 450 or more stalls have been found." Following this discovery it was found that many pillars, assumed hitherto to be sacred pillars or masseboth in various excavations, such as Ta'annek, Tell el-Farah, Tell el-Hesi, Tell el-Qedah (Hazor) are really pillars of similar horse stables." Thus evidence for SOLOMON's chariots and 12 000 chariot horses and for chariot cities from Beersheba almost to Dan accumulates. It is not likely that 12 000 stalls could be found, and surely not all of those discovered were built by SOLOMON, but enough have been found to substantiate I Kings (10 : 26-29), that SOLOMON was a great horse trader, accumulating a force of no mean proportion for the defence of his kingdom and at the same time using the increase from his stables to add to his wealth. The discovery of the same telltale rows of pillars at Gezer, Megiddo and Hazor exactly agrees with the statement in I Kings that SOLOMON built, or rather rebuilt, these three cities."

ALBRIGHT (1943; cf. also PEET 1924) translates the quoted passage, strongly supported by the text of the Septuaginta: "And SOLOMON's horses were exported from Cilicia: the merchants of the king procured them from Cilicia at the current price; and a chariot was exported from Egypt at the rate of 600 shekels of silver and a horse from Cilicia at the rate of 150; and thus (at this rate) they delivered them by their agency to all the kings of the Hittites and the kings of Aram." The important change is the translation for the land of horse export as being Cilicia instead of Egypt. This change well agrees with other documents, which mention the Cilician horse as being the best horse of that period. The famous horse-breeding centres of Arabia and Irak are of much later date. The oldest document mentioning horses from Arabia at all is a record of SARGON on tribute received from ITAMAR the Sabaean in the 8th century B.C., where gold and horses are mentioned. It is rather questionable, if horses were bred in any considerable number in ancient Egypt before the Hellenistic age. MEYER (1912) interprets the passage of Deuteronomy 17 : 16: "But he shall not multiply horses for himself (the King of Judah, about 620 B.C.), nor cause the people to return to Egypt, to the end that he should multiply horses" when describing a bartering trade between the kings of Judah and of Egypt, which exchanged Jewish mercenaries for Egyptian horses (cf. Elephantine). The possibility exists that since the Hyksos, or at least during the reign of the Hyksos, horses were bred in Egypt for the army.

Interesting is the fact that the stables of the Solomonic period were apparently built for chariot horses only. Cavalry horses are not mentioned, although this arm of service was developed at that time in Assyria.

At Megiddo a stele was found of SHESHONK, the SHISHAK of the Bible, who looted or occupied the town during the reign of REHOBEAM. MCCOWN (1943 p. 171) even suggests that this very campaign was held in quest of the horses of Megiddo.

The earlier excavations of Megiddo or Tell el Mutesellim by SCHUMACHER and BENZINGER (1903 to 1905) had brought to light a most beautiful lion seal with the inscription: SHEMA, the servant of REHOBEAM (pl. XXVI).

In this connection we propose to discuss some more details about King SOLOMON. His position in the legend of all peoples of the country will be mentioned on various occasions. His rule indicates a peak of local civilisation. We may first mention the trade and training of horses and chariots for the army by quoting (I. Kings 10 : 26): And SOLOMON gathered together chariots and horses: and he had 1400 chariots and 12.000 horses, which he bestowed in the cities for chariots, and with the king at Jerusalem.

N. GLÜCK (1940 p. 50 ff., 89 ff.) has described SOLOMON's copper mines in the Wadi

Araba and the Red Sea port Ezion Geber, from which ships were sent to Ophir. Once in three years the navy came to this port loaden with gold and silver, ivory and monkeys. The *"qofim we-tukim"* (I Kings 10 : 22) were usually translated as monkeys and peacocks (or parrots). Yet the ivory was doubtless of East-African origin. This makes the traditional translation for *tukim* improbable. ALBRIGHT (1942 p. 212) has given a better interpretation to the *tukim*. In the old Egyptian story of the Shipwrecked Sailor (about 1900 B.C.) the serpent-king of Punt gives the sailor precious presents, including ivory and, at the end of the list, two kinds of monkeys (*gf* and *ky*). *Gf* is doubtless the same as the Hebrew *qof*, *ky* being identical with *tuki*. Also the scene of this Egyptian story lays somewhere in East-Africa.

In order to describe the splendour of SOLOMON's court the daily provisions are listed, among which we find: ten fattened oxen, twenty oxen out of the pastures, a hundred sheep, being identical with *tuki*. Also the scene of this Egyptian story lays somewhere in East-Africa. almost always been referred to fowl. We agree with this interpretation (BODENHEIMER 1946), in spite of the use of the word *avussim* being as a rule apparently reserved for the fattening of mammals by the trough. The sequence almost certainly excludes a mammal. UNGNAD's connection of *barbur* with the Accadian berberu (wolf) makes no sense, as wolves were neither fattened nor permitted as food. The context obviously refers to a common dish. Translations such as swans can therefore be dismissed. Domestic fowl was, if kept in some quantity, used mainly for the eggs. Ducks and rock-partridges were caught by snares and in other ways of game, but they certainly were not fattened. Yet the goose was a very common food in Egypt since ancient times (A. WIEDEMANN 1920 p. 292). Goose-cramming is depicted on some tombs of Sakkara. Goose-keeping is also represented in one of the ivories of the 11th century at Megiddo (fig. 41, 1). And it was known in the Odyssee as a domestic bird. On all those lines of argument we come to the conclusion that the "barburim avussim" can only refer to fattened geese.

We have mentioned before the bulls and the lions on the vessels of the temple of SOLOMON (I Kings 7). On the throne of his palace, which was of ivory overlaid with gold we find two lions beside the steps (I Kings 10 : 18-20). In the long prayer on the opening of the temple we heard the request that God may listen and fulfil all prayers in times of famine, of pestilence, of blasting and mildew (*shidaphon* and *jerakon*), of the arrival of the flying and of the hopping locusts, etc. (I Kings 8 : 37-39).

And the description of his wisdom shows, that legends had been formed even during or shortly after his period (I Kings 4 : 33): And he spake to trees, from the cedar tree of the Lebanon even unto the hyssop that springeth out of the wall. He spoke also to the beasts, and to the birds, and to the creeping animals, and to the fishes.

3. 56. SAMARIA

Samaria or Sebaste, the ancient capital of the northern kingdom, excavated by a Havard University expedition, shows traces of an early Bronze settlement. But the town was founded about 875 B.C. by Omri and existed until the Crusader period. In this sequence the destruction by SARGON in 722 B.C. was a mere episode. Samaria is repeatedly mentioned in the Bible in connection with its highly developed art of ivory carving. In I Kings (22 : 39) reference is made to "the ivory house which AHAB made". And AMOS thunders against the "beds of ivory upon which they lie" (6 : 4) and announces that "the houses of ivory shall perish" (3 : 15). Now a great deal of fragments of highly artistic ivory carvings and inlays were found all over the town in the Israelite stratum. They were used as ornaments and inlays on furniture and on wooden walls. Beds and walls with ivory and inlay of a very similar character have also been discovered in N. Syria, especially at Arslan Tash. These are dated to King HAZAEL (about 842 B.C.). The Samaria ivories belong to the same period and to the same school of artists. A piece of unworked ivory was also excavated. There is not the slightest doubt about the local provenance of these carvings. Their motives show strong Egyptian and Mesopotamian influences. Some of the most beautiful carvings were apparently covered with a thin layer of gold (those from the beds, for instance), others had polychrome inlays. Among the animal motives we mention some lion half-reliefs forming part of the decoration of a luxury bedstand. Battling animals include a beautiful fight between lion and bull. A fine piece of work of Mesopotamian influence is the scene of pasturing stags. All these ivories have been adequately published by the CROWFOOTS. Pl. XXII shows some of the most pretty animal ivories. A great number of ivory fragments was found near the centre of the northern city wall. McCOWN (1943 p. 197) takes this as possible evidence that the "house of ivory" stood near the northern side of the hill. We have mentioned before that in expert judgement the ivories of Samaria have been worked from tusks of the African, not of the Indian elephant.

3.6. ASSYRIAN INFLUENCES IN THE FIRST MILLENNIUM B.C.

The dominance of Egypt declined during the first millennium B.C. For some centuries still Egypt struggles with Assyria, the rising empire. Towards the later part of the millennium Persians, Greeks and Romans are the dominating political forces. The Bible is in many ways the most comprehensive document of the animal life in this period. Before letting pass before our eyes an adequate epitome of this source, we will discuss a number of foreign documents and influences.

In these centuries the annals of the Assyrian kings are a valuable source for wars in Syria/Palestine, some of which we quote from GRESSMANN (1909 I p. 108 ff): ASSURBANIPAL records (about 870 B.C.):

> At that time I marched along the Lebanon unto the big Sea of the land of Amuru. In the big sea I cleaned my weapons and sacrificed to my Gods. I received tribute from the kings of the shores of the sea, from Tyre, Sidon, Byblos, Mahallat, Maisa, Kaisa, of Amurru and Arwad in the sea: silver, gold, lead, copper, copper vessels, multicoloured cloths, linen, a big pagutu (animal), wood from Ushu and Urkarinnu trees, the teeth of a big whale. I climbed into the Hamanu mountains and cut wood of cedars, cypresses, junipers and pines....

SALMANASSAR II (about 854):

From Aleppo I approached ..... Karkara, which I destroyed and burned. They were supported by 1200 chariots, 1200 cavalry and 20 000 foot-soldiers from Damascus, 700 chariots, 700 riders and 10 000 footsoldiers from Hamat, 2000 chariots, 10 000 foot-soldiers from Ahabbu, the Shirilaean (read: Ahab of Israel) .... and by 1000 camels of the Arab Gindibu.

The black obelisk from Nimrud describes this expedition much shorter. This monument may be described here, as it contains a number of interesting animals. The illustrations are arranged in five rows with one picture on every side. The first row describes the tribute of Sua of Gilzan (silver, gold, lead, vessels of copper, horses and two-humped camels), the second four pictures with the tribute of IAUA (JEHU) the son of HUMRI (OMRI). But HUMRI was the Assyrian name for the territory of Israel (silver, gold, lead and bowls, dishes, cups and other vessels of gold). The third row illustrates the tribute of Musri (part of Cilicia), which consists of two Bactrian camels, wild bull, unicorn and wild goat, Syrian elephant, followed by four monkeys with humanized faces. Row four with the tribute of the land of Sukhu begins with a landscape, a mountain forest with a pair of lions and fallow deer, and the usual tribute, among which ivory, also figures, as is the case in the fifth row with the tribute .of Khattina.

On his second campain against Damascus SALMANASSAR II (849 B.C.) received the following tribute from Patin: silver, gold, lead, horses, cattle, sheep, clothes and linen. He climbed the Hamanu mountains and cut cedarlogs.

Tiglatpileser IV (738 B.C.) received the following tribute from the kings KUMMUH, Damaskus, from MENAKHEM of Samaria, of Tyre, Byblos ... and from two kings of Arabia: gold, silver, lead, iron, elephant skins, elephant tusks, coloured clothes, linen, clothes dyed in violet and in red purple, wood of Ushu and Urkarinnu trees, many precious objects, many sheep, the furs of which were dyed in red purple, feathered birds of heaven, the wings dyed in violet purple, horses, mules, cattle, sheep and goats, camels and she-camels with their fillies. Similar tribute was obtained in Palestine which he invaded in 733/32 B.C. attaining in the south to Askalon and Gaza. SARGON destroyed Samaria in 722 B.C. and made campaigns to the far south of Palestine in the following years.

King SENNACHERIB laid siege to Jerusalem (701 B.C.). His own report on this feat is:

> And Hazakiau of Juda had not subjected himself to my yoke. 46 of his walled fortresses and the small towns around them did I lay siege to exposing them to the work of my siege-machines, by the fight of my foot-soldiers, by mines, breaches and ...., and I occupied them all. 200.150 men, big and small, men and women, horses, mules, asses, camels, cattle and sheep without number did I catch there as my prey. The king himself was enclosed in Jerusalem, his capital like a bird in its cage. I erected bulwarks and I punished whoever left the town. The conquered towns I separated from his country and gave them to the kings of Asdod, Amkarruna and Gaza, and thus reduced his kingdom... But Hazakiau was smitten by the fear of the splendour of my power. His allies took flight. He ordered to bring into my residence at Niniveh 30 talents of gold, 800 talents of silver, jewels, cosmetics, ivory beds and ivory thrones, elephant skins and ivory, wood of Ushu and Urkarinnu trees, his daughters and their servants, and musicians of both sexes. He sent a special ambassador to me to pay me hommage.

In this report it is not mentioned that King SENNACHERIB had to give up the siege of Jerusalem by reason of an epidemic disease:

> „And it came to pass that night that the angel of the Lord went out, and smote in the camp of the Assyrians 185.000 men: and when they arouse early in the morning, behold, they were all dead corpses. Sennacherib king of Assyria departed, and went and returned, and dwelt at Nineveh." And as he was worshipping in the temple of his God, two of his sons killed him and Esarhaddon his son reigned in his stead. (II Kings 19, 35, 36, 37).

According to Herodotus (2 : 141) Sennacherib had marched with his main force to attack Egypt and both armies camped at Pelusium. There a vast army of mice devoured the bow-strings and shield-thongs of the Assyrians, so that morning found them an unarmed prey to the Egyptians. PEET (1924) makes an understatement when he says that it is tempting to see in them the record of the same event. If there was a plague before Jerusalem, its character is entirely unknown. It may have been typhus as well as bubonic plague or something very different, even a form of Spanish influenza. It is just as possible that some disease, and then the mention of mice would suggest bubonic plague, or other disaster prevented continued action of the main force and the small besieging-army of Jerusalem was ordered back during the return of the main army to Ashur, after some kind of contract was made with Hezekiah.

On their expeditions to Arabia and into Egypt the Assyrian rulers learned to fear desert expeditions. Some Arabian princes took flight before SENACHERIB to Adummatu, whose place is a place of thirst without food and cisterns. Or the Sinai march of ESARHADDON (670 B.C.) to Egypt: He collected camels "without number", snakes with two heads (horns?) caused damage, the pointed stones of the desert caused wounds, until finally the frontier was reached. Finally we mention a stele of NEBUKADNEZAR (ab. 585 B.C.) for his care of the cedars of the Lebanon and the erection of his portrait as a sign of his special protection of the people of the Lebanon, that they may live quietly and furnish him with cedar logs.

The powerful language of the Assyrian kings is amply illustrated by their inscriptions, which often use animals as parables, of which we chose the following selection (All from vol. 2 of D. D. LUCKENBILL, *Ancient Records* 1927): SARGON (724-705 B.C.):

> 2, 22: And with his own dagger he stabbed himself through the heart, like a pig.
> 2, 39: I caused my picked fighters to fly across the ditches like eagles.
> 2, 67: Like a rat(?) he crept along the side of the city wall and entered his city.
> 2, 118: (Sargon), the mighty in battle, who caught the Ionians out of the midst of the sea in shoals(?) like fish.
> 2, 126: (The gods may) make firm his dynasty, keep his steeds fit, his teams well preserved .....

2, 142: I kept at the head of my army and made my chariots, cavalry and infantry fly over that (peak) like brave eagles ... The camels and bagages asses scrambled to the summit of the peak like wild goats, natives of the mountains.

2, 154: His warriors I slaughtered about his feet like lambs.

2, 155: Like (an animal) flewing before the hunter, he trod the slope of his mountain.

2, 158: Like swarming locusts I turned the beasts of my camps into its meadows, and they tore up the vegetation on which they depended, they devastated their plain (cf. also 2, 163).

2, 164: My brave warriors cast themselves on the mountain sides, like stray sheep. With the widespreading armies of Assur I covered all their cities like locusts.

SENNACHERIB (705-681 B.C.):

2, 242: I loaded them into ships and fled like a bird to the city of Nagitarakki, which is in the midst of the sea.

2, 244: Like a young ibex I mounted the high peaks in pursuit of them.

2, 252: Like the onset of the locust swarms of the spring-time they kept steadily coming on against me to offer battle.

2, 254: The terror of my battle overpowered their bodies like a bull.

2, 256: Sennacherib, the mighty king, ... the prayerful shepherd ....

2, 259: I raged like a lion, I stormed like a tempest ...

2, 263: Bel-ikri, son of a master-builder, who had grown up in my palace like a puppy.

2, 277: In the midst of the high mountains of the Kassites I rode on horseback, where the terrain was difficult, and had my chariot drawn up with ropes; where it became too steep, I clambered up on foot like a wild-ox.

2, 296 (and 2, 316): Where it was too steep for my (sedan) chair, I advanced on foot like a young ibex.

2, 316: Whose abodes are situated on the peaks of Mt. Nippur, a difficult mountain, like the nests of the eagle.

ESARHADDON (680-669 B.C.):

2, 509: The seditious rebel heared of the advance of my hosts and fled to Elam like a jackal (written: fox).

2, 511: Like a fish I caught (the king of Sidon) out of the sea and cut off his head.

2, 513: Like a bird I snared him out of (his) mountain and cut off his head.

2, 515: Beside the gate inside the city of Niniveh (I kept him tied along with) dogs and swine.

2, 521: The gods in whom they trusted, captives ... like sheep I carried away.

2, 550: By (the side of the gate of Niniveh) I tied him up like(?) a pig, in chains.

2, 668: The trustworthy shepherd, who shepherds the black-headed (Assyrians).

2, 740: In war and battle fight furiously at my side, let me wipe out my foes like ants!

ASSURBANIPAL (668-626 B.C.):

2, 795: Their dismembered flesh I fed to the dogs, swine, wolves and vultures, to the birds of heaven and the fish of the deep.

2, 819: I put him into a kennel. With jackals(?) and dogs I tied him up and made him guard the gate in Niniveh.

2, 823: Across the parched and thirsty desert, wherein no bird of heaven is seen, in which no onagers or gazelles graze for a stretch of 100 double hours from Niniveh... Between the cities of Iarki and Asella, in the desert, a far-off place, where there are no animals of the plain and (where) the birds of heaven build no nests, I defeated the tribe of the Isamme' ... People, asses, camels and sheep in countless numbers I took from them as booty.

2, 827: Through thirst and deprivation they perished. Those who were left ripped open their riding-camels and, (to quench) their thirst, drank the blood and the urine.

2, 829: Through the jaw of his face I passed a rope, put a dog chain upon him and made him occupy a kennel of the east gate of Niniveh.

2, 832: From out of the mountains, his place of refuge, whither he had flown, I hunted him like a falcon(?) and took him alive to Assur.

2, 855: The Elamite is covering Akkad like a dense(?) swarm of locusts.

2, 857: Bel-ikishe, who had cast off the yoke of my rule, lost his life through the bite of a wild boar.

2, 989: The gods of Sumer and Akkad, like whimpering puppies(?), deported themselves strangely before him.

2, 1109: Their flesh I fed to the vultures.

ASSURBANIPAL conquered TIRHAKAH, the king of Kush: Gold, silver, ... mighty horses, people, male and female, monkeys(?), apes(?), giraffes (wrongly proposed for: okapis(?)), they brought out of his gates (2, 917). And Ikkilu, king of Arvad, whose abode, like that of a fish, is in the unmeasured waters, made his submission. The (payment of) gold, dark-red wool, black wool, fish and birds, I imposed upon him as annual tribute (2, 912). ASSURBANIPAL also left a number of hunting records:

2, 935: Since I took my seat upon the throne of the father who begot me, Adad has sent his rains, Ea has opened up his fountains, the forests have been thriving exceedingly, the reeds of the marshes have shot up so high there is no getting through them. The young of the lions throve therein, in countless numbers, .. They became fierce and terrible through their devouring of herds, flocks and people. With their roaring the hills resound, the beasts of the plain are terrified. They keep bringing down the cattle of the plain, they (keep) shedding the blood of men. As if the plague had broken loose, there were heaped up the corpses of dead men, cattle and (sheep). The shepherds and herdsmen weep at the lions... The villages are in mourning day and night. Of the deeds of these lions they told me. In the course of my march (campaign), into ... their lairs I broke up......

3.7. THE OLD TESTAMENT AND ITS ANIMALS

3.71. THE OLD TESTAMENT AS SOURCE OF ANIMAL LIFE

The Old Testament is to some a book of revelation, to others a historical literary document, which was written down, after centuries of oral tradition, since the beginning of the 9th century B.C. The oldest books of the Bible are composed of various old sources, which are defined since the 9th century A.D. as the Jehovah or Judaean report (J), the Elohim or Ephraimite report, representing the often divergent traditions of the Northern and the Southern kingdom (E), a unification from both these sources about 722 B.C. (JE) and the priestly code (P). The oldest source (J) was written down in the early 9th century, the Ephraimite code slightly later. The priestly code was written by a school of priests and is mainly concerned with the ritual and with the teachings and institutions of theocracy. Its final wording took place after the restitution in 537 B.C. (DRIVER and PEAKE 1929). A final wording of the Hebrew text was apparently performed by a synod about 100 A.D., after the fall of Jerusalem (KENYON 1936). It seems that this same synod also established rules in order to ensure accurate copying of the sacred text. Since that date probably minor changes only in the Hebrew text have occurred. Many allusions and words were obscure even at that period. The excavations of Ras Shamra and of Assyria recently have helped to get a correct interpretation of many of such obscure sentences and words. Especially H. TORCZYNER deserves much commendation for his work in this field. Translations into Greek, Aramaic, and other languages date back to the 3rd century B.C., when Ptolemy arranged for the famous Septuaginta- translation at Alexandria, and somewhat later the Aramaic Peshitta. Both these translations as well as the famous Samaritan Pentateuch were made many centuries before the final wording of the Bible. Hebrew texts were used, which in many places differed considerably from the later codified Hebrew text, even if minor differences may be ascribed to free translation. The oldest preserved Hebrew manuscripts of the Old Testament dated only from the 9th century A.D., of course till some books were discovered recently in the famous scrolls (2nd or 1st cent. B.C.; SUKENIK 1948). Some Greek manuscripts go back to the 4th and 5th centuries A.D., such as the *Codex Sinaiticus,* the *Codex Vaticanus* and the *Codex Alexandrinus.* Comprehensive fragments of an earlier Greek text, the Chester Beatty papyri, dating from about 140 A.D., have recently been discovered.

Whilst many nomad and semi-nomad traditions from the period preceding the conquest of Palestine are preserved in the two older codes, the priest code refers to the period of fixed agriculture, apart from its interest being concentrated on questions of ritual mainly. It should be added however that this separation of ancient Bible sources into Jahve, Elohim, Priest code, etc. texts is strongly refuted by U. CASSUTO. In an authoritative study on the question of the Genesis (1934) he points out, that an abundance of traditions of various origins, characters and aims had accumulated in the culture of early Israel, intermixed, often in variations of its own, with the original cultural creations of Israel, all transmitted orally from generation to generation, with even active transformation during this transmission, and that even the official wording of the Bible contains only a small selection of these traditions. The wealth of variations of well-known Biblical subjects in the early midrashim is ample proof for this restriction. Of course, many of these traditions have their source in the special tribal traditions which were formed under different conditions of regional history and of cultural contacts. The decision whether the wording of the Thorah was a mere unification of pre-existing separate texts, which can be recognised by simple philological criteria, or whether it represented a real creation drawing from the manifoldness of Israel's tradition must be left to future research.

A colleague in botany, in a recent discussion about the Old Testament expressed his great desillusion and disappointment about the little amount of natural history and of the conspicuous lack of interest in nature. He maintained that the old writers had a very low knowledge of and little gift for observation of nature and of natural things. We cannot agree with this judgement. First of all it was not the aim of any of the Books of the Bible to elucidate or describe and compile natural phenomena. These books were written as historical, religious, theological, political, moral or poetical works. It is unjust to measure the knowledge of a people and of a period from the natural knowledge expressed in books of that type. How poor would the splendid early zoology of the Greeks be, when we should have to reconstruct them from the works of HOMER, of SAPPHO, of THUCYDIDES and of PLATO! There cannot be the slightest doubt that these old nomads had no better and no worse measure of observation and experience with regard to the fauna and flora of their environment than the ageless oral tradition of all recent nomads in Asia and Africa possesses. And what wealth of sayings, fables, omina, etc. do we find among all the various fellaheen populations of the Middle East, whether they are Semites or non-Semites; this wealth, which is based on a co-ordination of phenomenological correlation and of splendid observation, was accumulated and transmitted throughout many centuries. DALMAN has recently compiled the current agricultural and natural history tradition of the Palestine peasants, which often still are identical with similar traditions alluded to in the scriptures. If few of the earlier sayings on animals and plants have penetrated the codified text, another collateral reason explains this easily. The codifying priests of the 7th and 6th century B.C., with only one aim before their eyes, namely to serve the establishment of a theocracy, were not much interested in nature, and almost certainly they were just the class farthest away from nature, with exceptions of course, with the lowest knowledge of natural history and regarding natural observation as futile. In many cases the sense of the oral tradition referring to observations from the nomad period was obscure to them. We have analysed such a situation step by step for the manna tradition of the Exodus (BODENHEIMER 1929): every description of the older codes fits the facts, whilst the additions of the priest code often make no sense at all.

Anyhow, the writer is confident that many, and perhaps most, observant readers of the Bible will agree with him that even thus the wealth of animal and plant lore in the Bible is by no means to be belittled. We refer to the careful and pleasant compilations and commentaries of Canon TRISTRAM (Natural History of the Bible), of A. WÜNSCHE (1906), and others. In referring to these extensive studies we feel no need to give exhaustive quotations of the animal lore of the Bible in the following pages. We will just select a few descriptions, a few problems. One fact should suffice to warn us, that we are not yet entitled to pass judgement on the natural history of the Old Testament. Apart from the domestic animals we can determine less than 20 % of the animal names of the Old Testament. For a group of similar size we can guess from the context or by philological analysis at an uncertain, but possibly correct interpretation. But the large majority of all animal names of the Old Testament are definitely *nomina nuda*: empty names which cannot be ascribed to any species, and often even not to a definite class of animals. They have been translated somehow, but should much better be reproduced as Hebrew names of unknown meaning in mentioning that it refers to some animal, mammal or bird. And in spite of all these shortcomings the wealth of animal, plant, and stone lore, which is alluded to, is no small one. Many allusions and names remain obscure to us, many were probably obscure to the codifying priests. Many such allusions, parables and allegories may have been discarded even then from the text during the final wording.

These introductory words were needed, as an unjustified enthusiasm on the overwhelming riches of natural history of the Bible, as well as an equally unjustified belittling of it are the two extreme, but most common attitudes encountered. Within reasonable limits we have every reason to delight in the animal lore of the Bible, and to be grateful for the many hints and allusions which have survived the final wording. In this spirit we now turn to this important source itself, leaving only the domestic animals for a later discussion.

3. 72. ANIMAL QUOTATIONS FROM THE OLD TESTAMENT

Mammals. The wild ass, "whose house I have made the wilderness, and the barren land his dwellings. He scorneth the multitude of the city, neither regardeth he the crying of the driver. The range of the mountains is his pasture, and he searcheth after every grey thing" (Job 39, 6-8).

They "be mighty men, and they be chafed in their minds, as a bear robbed of her whelps in the field" (2 Sam. 17, 8).

"The boar out of the wood doth waste it" (Ps. 80, 13).

"The conies are but a feeble folk, yet make they their houses in the rocks" (Prov. 30, 26). "The coney because he cheweth the cud, but divideth not the hoof, he is unclean to you" (Lev. 11, 5).

Jackals are mentioned in the story of Samson, who caught 300 of them and put firebrands between their tails to burn the fields of the Philistines. They are also mentioned as devouring the grapes in the vineyards (Solomon's Song 2, 15).

"Knowest thou the time when the ibex of the rocks bring forth?" (Job 39, 1).

"The high hills are a refuge for the ibex" (Ps. 104, 18).

"The hare, because he chewest the cud, but divideth not the hoof, he is unclean to you" (Lev. 11, 6).

"Let her be as the loving hind and pleasant roe (read: gazelle) (Prov. 5, 19). "As the hart panteth after the water brooks, so panteth my soul after thee, O God" (Ps. 42, 1). "The Lord is my strength, and will make me walk my feet like hinds' feet, and he will make me to walk upon mine high places" (Hab. 3, 19).

"As a leopard by the way will I observe them" (Hos. 13, 7). "Can the Ethiopian change his skin, or the leopard his spots? (Jer. 13, 23).

"A lion is strongest among beasts, and turneth not away for any" (Prov. 30, 30) DAVID, when a youth, had killed both a lion and a bear, when they attacked his father's flock (1 Sam. 17, 36). Ezekiel (19. 4, 8) describes his capture in pits: "He was taken in their pit, and they brought him with chains unto the land of Egypt ... The nations set him ... and spread their net over him: he was taken in their pit" "The lion roared, who will not fear?" (Am. 3, 8). "They shall roar like young lions: yea, they shall roar, and lay hold of the prey, and carry it away safe" (Isa. 5, 29).

Voles were sent as a visitation upon the Philistines, when they retained the ark of the Lord. When the ark was restored, they sent with it five golden voles, images of those which had marred their land (1 Sam. 6).

"Harts and gazelles and fallow-deer and fatted geese" (1 Kings 4, 23) were provided for the table of Solomon. Asahel "was as light of foot as a gazelle" (2 Sam. 2, 18). "Deliver thyself as a gazelle from the hand of the hunter, and as a bird from the hand of the fowler" (Prov. 6, 5).

"Will the aurochs be willing to serve thee, or abide by thy crib? Canst thou bind the aurochs with his band in the furrow? or will he harrow the valleys after thee? Wilt thou trust him, because his strength is great? or wilt thou leave thy labour to him?" (Job 39, 9-11). "He hath the strength of an aurochs" (Numb. 23, 22).

"God created great whales, and every living creature that moveth, which the waters brought forth abundantly, after their kind (Gen. 1, 21). Obviously a whale was also the great fish that swallowed up Jonah (Jon. 1, 17).

"Benjamin shall ravin as a wolf; in the morning he shall devour the prey, and at night he shall divide the spoil" (Gen. 49, 27). In the times of Messiah "the wolf shall dwell with the lamb" (Isa. 11, 6).

Birds. Birds unclean to eat are birds of prey and feeders on carrion and fish (Lev. 11, 13-19). Beautiful are the allusions to seasonal rhythm in bird life: "Yea, the stork in the heaven knoweth her appointed time; and the turtle and the crane and the swallow observe the time of their coming" (Jer. 8, 7). "Lo! the winter is past, the rain is over and gone; the flowers appear on the earth; the time of the singing of birds is come, and the voice of the turtle is heard in our land" (Solomon's Song 2, 11-12). Other general observations of beauty are: "Yea, the sparrow hath found a house, and the swallow a nest for herself, where she may lay her young" (Ps. 84, 3). "As a bird that wandereth from her nest, so is a man that wandereth from his place" (Prov. 27, 8).

Bird snaring was common. "The proud have hid a snare for me and cords; they have spread a net by the wayside; they have set gins for me" (Ps. 140, 5) is only one of the many allusions to this activity. Also decoy birds were used for partridge and pigeons.

The sharp eye of the eagle is alluded to: "There is a path which no fowl knowth, and which the eagle's eye hath not seen" (Job 28, 7). The baldness of the vulture is described in "Make thee bald, and poll thee for thy delicate children; enlarge thy baldness as the vulture" (Micah 1, 16). In deserted places "the owl and the raven shall dwell (Isa. 34, 11). "The screech owl also shall rest there, and find for herself a place of rest" (Isa. 34, 14). Or regarding the raven: "He giveth to the beast his food, and to the young ravens which cry" (Ps. 147, 9). "Like a crane or like a swallow did I chatter" (Isa. 38, 14).

No birds are mentioned more often than the various pigeons and doves. Turtle-doves and pigeons are offerings for various occasions. Yet: "O my dove, that art in the clefts of the rock, in the secret places of the stairs, let me see thy countenance, let me hear thy voice". (Solomon's Song 2, 14). Another mention of the rock-dove is: "O ye that dwell in Moab, leave the cities, and dwell in the rock, and be like the dove that maketh her nest in the sides of the hole's mouth" (Jer. 48, 28).

Partridges were favoured game already in Biblical times: DAVID complains of his persecution by Saul: „The king of Israel is come out to seek a flea, as when one doth hunt a partridge in the mountains" (1 Sam. 26, 20). JEREMIAH (17, 11) compares those collecting riches to "a partridge sitting on eggs, and not hatching them". Its use as decoy bird is alluded to: "Like as a partridge taken and kept in a cage" (Eccles. 9, 30). Some remarks on quails, as well as more details on partridge, are found elsewhere in these notes.

The ostrich, fairly common in the Eastern deserts, is repeatedly mentioned (Job 30, 29) and Micah (1, 8) couples ostriches and dragons; also Isa. 14).

"As for the stork, the cypresses are her house" (Ps. 104, 17).

Reptiles and Amphibia. One famous passage in Job (41) seems to be applicable to the crocodile, as does Ezekiel (29, 3): "Behold, I am against thee, Pharaoh, king of Egypt, the great crocodile that lieth in the midst of his rivers, which hath said: My river is mine own, and I have made it for myself".

Among snakes the following passage is adapted to the cobra: "They are like the cobra that stoppeth her ear; which will not hearken to the voice of charmers, charming never so wisely" (Ps. 58, 5). Another serpent has been identified with the horned snake: "Dan shall be a serpent by the way, an adder in the path that biteth the horse heels, so that his rider shall fall backward" (Gen. 49, 17). "At the last it biteth like a serpent, and stingeth like an adder" (Prov. 23, 32) refers probably to the common Palestine Viper. We are inclined to regard the "viper and fiery flying serpent" (Isa. 30, 6) as being the efa, which in mediaeval tradition has been interpreted in the form of the thyrus snake with similar attributes.

Frogs are only mentioned as the second of the Egyptian plagues.

Fish. Fish without fins or scales are unclean and forbidden to eat. Yet not one of the Palestine fishes was honoured with a Hebrew name in the Bible, whilst such abound in the Talmud. Flavius Josephus (*Bell. Jud.* III, 7, 8) remarks: There are many kinds of fish in the Lake of Galilee, which differ in taste and form from those of other waters... Some have believed that this source of Kapharnaum be an arm of the Nile, as the Korakinos fish (*Clarias lacera*) is found in it, just as in the lake near Alexandria". This resemblance or identity of some fish, such as the cat-fish or the common bream (*Tilapia nilotica*) with those from the Nile, have evoked the interest of many later observers. The presence of a fish-market in ancient Jerusalem results from the name fish-gate (Neh. 3, 3 also Micah). Fishery on the lake of Galilee has become popular through the Apostles who originally were fishermen, and who created many of the most familiar metaphors and symbols of the Christian faith. The great part a fish plays in ancient Christian symbolism, however, has another origin. The Greek initials of "Jesus Christ, Son of God, Saviour" form the word Ichthys, Greek for fish. Drag-nets (Isa. 19, 8; Matt. 13, 47 ff.) and casting-nets (Matt. 4, 18; John 21) were and are used. Also fishing with hook and line (Isa. 19, 8; Matt. 17, 27) and fish spearing (Job 12, 7) were known. And Ezekiel (47, 10) is the first to mention the absence of fish in the Dead Sea. In his messianic prophecy he says: "And it shall come to pass, that the fishers shall stand upon it from Engedi even unto Eneglaim; they shall be a place to spread forth nets; their fish shall be according to their kinds, as the fish of the great sea, exceeding many."

Evertebrate animals. About a snail it is written: "As a snail which melteth, let every one of them pass away" (Ps. 58, 8). Pearls are mentioned several times as jewels in the New Testament (e.g. Matt. 13, 45). The mention of corals (Ez. 27, 16) seems to be slightly doubtful." "The leech has two daughters, crying: give, give!" (Prov. 30, 15). Scorpions were, of course, well-known, e.g. "Who led thee through that great and terrible wilderness, wherein were fiery serpents, and scorpions, and drought?" (Deut. 8, 15). They dwell in ruins and in deserted places. "Their torment was as the torment of a scorpion, when he strikes a man" (Rev. 9, 5). "Whose trust shall be a spider's web"? (Job 8, 14).

Lice and flea, flies and gnats are often mentioned in the Bible, as are insect pests of stores and of the fields (worm, moth, caterpillar).With locusts, bees, manna, Kermes, purple snail we shall deal separately. The other insects mentioned are ants (Prov. 6, 6-8; 30, 24, 25) and hornets (Deut. 7, 20).

3. 73. VOLES, PLAGUES AND WHALES IN THE OLD TESTAMENT

Little can be learned from the Bible about the human epilemics, transmitted by insects. One of the most interesting episodes is found in I Samuel, where a plague amongst the Philistines is described following the abduction of the ark of covenant. The Hebrew text and the Septuaginta show some divergencies:

VERS	HEBREW TEXT	SEPTUAGINTA
5 : 6.	And the hand of the Lord was heavy upon the men of Ashdod, and he destroyed them and smote them with emerods (°afolim), Ashdod and its neighbours.	And the hand of the Lord was heavy upon the men of Ashdod, and he punished them, and exanthemas occurred on their lower body parts. And inmidst of their places grew mice and a great destruction occurred in the town by death.
5 : 9.	...And there was a great disaster in the town and he smote its people, from small to big, and exanthemes broke out of them.	...And there was a great disaster in the town, and he smote them, from small to big, and he stroke them on their buttocks. And they made themselves (cushioned) seats.
6 : 4, 5.	...Wherefore you shall make images of your "emerods" and images of your mice, which destroy the country.	...And you shall make five golden buttocks ... and five golden mice, pictures of those mice which destroy the soil.

This epidemic has always been regarded as a bubonic plague. And the connection with mice was regarded as the first conscientious statement that both are correlated. The Hebrew text, however, does not justify this latter conclusion: the epidemic and the vole outbreak, not uncommon in the Philistine plain, appear as two independent scourges.

Yet even the diagnosis as bubonic plague aske for some remarks. The word °afolim (translated as boils or emerods) remains uncertain. It has been connected with the verb 'afol = project, which may well refer to boils. Nothing is said in the Hebrew text on the location of these boils. The Vulgata, LUTHER and the English Version translate the word jisathru as secret (in their secret parts). It seems, however, actually to be jisatru from splitting, erupting, in that case referring to the eruption of boils. The location of the 'afolim has been translated by the Septuaginta (in 5 : 6) as naus = ships, in the other places as hedras = buttocks. Dr. J. RIVLIN pointed out to us that the word ilfa = ship is used for the entire pelvic region in the Midrash Echa Rabati 1 : 3. This explains the otherwise unexplainable application of the word "ships" in the Septuaginta. Another hint of Prof. M. SCHWABE that ilfa and 'afolim, in spite of their different orthography, are probably the same word, finds support in the translation of the Septuaginta: 'afolim = hedrae (buttocks) (in 6 : 4) for instance. There remains the question of the origin of the addition to verse 5 : 6 in the Septuaginta. Dr. RIVLIN showed us a collection of old midrashim, the Jalkut Shimoni, where mice are connected with the plague in another way: They were supposed to have torn out the intestines from the belly. This clearly indicates that here, as is often, the case an old midrash tradition has been incorporated into the text of the Septuaginta. The connection of mice with the plague seems to be a later interpretation. The medical indications are too few to permit a definite diagnosis of the epidemic. The fact that boils broke out in the pelvic region makes bubonic plague a possible diagnosis (communication of Dr. ULITZKI). In that case the quoted plague would certainly be one of the oldest, if not the oldest, outbreaks of bubonic plague described from Mediterranean countries, long before the classical plague of Athens, described by THUCYDIDES. The connection between bubonic plague of men and rats is through the rat fleas which transmit the bacillus from infected rodents to men. Another historical outbreak of this plague occurred in NAPOLEON's army 150 years ago at Jaffa. Small epidemics occurred in the port towns of Palestine during the last two world wars. Prof. OLITZKI (1955) has shown in the mean time that Microtus is practically immune against *Bacillus pestis*.

The big epidemic which killed 185.000 Assyrian soldiers in one night before Jerusalem in the days of King HEZEKIAH (II Kings 19 : 35), cannot be connected with bubonic plague by any symptom. It may have been any of the big epidemics, so common before in armies, such as typhus, typhoid, cholera, etc.

No definite indication of malaria exists from ancient Palestine, except perhaps the diseases reported in the Middle Kingdom of Egypt of soldiers suffering from fever in the frontier stations of Retenu. RICHARD Cœur-de-Lion suffered heavily from malaria during the crusades. Possibly heavy malaria in normal times was connected with periods of agricultural neglect, as we have pointed out before.

The story of JONAH and the "great fish" (Jonah 1 and 2) has become one of the great legends. Sidi Yunis and Kafr Yunis and other places of burial of the prophet are spread in quantities fom Morocco to Irak. The most authentic tomb is, of course, that near Niniveh (Mosul). "Now the Lord had prepared a great fish to swallow up Jonah. And Jonah was in the belly of the fish three days and three nights .... And the Lord spoke unto the fish, and it vomited out Jonah upon the dry land."

We have not the slightest indication that this story is the report of a real occurrence. There might, however, be a germ of truth in it. Those interpreters who take the story seriously are divided with regard to the nature of the "great fish". Two animals may be connected with the legend. The sperm-whale (*Physeter catodon = Catodon macrocephalus* GRAY) is an Atlantic whale which appears at intervals on the Palestine coast (cf. BODEN-HEIMER 1935 p. 460). NORMAN and FRAZER (1938) say that an intact shark of three meters' length has once been taken out of one of these whales, the males of which reach up to twenty meters' length. It is probable that this shark was swallowed when dead. NORMAN and FRAZER connect this report with JONAH's tale. TH. MONOD (*Mer et Colonies,* August 1942 p. 25) however prefers to relate our story to the man-eating white shark (*Carcharodon rondeletti* M. HLE.), to which LINNAEUS also had ascribed the Biblical report. It seems unbelievable that an man can be swallowed unlacerated by this fish. By rational reasoning we have therefore the choice, to refer the story to a sperm-whale which had swallowed a man or a big animal intact, or to stories about the man-eating sharks, which lacerated their prey. No decision can possibly be made. A similar legend is mentioned by FRAZER (O.T. vol. II.) from New Guinea. Fig. 46 gives a charmingly naive illustration of the story from a mediaeval manuscript. JONAH is first thrown with his clothes into the open mouth of a whale and then vomited out by it quite naked, all his clothes having been digested. A third picture from one of the oldest Byzantine miniatures shows Jonah sitting in the stomach of the whale.

3.8. ANIMAL SACRIFICES IN THE BIBLE

3. 81. THE ISRAELITE SACRIFICES

Sacrifices of domestic and, to a lesser degree, of game animals were a very common usage of all the Semitic Middle East since the third Millennium B.C. The early Phoenician/Canaanite human sacrifice was successively suppressed and substituted by animal sacrifices, yet in Carthage and elsewhere it still persisted until the second half of the first millennium B.C. Many are its traces in the Bible, such as ABRAHAM's sacrifice of Isaac, JEPHTHA's sacrifice of his daughter MIRIAM, the leading of sons through the fire in the time of the monarchy, etc. Similar and other practices, such as child-sacrifices for every new house, were widely in usage in earlier, contemporaneous and later rituals in Canaan, Phoenicia and Carthage. The above mentioned story of ABRAHAM's intended sacrifice of ISAAC (Genes. 22) well indicates the period of substitution of animal for human sacrifice.

Ugaritic (1500 B.C.), Canaanite and late Carthaginian animal sacrifices, they all have a closely related ritual. The Canaanite rites of the 13th century B.C., such as revealed at Lachish or Beth-shan (cf. ALBRIGHT 1940 p. 225) show the most closest resemblance to those of the Priestly code (Leviticus). There has been left little doubt that the settling Israelites accepted part of the local Canaanite sacrificial ritual. Especially in the Northern Kingdom the penetration of the Canaanite ritual, and even gods, was very strong, even at late periods of the monarchy. Consequently there are many divergencies between the Ephraimite and the Judaic code of the Bible. The prophets still have to fight "pagan" Canaanite or Ephraimite conceptions with all their might (cf. also Psalm 106 : 35 ff.). On the other side, there has remained nothing substantial of the ingenious theory of YAHUDA, who tried to demonstrate the derivation of the Hebrew ritual from the Egyptian one. DUSSAUD (1941 p. 151) even suggests that the Egyptians borrowed the holocaust sacrifice (in most Semitic languages: *kalil*) under the name *chalil* from Palestine/Syria.

One of the oldest sacrifices of the Patriarchal age is the sacrifice of the covenant: "And (God) said to him (ABRAHAM): Take me a heifer of three years old, and a ram of three years old, and a turtledove, and a young pigeon. And he took unto him all these and divided them in the midst, and laid each piece one against another; but the birds divided he not (Genes. 15 : 9, 10, Jerem. 34). A similar covenant (*karat brith*) has been found in one of the Ras-Shamra reliefs (with loaves of bread; DUSSAUD 1941 p. 354).

And these are the main animal sacrifices of the Mosaic law:

1. The holocaust (or burnt-offering or olah).

"If his offering be a burnt sacrifice of the herd, let him offer a male without blemish: he shall offer it of his own voluntary will at the door of the tabernacle of the congregation before the Lord. And he shall put his hand upon the head of the burnt offering; and it shall be accepted for him to make atonement for him. And he shall kill the bullock before the Lord: and the priests, Aaron's sons, shall bring the blood, and sprinkle the blood round about upon the altar that is by the door of the tabernacle of the congregation. And he shall flay the burnt offering, and cut it into his pieces. And the sons of Aaron the priests shall put fire upon the altar, and lay the wood in order upon the fire: And the priests, Aaron's sons, shall lay the parts, the head, and the fat, in order upon the wood that is on the fire which is upon the altar: But his inwards and his legs shall he wash in water: and the priest shall burn all on the altar, to be a burnt sacrifice, an offering made by fire, of a sweet savour unto the Lord. And if his offerings be of the flocks, namely of the sheep, or of the goats, for a burnt sacrifice; he shall bring it a male without blemish. And he shall cut it into his pieces, with his head and his fat: and the priest shall lay them in order on the wood that is on the fire which is upon the altar: But he shall wash the inwards and the legs with water: and the priest shall bring it all, and burn it upon the altar: it is a burnt sacrifice, an offering made by fire, of a sweet savour unto the Lord. And if the burnt sacrifice for his offering to the Lord be fowls, then he shall bring his offering of turtledoves, or of young pigeons. And the priest shall bring it unto the altar, and wring off his head, and burn it on the altar; and the blood thereof shall be wrung out at the side of the altar: And he shall pluck away his crop with his feathers, and cast it beside the altar on the east part, by the place of the ashes. And he shall cleave it with the wings thereof, but shall not divide it asunder: and the priest shall burn it upon the altar, upon the wood that is upon the fire: it is a burnt sacrifice, an offering made by fire, of a sweet savour unto the Lord" (Levit. 1 : 3-17).

"And the priest that offereth any man's burnt offering, even the priest shall have to himself the skin of the burnt offering which he has offered" (Levit. 7 : 8). DUSSAUD (1941 p. 72) is of the opinion that the *olah* was only adopted after the settlement of the Israelites in Palestine. The imposing hand of the sacrificer upon the animal at the door of the tabernacle, the smikha, is an old Canaanite-Phoenician rite: by it the soul of the sacrificer enters into the animal, thus offering substitution for the offerer of the olah, and connecting it with God. Conditions necessary for the success of the sacrifice, i.e. its acceptance as atonement or propitiation, are: male sex of an entire and healthy animal, sometimes of a certain age, offered by free will in a certain place to be presented to God, and the smikha. The immolation takes place on the northern altar of the later temple by the sacrificer himself. Later the immolation was performed by the priests (DUSSAUD 1941 p. 74), as is evident from the translation of the Septuaginta. In the early period the priests offered the blood of the victim, or part of it, to God by sprinkling it on and around the altar. The priests bring the fire and arrange the logs on which the quarters of the divided victim are put, its head and its "fat". The smell of the burning victim is agreeable to God. Blood and "fat" play a specially important rôle in the olah, as in all other sacrifices. The blood was collected partly in a bowl and sprinkled around the altar. The blood, believed to be the bearer of the spiritual soul, the ruach, was impregnated with holiness. "The blood with which the life pours out, procures the atonement" (Mishnah, Pessachim). The "fat" (peder or chaleb) is not what we understand under that name: it included the kidneys with their fat, the membrane of the liver, the membrane and the fat of the intestines. These organs were believed to be the seat of the vegetative soul, the nephesh. The requirements of integrity and healthiness of the animal are defined in Leviticus 22 : 17-25 in detail: The turtledoves and the young pigeons are the olah of the poor man. They are burnt undivided. The priests receive the skin of the victim (which in Carthage could be substituted by a sum of money). DUSSAUD (1941 p. 89) proposes that this delivery of the skin to the priests is connected with the *smikha*.

2. The sacrifice of the communion (zebach shelamim).

"And if his oblation be a sacrifice of peace offering, if he offered it of the herd; whether it be a male or female, he shall offer it without blemish before the Lord. And he shall lay his hand upon the head of his offering, and kill it at the door of the tabernacle of the congregation, and Aaron's sons the priests shall sprinkle the blood upon the altar round about. And he shall offer of the sacrifice of the peace offering an offering made by fire unto the Lord; the fat that covereth the inwards, and all the fat that is upon the inwards. And the two kidneys, and the fact that is on them, which is by the flanks, and the caul above the liver, with the kidneys, it shall be taken away. And Aaron's sons shall burn it upon the wood that is on the fire: it is an offering made by fire, of a sweet savour unto the Lord" (Levit. 3 : 1-5).

"Ye shall eat no manner of fat, of ox, or of sheep or of goat. And the fat of the beast that dieth of itself, and the fat of that which is torn by beasts, may be used in any other use: but ye shall in no wise eat of it. For whosoever eateth the fat of the beast, of which men offer an offering made by fire unto the Lord, even the soul that eateth it shall be cut off from his people. Moreover ye shall eat no manner of blood, whether it be of fowl or of beast, in any of your dwellings. Whatsoever soul it be that eateth any manner of blood, even that soul shall be cut off from his people" (Levit. 7 : 23-27).

Repeated is the strict taboo on blood and "fat", i.e. on the consumption of the seat of the ruach and of the seat of the nephesh. In the zebach shelamim a perfect female is also accepted. The ritual is very similar to that of the olah. The requirements for the health of the victim are detailed in Leviticus 22 : 21-25. Calves, lambs and kids are acceptable only on the eighth day after birth, as in most eastern rituals, and the mother shall not be killed on the same day with the young. The consumption of the meat of any sacrifice not offered following the rules of the zebach shelamim is strictly prohibited (Levit. 7 : 3-7). The priests obtain the "fat" for burning, the breast and the right thigh as their due (Levit. 7 : 28-34).

3. The sacrifice pro peccato (for transgression of the religious law, the chattat).

"If the priest that is anointed do sin according to the sin of the people; then let him bring for his sin, which he has sinned, a young bullock without blemish unto the Lord for a sin offering. And he shall bring the bullock unto the door of the tabernacle..; and shall lay his hand upon the bullock's head, and kill the bullock before the Lord. And the priest that is anointed shall take of the bullock's blood, and bring it to the tabernacle..; And the priest shall dip his finger in the blood, and sprinkle of the blood seven times before the Lord, before the veil of the sanctuary. And the priest shall put some of the blood upon the horns of the altar of sweet incense before the Lord, which is in the tabernacle..; and shall pour all the blood of the bullock at the bottom of the altar of the burnt offering, which is at the door of the tabernacle... And he shall take off from it all the fat of the bullock for the sin offering: the fat that covereth the inwards, and all the fat that is upon the inwards. And the two kidneys, and the fat that is upon them, which is by the flanks, and the caul above the liver, with the kidneys, it shall he take away. As it was taken off from the bullock of the sacrifice of peace offerings: and the priest shall burn them upon the altar of the burnt offering. And of the skin of the bullock, and all his flesh, with his head, and with his legs, and his inwards, and his dung. Even the whole bullock shall he carry forth without the camp unto a clean place where the ashes are poured out, and burn him on the wood with fire: where the ashes are poured out shall he be burnt" (Levit. 4 : 3-12).

Similar prescriptions are for the chattat of the community (Levit. 4 : 13-21), of nobles and of simple men (Levit. 4 : 22-5 : 13).

4. The sacrifice of atonement pro delicto, the trespass offering or the asham.

"And if a soul sin and commit any of these things which are forbidden to be done by the commandments of the Lord; though he wist it not, yet is he guilty, and shall bear his iniquity. And he shall bring a ram without blemish out of the flock, with thy estimation, for a trespass offering, unto the priest: and the priest shall make an atonement for him concerning his ignorance wherein he erred and wist it not, and it shall be forgiven him. It is a trespass offering" (Levit. 5 : 17-19).

"The trespass offering is most holy. In the place where they kill the burnt offering shall they kill the trespass offering: and the blood thereof shall he sprinkle round about upon the altar. And he shall offer of it all the fat thereof; the rump and the fat that covereth the inwards. And the two kidneys, and the fat that is on them, which is by the flanks, and the caul that is above the liver, with the kidneys, it shall he take away: And the priest shall burn them upon the altar for an offering made by fire unto the Lord: it is a trespass offering. Every male among the priests shall eat thereof; it shall be eaten in the holy place: it is most holy. As the sin offering is, so is the trespass offering: there is one law for them: the priest that maketh atonement therewith shall have it" (Levit. 7 : 1-7).

We have heard that the ritual of the olah is probably a late assimilation of Canaanite rituals after the settling in Palestine. One of the main reform of Moses was apparently the replacement of El, the God of the patriarchs, by Yahve as tribal God (DUSSAUD 1941 p. 346). This principle is well expressed by MICAH (4 : 5): "For all the people will walk every one in the name of his god, and we will walk in the name of Yahve our God for ever and ever." The same motive is expressed in the Judges (11 : 24): "Will thou not possess that which Chemosh thy god giveth thee to possess? So whomsoever the Lord our God shall drive out from before us, them will we possess." The rite of the covenant of MOSES is described in Exodus (24 : 5-8): „And (MOSES) sent young men of the children of Israel, which offered burnt offerings, and sacrificed peace offerings of oxen unto the Lord. And MOSES took half of the blood, and put it in basins; and half of the blood he sprinkled on the altar. And he took the book of the covenant, and read in the audience of the people: and they said: All that the Lord hath said will we do, and be obedient. And Moses took the blood, and sprinkled it on the people, and said: Behold the blood of the covenant, which the Lord hath made with you concerning all these words."

This transition is well recognizable in GIDEON's story (Judges 6 : 25-28):

> „And the Lord said unto him, Take thy father's young bullock, even the second bullock of seven years old, and throw down the altar of Baal (= El) that thy father hath, and cut down the grove that is by it: And build an altar unto the Lord thy God upon the top of this rock, in the ordered place, and take the second bullock, and offer a burnt sacrifice with the wood of the grove which thou shalt cut down. And Gideon took ten men of his servants, and did as the Lord had said unto him and so it was, because he feared his father's household, and the men of the city, that he could not do it by day, that he did it by night. And when the men of the city arouse early in the morning, behold, the altar of Baal was cast down, and the grove was cut down that was by it, and the second bullock was offered upon the altar that was built."

DUSSAUD (1941 p. 68) regards the legend of the golden calf as an original attempt of justification of this cult in favour of the Northern Kingdom.

He explains (l.c. p. 241) that the Judaic tradition attaches to ABRAHAM and to Yahve the following old sanctuaries: Shechem, Bethel, Hebron, Beersheba and Jerusalem, the old Ephraimite tradition to Isaac and Jacob and the God Bethel (= Baal, Hadad, or El) the sanctuaries of Beersheba, Bethel, Machanaim, Shechem and Gilgal. (cf. also Amos 7 : 9, 16). Whilst the cult of Jahwe was restricted to Jerusalem, at least from the second prophetic period onwards and especially since the Solomonic temple, the contamination with the local Canaanite gods was so strong in the Northern Kingdom that Yahve and Bethel were completely identified (DUSSAUD 1941 p. 242). In the story of the golden calf (Exodus 32) only the first six verses belong to the old Ephraimite text: "And all the people brake off the golden earrings which were in their ears, and brought them unto Aaron. And he received them at their hand, and fashioned it with a graving tool, after he had made it a molten calf; and they said: These be thy gods, O Israel, which brought thee up out of the land of Egypt. And when Aaron saw it, he built an altar before it; and Aaron made proclamation, and said, To morrow is a feast to the Lord. And they rose up early on the morrow, and offered burnt offerings, and brought peace offerings; and the people sat down to eat and to drink, and rose up to play" (Exod. 32 : 3-6). The rest of the chapter is devoted to the refutation of this Ephraimite text. But the tendency is fully confirmed by a parallel in the story of the images of Micah and at Dan (Judges 17 and 18). Under this aspect the history of the golden calf is again a reflection of later events, following the settlement in the hills of Palestine, to the earlier history of Israel, in order to justify the adoration of Baal *in loco* of Jahve. This statement is important for the interpretation of the bull statues in Palestine in the Israelite period.

We now proceed to the description of animal sacrifices for purification. The first concerns purification from the touch of a dead body:

"Speak unto the children of Israel, that they bring thee a red heifer without spot, wherein is no blemish, and upon which never came yoke: And ye shall give her unto Eleazar the priest, that he may bring her forth without the camp, and one shall slay her before his face: And Eleazar the priest shall take her blood with his finger, and sprinkle of her blood directly before the tabernacle of the congregation seven times: And one shall burn the heifer in his sight: her skin, and her flesh, and her blood, with her dung, shall he burn. And the priest shall take cedar wood, and hyssop, and scarlet, and cast it into the midst of the burning of the heifer. Then the priest shall wash his clothes ......" (Numbers 19 : 2 ff.).

The second ritual is that of the purity declaration of a healed leper:

"This shall be the law of the leper in the day of his cleansing: He shall be brought unto the priest... Then shall the priest command to take for him that is to be cleansed two birds alive and clean, and cedar wood and scarlet, and hyssop. And the priest shall command that one of the birds be killed in an earthen vessel over running water: As for the living bird, he shall take it, and the cedar wood, and the scarlet, and the hyssop, and shall dip them and the living bird in the blood of the bird that was killed over the running water. And he shall sprinkle upon him that is to be cleansed from the leprosy seven times, and shall pronounce him clean, and shall let the living bird loose into the open field ..... And on the eighth day he shall take two he-lambs without blemish, and one ewe lamb of the first year without blemish, and three tenth deals of fine flour for a meat offering...... And the priest that maketh him clean shall present the man that is to be made clean, and those things before the Lord, at the door of the tabernacle. And the priest shall take one he-lamb, and offer him for a trespass offering. And he shall slay the lamb in the place where he shall kill the sin offering and the burnt offering... And the priest shall take some of the blood of the trespassing offering, and the priest shall put it upon the tip of the right ear ..... And afterward he shall kill the burnt offering" (Levit. 14 : 2 ff.).

The Passah ritual combines an old nomad tradition in the sacrifice of the lamb with an agricultural one, the feast of the unleavened breads. Many authors, among them STEUERNAGEL and EDWARD MEYER—the latter basing themselves upon deviations in the ritual of the Elephantine papyri—regard the combination of both these traditions as a rather late occurrence, even dating it to the Persian period only. We entirely agree with DUSSAUD (1941 p. 332 ff.) that the combined Passah feast is a very old tradition. It has been traced to the Ras Shamra period and to the Canaanite settlements in Palestine of the 14th century B.C. These rites were passed on to the Hebrews of the Negeb. And if these Hebrews were no full agriculturists, ALBRIGHT (1942 p. 99) has demonstrated that they were half-settled, of nomad habits with regular cyclic migrations, but with sowing of their own. There still exist even today Arab tribes in Palestine and Transjordan who sow, leave the spot for their migrations, and return for the harvest. The writer has met such tribes near Rafa. The sacrifice of the Passah lamb is described in Exodus (12 : 3-11):

"In the tenth day of this month they shall take to them every man a lamb, according to the house of their fathers, a lamb for one house: And if the household be too little for the lamb, let him and his neighbour next unto his house take it according to the number of the souls... Your lamb shall be without blemish, a male of the first year: ye shall take it out from the sheep, or from the goats: And ye shall keep it until the fourteenth day of the same month: and the whole assembly of the congregation of Israel shall kill it in the evening. And they shall take of the blood, and strike it on the two side posts and on the upper door post of the houses, wherein they shall eat it. And they shall eat the flesh in that night, roast with fire, and unleavened bread; and with bitter herbs they shall eat it. Eat not of it raw, nor sodden at all with water, but roast with fire; his head with his legs, and with the purtenance thereof. And ye shall let nothing of it remain until the morning; and that which remaineth of it until the morning ye shall burn with fire. And thus ye shall eat it; with your loins girded, your shoes on your feet and your staff in your hand; and ye shall eat it in haste: it is the Lord's passover."

It must be assumed that the connection of the Passah feast with the exodus from Egypt is a secondary one. It is obvious that this sacrifice has an apotropaic intention, which DUSSAUD (1941 p. 339) ascribes to the bad spirits of the corn. By the Passah sacrifice the people were purified and protected, and could now proceed to cut the corn (barley), and to offer its firstlings to the priests without danger from the spirits of the corn. The interdiction to eat leavened bread belongs to this preparatory purification.

The end of the harvest (wheat) is marked by another feast, seven weeks later, the *Shevuoth,* to which the following sacrifice applies:

> „Also in the day of the first fruits, when ye bring a new meat offering, unto the Lord, after your weeks be out, ye shall have an holy convocation; ye shall do no servile work: But ye shall offer the burnt offering for a sweet savour unto the Lord; two young bullocks, one ram, seven lambs of the first year; And their meat offering of flour mingles with oil, three tenth deals unto one bullock, two tenth deals unto one ram, a several tenth deal unto one lamb, throughout the seven lambs; And one kid of the goats, to make an atonement for you. Ye shall offer them beside the continual burnt offering, and his meat offering ... and their drink offerings" (Numbers 28 : 26-31).

Another highly refined sacrifice is connected with the sending of the scapegoat into the desert, during the feast of the atonement:

> „Thus shall AARON come into the holy place: with a young bullock for a sin offering, and a ram for a burnt offering ... And he shall take of the congregation of the children of Israel two kids of the goats for a sin offering, and one ram for a burnt offering. And AARON shall offer his bullock of the sin offering, which is for himself, and make an atonement for himself, and for all his house. And he shall take the two goats, and present them before the Lord at the door of the tabernacle of the congregation. And AARON shall cast lots upon the two goats; one lot for the Lord, and the other lot for the scapegoat. And AARON shall bring the goat upon which the Lord's lot fell, and offer him for a sin offering. But the goat, on which the lot fell to be the scapegoat, shall be presented alive before the Lord, to make an atonement with him, and to let him go for a scapegoat into the wilderness. And Aaron shall bring the bullock of the sin offering . . . . . And he shall take of the blood of the bullock, and sprinkle it with his finger upon the mercy seat eastward; and before the mercy seat shall he sprinkle of the blood with his finger seven times. Then shall he kill the goat of the sin offering, that is for the people, and bring his blood within the veil, and do with that blood as he did with the blood of the bullock, and sprinkle it upon the mercy seat, and before the mercy seat . . . . And there shall be no man in the tabernacle of the congregation when he goeth in to make an atonement in the holy place, until he come out, and have made an atonement for himself and for his household, and for all the congregation of Israel. And he shall go out unto the altar that is before the Lord; and shall take of the blood of the bullock, and of the blood of the goat, and put it on the horns of the altar round about. And he shall sprinkle of the blood upon it with his finger seven times, and cleanse it, and hallow it from the uncleanness of the children of Israel. And when he hath made an end of reconciling the holy place ..., he shall bring the live goat: And AARON shall lay both his hands upon the head of the live goat, and confess over him all the iniquities of the children of Israel, and all their transgressions in all their sins, putting them upon the head of the goat, and shall send him away by the hand of a fit man into the wilderness: And the goat shall bear upon him all their iniquities unto a land not inhabited: and he shall let go the goat in the wilderness" (Levit. 16 : 3-22).

This scapegoat, which is sent once every year in to the desert, loaden with all the past year's sins of Israel, is a procedure widely spread among primitive tribes all over the world. FRAZER (1945 p. 566 ff.) compiles a number of them. The smikha, the laying of the high-priest's hand upon the head of the goat, symbolises the transfer of the sins upon his head.

We conclude this by no means complete list of animal sacrifices with the ritual of dedication of the Levites (Numbers 8 : 6-18):

"Take the Levites from among the children of Israel, and cleanse them . . . . Then let them take a young bullock with his meat offering . . and another young bullock shalt thou take for a sin offering . . . . and the children of Israel shall put their hands upon the Levites. And Aaron shall offer the Levites before the Lord for an offering of the children of Israel, that they may execute the service of the Lord. And the Levites shall lay their hands upon the heads of the bullocks: and thou shalt offer the one for a sin offering, and the other for a burnt offering, unto the Lord, to make an atonement for the Levites. And thou shalt set the Levites before AARON and before his sons, and offer them for an offering unto the Lord . . . . and the Levites shall be mine. . . . For they are wholly given unto me from among the children of Israel; instead of such as open every womb, even instead of the firstborn of all the children of Israel, have I taken them unto me. For all the firstborn of the children of Israel are mine, both man and beast: on the day I smote every firstborn in the land of Egypt I sanctified them for myself."

The hints to the ancestral sacrifice of the firstborn is obvious. The dedication of the Levites by the people is accompanied by the same *smikha* which reappears in all sacrifices of animals dedicated to God.

Meat, an occasional food only, being originally only slaughtered in the temple and found predominant in the list of the animal sacrifices, we are astonished by the exclusion of milk and eggs from this list.

Milk—mainly goat's milk—was, together with bread, the main food of the patriarchal age. Milk includes a number of milk products, such as cheese, lebben (sour milk), butter and butter milk. It is therefore surprising not to find any of these milk products to be included among the sacrificial offerings. A number of facts may explain this situation. The possession of goats was so common in all strata of the population, including the priests and their servants, that no milk was needed as contribution for their maintenance. DOUGHTY (I p. 215, II p. 443) describes that it is a shame in Arabia to sell milk. It has little monetary value and is given freely to any passing wanderer. For this reason W. R. SMITH (1899 p. 184) refuses to recognise the libation of milk before certain old Arab gods or on holy stones as a sacrificial act, sacrificial acts being restricted to more valued property. Yet milk libations are widely spread in ancient Semitic rites, from Arabia over Ras Shamra and Phoenicia in general to Carthage (cf. *Corpus Inscript. Semit.* Paris, 1885, Vol. I no. 165 1.14, no. 167 1.10). SMITH's tentative explanation (1889 p. 167), that milk was refused as a quickly fermenting substance, is most improbable, considering the ritual use of wine. Milk being so perishable in warm climates is an unsatisfactory explanation, as it does not apply to cheese and other milk products. Of no help is also the theory, that milk was regarded as a substitute for blood, and therefore refused. If that be true, milk would have been excluded from the diet, which was obviously not the case.

It is more easy to explain the absence of domestic fowl from the list of sacrificial animals. It was unknown to the patriarchs. Whilst certainly being present in the time of the later kingdom (7th century B.C. at least), we have no information, how abundant it was at that period. The absence of eggs from the sacrifices may have been caused either by the same reason which prevented milk from being included into this list, being too common and too little valued, or because of the conspicuous connection of domestic fowl with pagan rites, such as those of Nergal.

Some vivid descriptions of the sacrifices have been preserved in some of the apocryphal and pseudo-epigraphic books. Apart from the apocryphal book of Esdras (1 : 7-9 and 7 : 7; cf. also II Chron. 35 : 7-9 and Ezra 2 : 17) we read in the Letter of Aristeas (88-96):

"The Temple faces the east and its back is toward the west. The whole of the floor is paved with stones and slopes down to the appointed places, that water may be conveyed to wash away the blood from the sacrifices, for many thousand beasts are sacrificed there on the feast days. And there is an inexhaustible supply of water...... There are many openings for water at the base of the altar which are invisible to all except to those who are engaged in the ministration, so that all the blood of the sacrifices which is collected in great quantities is washed away in the twinkling of an eye.... The service is carried on without interruption —some provide the wood, others the oil, others the fine wheat flour, others the spices; others again bring the pieces of flesh for the burnt offering, exhibiting a wonderful degree of strength. For they take up with both hands the limbs of a calf, each of them weighing more than two talents, and throw them with each hand in a wonderful way on to the high place of the altar and never miss placing them on the proper spot. In the same way the pieces of the sheep and also of the goats are wonderful both for their weight and their fatness. For those, whose business it is, always select the beasts which are without blemish and specially fat, and thus the sacrifice is carried out... The most complete silence reigns..., though there are actually seven hundred men engaged in the work, besides the vast number of those who are occupied in bringing up the sacrifices. Everything is carried out with reverence and in a way worthy of the great God."

References to the sacrifices of Genesis are contained in the Book of Jubilees (14 : 9-12, 16 : 23, 21 : 6 ff.). A more detailed ritual of an old fragment of another manuscript of the Testament of Levi has been published by CHARLES (1913 II p. 364 f.).

3.82. SEMITIC ANIMAL SACRIFICES IN GENERAL

The rituals of the various sacrifices in Syria and Carthage, where they were brought by the Tyrian founders of the city, are very similar. DUSSAUD (1941 p. 140 ff.) was given a fair comparison, from which we quote a few formal points only. The names of the animal sacrifices were:

TYPE	CARTHAGE	JERUSALEM
Holocaust	*shelem-kalil*	*olah*
Sacrifice of communion	*sevaat*	*zebach shelamim*
Expiatory sacrifice	*kàlil*	*chattat* and *asham*

The ritual shows many parallels to those of Leviticus. The tariff of Carthage regulates the payment for each sacrifice, due to the priests, as follows:

VICTIM	PAYMENT
Kalil	
Bull	10 sicles of silver to each priest and 300 sicles of weight in meat.
Calf, ram	5 sicles of silver to each priest plus 150 sicles of weight in meat.
Sheep, he-goat	1 sicle and 2 zars to each priest.
Lamb, kid, stag (?)	3/4 sicle and 2 zars to each priest.
Sevaat	
Bull	10 sicles of silver to each priest and the breast and one thigh. The skin, legs, paws and the rest belongs to the sacrificer.
Calf, ram	5 sicles to each priest, rest as above.
Sheep, he-goat	1 sicle and 2 zars to each priest, rest as above.
Lamb, kid, stag (?)	3/4 sicle and 2 zars to each priest, rest as above.
Shelem-kalil	
Bull	10 sicles of silver to each priest.
Calf, ram	5 sicles to each priest.
Sheep, he-goat	1 sicle and 2 zars to each priest.
Lamb, kid, stag (?)	3/4 sicle and 2 zars to each priest.
Rooster, hen	3/4 sicle and 2 zars to each priest.

The tariff for the *kalil* and the *sevaat* in the fragment of the Louvre is as follows (DUSSAUD 1941 p. 150):

Bull, ram	The skin to the priests, the horns (?) to the sacrificer.
Sheep, he-goat	The skin, the fat of the intestines and the feet to the priests.
Lamb, kid	The skin to the priest.
Rooster, hen	2 zars to the priest.

In his famous *Lectures on the Religion of the Semites* (1928, 1899) W. R. SMITH has attempted to trace the origins of the Biblical sacrifices to more primitive conditions, such as still survived in the bedawi tradition of Arabia in historical times. We doubt if such comparative constructions are rigorously justified, as much of Jewish thought depended upon the religious background of the high civilisations of Irak and Egypt. The Hebrews may have lived in a similar spiritual environment to that of the later bedawi of Arabia, but at the Patriarchal age that periode belonged to a remote past, buried beneath many and more recent layers of religious experience and thought. We call to mind that ALBRIGHT has convincingly demonstrated, that the pre-invading Hebrews were no true desert nomads any more. Thus we may *prima facie* apply many of Smith's conclusions only to the Arab bedawi of the desert, but not to the early Hebrews who approached rapidly the stage of agricultural settlement.

The jins or demons often take animal shape. They inhabit mainly the desert and the wilderness, the land which did not belong to the "Beth ha-Baal", the land protected by the local deity. The jins rule in such places and protection has to be sought by every traveller going through their areas. In some of the later books of the Old Testament we still find strong remembrances of such assumptions.

SMITH also gives a peculiar interpretation of totemism, which goes together with the proper understanding of animal sacrifices. In the totemistic period of its development every tribe adopts some kind of animals as its relatives, as its brethren. Primitive people generally have a rather direct relation to animals as rational beings. Ancient magic proves this again and again. JACOBUS of Edessa (Quaestiones 44), for instance, quotes an ancient Syrian rite for the control of caterpillars injurious to the plants of a garden. A group of girls comes together, takes one of the caterpillars and then chooses one from the girls as the 'Mother of the Caterpillar'. The collected caterpillar is now mourned and buried. The adaptive mother is brought to the garden under loud mourning of the other girls, and all caterpillars rapidly leave the garden. This habit supposes, of course, that the caterpillars understand the procedure and direct their behaviour consequently. The background of animal fables and of animal omina is often a similar one.

The absence of true totemistic relics in the established Semitic religions is explained by the long interval between the early period of true totemism and the foundation of the first temples. This is possibly, and even probably, correct. SMITH regards certain traditions as being such relics, such as the tale of ARISTOTLE that certain serpents of the Euphrates never bite the local inhabitants; the mourning and burial rites of the S. Arabian Banu Harith for a gazelle found dead; the acclamation of the coney as a brother by certain bedawi of the Sinai, who never eat its meat, as he who eats a coney will never see his parents again; the veneration of the founder of Baalbeck in the form of a lion, etc.

Sacrificial animals are mainly the pure, eatable domestic animals, such as ox, sheep and goat. In Arabia, where the camel is eaten, it is also sacrificed. Gazelles and deer can be eaten, but are rarely sacrificed. Even with the Arabs the gazelle is an incomplete substitute only for a sheep. Doves and turtle-doves are only burnt as holocaust and under special conditions.

The sacrifice of the Semites was not primarily a gift to the deity, but an act of community and of communication, where the deity and the adorers were united in the enjoyment of the meat and of the blood of the sacrificial animal, thus renewing and fortifying the mutual covenant. Every covenant was confirmed by a sacrifice and/or a sacrificial meal. The normal human unit for a sacrificial meal was the family (cf. the Passah rules). On a higher level were the sacrifices of the tribe or of the town. Certain animals may be slaughtered for consumption only on such occasions. Thus, it was forbidden in Arabia, to slaughter a camel for family use. It could be slaughtered in a public ritual open to all members of the tribe.

SMITH assumes that originally all sacrificial animals were regarded as members of the tribe, which only under religious supervision could be slaughtered. In this respect FRAZER's analysis of certain African husbandry tribes may be remembered (1925). A strong tendency to preserve the stock of the herds for milk production—milk and vegetables forming the main food—is often hidden under rituals of taboos. Originally, and this is still recognisable in the early books of the Bible, every legitimate slaughtering for consumption was sacrificial. This connection was lost in due time. But now two classes of sacrifices became conspicuous, at least in the pagan rites: ordinary sacrifices of animals which usually were eaten and certain extraordinary sacrifices of animals, which were forbidden as food.

With regard to the ordinary sacrificial animals it must be remembered, that in primitive tribes the life of the tribe depended mainly upon one kind of domestic animal: either upon sheep and goats, or upon cattle, or—in later days—upon camels. Correspondingly we find a cow-Astarte in one, a sheep-Astarte in another place or tribe. The Hebrews of the patriarchal age as well as their kinsmen, the Moabites (Deuter. 7 : 13; II Kings 3/4) were definitely sheep-nomads, whilst cattle breeding was more concentrated in the settled areas. Also the name of Rachel (= mother sheep), the mother of the house of Joseph, points in this direction.

Historical illustrations are the dove-Astarte of Ascalon, the cow-Astarte of Sidon (perhaps the model for the legend of Europe and Zeus) and of Byblos where the goddess was represented with horns (or with a bull's head above her own head) and finally the sheep-Astarte of Canaan, the *Astheroth zoncha* of the Deuteronomy (7 : 13). SMITH connects this sheep-Astarte with the Passah ritual, which finds its analogy in the Arab sacrifices in the month of Ragab. An atonement sacrifice of parallel character was the sheep which was burnt alive in Cyprus on the first of April; the burning of a living sheep in the great spring-festival at Hierapolis, and certain atonement sacrifices of the Harranians, who maintained pagan rites until the Middle Ages, in the first half of Nisan. The ram was, apart from the pig, the most usual ancient animal for atonement sacrifices, a fact well reflected in the ram put into the desert on the eve of the Hebrew atonement day.

W. R. SMITH also discusses a number of extraordinary sacrifices in the Semitic Middle East. The pig was sacrificed and consumed once a year only by the pagan Harranians (AL NADIM, *Orat.* V p. 176). In Cyprus wild boars were sacrificed to Astarte and to Adonis every year on the second of April (LYDUS, *De mensibus* IV : 64). Similar extraordinary boar sacrifices are reported from Argos (ATHENAEUS 3 : 49), from Pamphylia (STRABO 9 : 5 : 17), from Syria (LUCIAN, *De dea Syria* 54). In J'rapta the sacrifice of a sow is represented in a rock relief (RENAN, *Miss. de Phénicie* pl. 31). And finally we have to record the famous passage in Isaiah (65 : 4, 66 : 3). An old family of priests of Judah bears the name Bne Chasir (Sons of the pig). Apart from two quotations in the Bible (I Chron. 24 : 15; Nehemiah 10 : 21) we find this name in an old family tomb near ABSALOM's tomb at Jerusalem (SAULCY II 1854 p. 206; AVIGAD 1946 p. 58). Considering all these facts we are not so definite any more in our rejection of Frazer's theory, that the uncleanness of the pig is the consequence of deification or a totemistic taboo in a remote past. But this period, if the assumption is correct, must have been very remote, at the latest during the sojourn at Padan-Aram or before.

The dog is also mentioned, together with the mouse, in Isaiah 66 : 3. And dogs have apparently been occasionally sacrificed at Carthage (JUSTINIAN 18 : 1 : 10). Horses were given "by the kings of Judah to the sun" (II Kings 23 : 11). At Rhodes, of Semitic ritual, four horses were thrown into the sea as a sacrifice during the annual feast of the sun. Similar is an annual deer-sacrifice to Astarte at Laodicea on the Phoenician coast, which was traditionally regarded as a substitution for the annual sacrifice of a virgin. Gazelles and deer occur as early as at Ras Shamra in sacrifices. SMITH proposes to regard the passage in II Samuel 1 : 19 "The gazelle, o Israel, is slain upon thy high places" as the reminescence of similar old sacrifices. The onager was eaten by the Arabs, but forbidden to the Harranians.

Doves were neither consumed nor killed by the Semites, whilst in Rome they were sacrificed to Venus. The dove is the bird of Astarte. We think that the old Syrian taboo of the dove is connected with the widely spread popular belief that the doves are soul-birds, bearers of the souls of the dead. Quails were sacrificed bij the Phoenicians at Eudoxus in remembrance of the resurrection of Heracles (ATHENAEUS 9 : 47). At Tyrus quails were annually sacrificed to Baal in the month of Peritius (February/March), at the season of the appearance of enormous swarms of quails in one night (cf. FLAVIUS JOSEPHUS, *Antiq.* 8 : 5 : 3).

Fish were eaten by the Jews, but not sacrificed. Their Syrian and Canaanite pagan neighbours held all or some fish in taboo as forbidden for consumption, but they were only seldom sacrificed. In remembrance of the ancient fish cult of Atergatis, bread was thrown into the sea still recently at Gaza (Q. St. P.E.F. 1893 p. 26). In Mesopotamia Ea is often represented as a fish, occasional fish sacrifices are illustrated, and the adorers of Ea often bear a fish skin as a robe.

SMITH regards these extraordinary and rare animal sacrifices as remembrances of more extensive cults and rituals of an often rather remote past. We have pointed out before that many ancient sacrifices are secondary substitutions for original human sacrifices. For many more stimulating suggestions and for many further details the reader is referred to the book of W. R. SMITH.

3.9. THE ZOOLOGY OF THE BIBLE IN THE LIGHT OF FRAZER'S ANALYSIS OF COMPARATIVE FOLKLORE

The books of the Bible contain a rich crop of ancient folklore. This holds good especially for the oldest sources, which apparently were first worded about 800 B.C., more than for the Priestly code which comprises, late intercalations from the sixth century B.C. The five books of Moses contain most of this ancient folklore recalling the early pastoral stages of the Hebrew tribes, before they settled down to an agricultural life in the promised land of milk and honey. The modern critical analyses of the development of the sources and the composition of the various layers of the Bible have contributed much to the preparation of the historical analysis of the development of Jewish thought. Perhaps one of the most striking examples is the decalogue. This splendid crystallization of ethical thought had a very different form in its earlier stages of development. This first old tribal decalogue is buried, but still clearly discernible in Exodus 34 : 14-26. R. H. KENNETT gives the primary decalogue, following the lead of BUDDE and WELLHAUSEN, as follows:

1. I am Jehovah thy God, thou shalt worship no other God (v. 14).
2. The feast of the unleavened cakes thou shalt keep: seven days thou shalt eat unleavened cakes (v. 18).
3. All that openeth the womb is mine; and all thy domestic stock that is male, the firstlings of ox and sheep (v. 19).
4. My sabbaths shalt thou keep; six days shalt thou work, but on the seventh day thou shalt rest (v. 21).
5. The feast of weeks thou shalt celebrate, even the first fruits of wheat harvest (v. 22).
6. The feast of ingathering thou shalt celebrate at the end of the year (v. 22).
7. Thou shalt not sacrifice (lit. slay) my sacrificial blood upon leavened bread (v. 25).
8. The fat of my feast shall not remain all night until the morning of Passover; (v. 25).
9. The first of the first fruits of thy ground thou shalt bring into the house of the Lord thy God (v. 26).
10. Thou not seethe a kid in its mother's milk (v. 26).

This old decalogue is a purely ritual prescription, far from containing any moral implications. The development from this first tribal to the second humanitarian decalogue is the decisive spiritual development of Israel. However, here we are primarily interested in its older form, as the tenth commandment gives us an opportunity to dive into the world of the thoughts of Sir JOHN G. FRAZER. The importance of FRAZER's study of comparative folklore as a guide to the development of culture and rites cannot be overstressed. This method still promises rich results in the study of many animal taboos, such as that of the camel, to which it has scarcely been applied.

The introduction of the interdiction of the old decalogue to seethe a kid in its mother's milk certainly stresses its great importance. FRAZER (O.T. p. 360 ff.) collected rich material of similar, very widespread dietary rules amongst peoples all over Africa. Contact of meat and milk either in the boiling pot or in the stomach have a dangerous consequence upon the milk production of the cow which produced the milk, even leading to a stoppage of the milk production. In our case it is clear, why the kid (or lamb), but not the calf, was mentioned in Exodus: cattle may have been wanting at least during part of the nomad period. And even in the time of agricultural settlement, the cattle was the beast of the plough, but not the milk-producer. This was predominantly the goat. The question still remains, why this (inclusive) prohibition of consuming milk and meat together (as practised in all traditional Jewish ritual) was formulated: "in its mother's milk". It is certain that humanitarian motives can be excluded. FRAZER interprets it *per analogiam* as a common rule amongst nomadic herdsmen subsisting mainly on the milk of their (cattle or in our case) goats and sheep, who are afraid of diminishing this milk supply by too greedy a consumption of meat. And kids and lambs give and gave the preferred meat to the nomads.

MERKER (1910 p. 33) touched upon this problem in his monograph on the *Massai*. Whilst there the consumption of milk and meat on the same day is interdicted, this taboo does not extend to the drinking of milk and blood. A mixture of both is even a preferred diet for wounded warriors. Another interesting interpretation has been given by MAIMONIDES (*Moreh Nebuchim* 3 : 48), who suggests that meat and cooked milk was a common sacrifice of the pagans and hence the interdiction to imitate pagan rituals. Recently also psycho-analysis has discussed the prohibition of drinking milk and eating meat at the same time, including the cooking of the suckling in the mother's milk, interpreting it as relics of the early struggle between matrilinear and patrilinear society, and of the analogous conflict between the conception of way of life in nomadic and agricultural society. M. WOOLF's (1945) additional assumption that ancient mythology has attributed to these rites is rejected by A. FODOR (1946).

Before proceeding to the further rules of the cleanness of animals (of which we here discuss only those concerning animal species, not those of conditions of cleanness of permitted animals and their parts) we reproduce the basic pertinent verses (Deuteronom. 14 : 3-20; Levit. 11):

Thou shalt not eat any abominable thing. These are the domestic animals which ye shall eat: the cattle, the sheep, and the goat. (Also, from wild animals:) the deer, the gazelle, the fallow deer, the *ako,* the *dishon,* the *theo* and the *samer.* And every animal that parteth the hoof, and cleaveth the cleft into two claws, and cheweth the cud among the animals, that ye shall eat.

Nevertheless these ye shall not eat of them that chew the cud, or of them that divide the cloven hoof; as the camel, and the hare, and the coney: for they chew the cud, but divide not the hoof; therefore they are unclean unto you. And the swine, because it divideth the hoof, yet cheweth not the cud, it is unclean unto you; ye shall not eat of their flesh, nor touch their dead carcase.

These ye shall eat of all that are in the waters: all that have fins and scales you shall eat. And whatsoever hath no fins and scales ye may not eat; it is unclean unto you.

Of all clean birds ye shall eat. But those are they of which ye shall not eat: the vulture, the lammergeyer and the *asniah.* And the *raah,* the *ayah* and the *dayah* after his kind. And every raven after his kind. And the ostrich, the *thachmoss,* the *shachaf* and the hawk after its kind. And the little owl, the eagle owl and the barn owl. And the *kaath,* the *rachamah* and the *shalach.* And the stork, the heron after its kind, the hoopoe and the bat.

All flying creeping things (= insects), going upon all four, shall be an abomination unto you. Yet these may ye eat of every flying creeping thing that goeth upon all four, which have legs above their feet, to leap withal upon the earth. Even these of them ye may eat: the locust after his kind, the salam after his kind, the chargol after his kind, and the chagab after his kind (probably all Orthoptera). But all other flying creeping things which have four feet, shall be an abomination unto you.

These also shall be unclean unto you among the creeping things that creep upon the earth: the mole-rat, the mouse, and the tortoise after his kind. And the *anakah*, the *koach*, the lizard, the gecko and the *thinshemeth*.

FRAZER enlarges (O.T. p. 376 ff.) his comparative analysis of the reason for the aversion of pastoral tribes to the eating of game. The contact of milk and meat of game in the stomach still endangers the milk production of the domestic stock. "The remarkable exceptions which some of these tribes make to the general rule, by permitting the consumption of wild animals that bear a more or less distant resemblance to cattle, suggests a comparison with the ancient Hebrew distinction of clean and unclean animals. Can it be that the distinction in question originated in the rudimentary zoology of a pastoral people, who divided the whole animal kingdom into creatures which resembled, and creatures which differed from, their own domestic cattle, and on the basis of that fundamental classification laid down a law of capital importance, that the first of the classes might be eaten and that the second might not? The actual law of clean and unclean animals, as it is set forth in the Pentateuch, is probably too complex to admit of resolution into elements so simple and so few; yet its leading principle is curiously reminescent of the practice of some African tribes which we have been discussing ...... The test of an animal's fitness to serve as human food is its zoological affinity to domestic ruminants, and judged by that test various species of deer and gazelles are, correctly enough, included among the edible animals, exactly as the Masai and Bahima, on similar grounds, include various kinds of antelopes within their dietary. However, the Hebrew scale of diet is a good deal more liberal than that of the Masai, and even if it originated, as seems possible, in a purely pastoral state, it has probably been expanded by successive additions to meet the needs and tastes of an agricultural people."

The zoological knowledge about the correlation of hooves and rumination of the ungulates is remarkable, and in this respect fortifies FRAZER's argumentation. We have, however, to reject another theory of FRAZER (G.B. p. 472), which sprang from his study of the corn-spirit in folklore, often impersonated as an animal. This study led him to the generalisation: "In general it may be said that all so-called unclean animals were originally sacred; the reason for not eating them was that they were divine." It is without parallel that all insects and all creeping things have ever been divine anywhere. There is no reason why hare and coney or owls should ever have been divine. We have not the slightest indication that the camel has ever been divine. Yet FRAZER stresses this theory especially with regard to the pig. Whilst the prescriptions about the pig agree well with the above mentioned theory, he explains (G.B. p. 472 f.): "The attitude of the Jews to the pig was as ambiguous as that of the heathen Syrians towards the same animal. The Greeks could not decide whether the Jews worshipped swines or abominated them (PLUTARCH, *Quaest. Conviv.* 4 : 5). On the one hand they might not eat swine; but on the other hand they might not kill them. And if the former rule speaks for the uncleanness, the latter speaks still more strongly for the sanctity of the animal. For whereas both rules may, and one rule must, be explained on the supposition that the pig was sacred; neither rule must, and one rule cannot, be explained on the supposition that the pig was unclean. If, therefore, we prefer the former supposition, we must conclude that, originally at least, the pig was revered rather than abhorred by the Israelites. We are confirmed in this opinion by observing that down to the time of Isaiah some of the Jews used to meet secretly in gardens to eat the flesh of swine and mice as a religious rite (Isaiah 65 : 4, 66 : 17). Doubtless this was a very ancient ceremony, dating from a time when both the pig and the mouse were venerated as divine, and when their flesh was partaken of sacramentally on rare and solemn occasions as the body and blood of gods ..... Again, the rule that, after touching a pig, a man had to wash himself and his clothes, also favours the view of the sanctity of the pig. For it is a common belief that the effect of contact with a sacred object must be removed, by washing or otherwise, before a man is free to mingle with his fellows. Thus the Jews wash their hands after reading the sacred scriptures."

These arguments are rather weak. Firstly because the Greeks and other pagans had always great difficulty in understanding the Jewish belief in an immaterial God and many points of the Jewish ritual. This difficulty was strengthened by an ironical feeling of superiority towards people who refuse pig-meat. Secondly the argument from Isaiah is especially weak. The quotations belong to the late Deutero-Isaiah. And there is not the slightest proof that the pig-eating fraternities took from old Jewish traditions. It is almost certain that they acted under the influence of contemporaneous pagan influences. Thirdly, KAUTZSCH (1922 p. 177) refers the sentence "and their carcase ye shall not touch" (Levit. 11 : 8) to a later addition of the late Priestly Code. There is no reason to regard the corresponding passage in Deutero-nomium as older. Thus, just the critical passage of FRAZER's argumentation refers to a very late addition of the original text, where the swine was treated just as the camel, hare and coney. Fourthly in the deserts wild pigs are rather rare, and there is no reason why it should have attracted divine veneration. We are rather inclined to regard the added glossary as an expression of a secondary situation, where eating pig-meat or its interdiction was a conspicuous difference between Jews and the dominant gentiles. The addition of hare and coney, is of course, an error, probably caused by the continuous motion of the lips of these animals. Whilst the explanation of the unclean animals as totem animals of the early Hebrew clans and tribes finds little background, we wish to hint at another point, which may offer an additional explanation of the distinction between clean and unclean animals. A very widespread popular belief is that food forms and influences the character and the qualities of the eater, of man as well as of animals. Ev enin higher civilizations this belief has persisted (cf. DE LA METTRIE's: "L'homme est ce qu'il mange"). This belief may well have brought about the interdiction of the carnivores. With them the old Jewish taboo of blood, assumed to contain the soul or life of the animal, must have been another strong reason for not eating them. FRAZER (G.B. p. 228) points out another blood taboo. The Jewish hunters poured out the blood of game they had killed and covered it up with dust. With regard to the creeping things (small mammals, reptiles, amphibians, etc.) and to the flying creeping things (insects with six legs. In grasshoppers, etc. the big jumping hindlegs were not counted as legs) the food was known or suspected as unclean. The locusts are conspicuous phytophages. The wild pig may have fallen in the same category. We see, however, no reason why the argument from pastoral life needs any enforcement, in order to explain the addition of swine or camel. Finally the parallel from Demeter whose sacred animal was the pig, has no connection with Jewish life. It results from agricultural conditions, during which the Jews never bred pigs. In none of FRAZER's other examples pig veneration, or what he interprets as such, refers to pastoral people. FRAZER also remarks on two other important zoological texts of the Old Testament. The first concerns the divergencies of the report on the creation in the first two chapters of Genesis. In the second chapter man is created before the other terrestrial animals, in the first after them (O.T. p. 1 ff.). For both legends of creation widespread analogies exist all over the world. Genesis 1 : 26 is of special interest, because it is the nucleus of systematics of all Biblical zoology, and because it is identical with the zoological system of the old Sumerians, as expressed in the Harra-hubullu: fish, fowls, domestic and wild animals (the big ones), the creeping things (including the small mammals) and, above all, man. Only the flying creeping things, the insects, have been added later as a further category.

Two divergent reports are also given in the description of Noah's ark and the great flood (Genesis 6 versus 7). In the second report clean and unclean animals are distinguished, seven of the former, two of the latter being permitted to enter. In the sixth chapter no such distinction is made and a pair of every animal enters the ark. This report belongs to the late Priestly Code, arguing probably that the clean animals had only been revealed to God by Moses, and that Noah could not yet distinguish between clean and unclean animals. With regard to the life of the animals in the ark, Jewish folklore has produced many legends and fables, which it is not here the place to discuss (cf. FRAZER O.T. p. 65 f. and BIN GORION 1917 p. 85 ff.).

A number of other points concerning the relation of man and animal in the Bible have been pointed out by FRAZER. Thus the prescription about the goring ox, which shall be put to death (Exod. 21 : 28/29), shows an early stage, where little distinction was made between man and brutes. Savages usually take vengeance on animals or even on inanimate things that hurt or offended them. In a later stage the killing of the goring ox may have become of additional importance, in order to prevent further damages. Until a few centuries ago animal processes were quite regular in many countries of Europe. Ecclesiastical as well as civil courts accused the animals of damage, for which they were held responsible (FRAZER O.T. p. 397 ff.). The scapegoats (Levit. 16 : 5), to which the High-priest transferred all the sins of the Children of Israel, before it was sent into the wilderness on the Day of Atonement, again has an abundance of parallels in the rituals of primitive people all over the world (FRAZER G.B. p. 569 ff.). The Fall of Man in the Garden of Eden is reconstructed in a rather divergent form by the comparison with old Semitic legends (FRAZER O.T. p. 15 ff.). "As a crowning mercy of paradise the Creator planned for our first parents the great gift of immortality, but resolved to make them the arbiters of their own fate by leaving them free to accept or reject the proffered boon. For that purpose he planted in the midst of the garden two wondrous trees that bore fruits of very different sorts, the fruit of the one being fraught with death to the eater, and the other with life eternal. Having done so, he sent the serpent to the man and woman, and charged him to deliver this message: "Eat not of the Tree of Death, for in the day ye eat thereof ye shall surely die; but eat of the Tree of Life and live for ever." Now the serpent was more subtle than any beast of the field, and on his way he bethought him of changing the message; so when he came to the happy garden and found the woman alone in it, he said to her, "Thus saith God: Eat not of the Tree of Life, for in the day ye eat thereof ye shall surely die; but eat of the Tree of Death, and live for ever." The foolish woman believed him, and ate of the fatal fruit, and gave of it to her husband, and he ate also. But the sly serpent himself ate of the Tree of Life. That is, why men have been mortal and serpents immortal ever since, for serpents cast their skins every year and so renew their youth. If only the serpent had not perverted God's good message and deceived our first mother, we should have been immortal instead of the serpents; for like the serpents we should have cast our skins every year, and so renewed our youth perpetually."

Some other animal legends of the Bible are only discussed in the complete edition of FRAZER's Folklore in the Old Testament (3 vol., 1919). In the second volume the bird sanctuary of the Temple at Jerusalem (Psalm 84 : 3) is compared with other bird sanctuaries of sacred places (2 p. 19). The ravens which brought food to Elijah are discussed (2 p. 22). A parallel legend to Jonah and the whale is found in New Guinea (2 p. 82). He comments on the lions, which brought the idolaters settling in destroyed Samaria to Jehova (II Kings 17 : 24 ff., 2 p. 84). FRAZER's work in general has enormously contributed to a better understanding of the relation between old Semitic legends and beliefs and their development within Israel. The origin of primitive knowledge about animals comes into the immortal store of nomads. There was probably often little difference between that of the Jewish tribes and that of the bedawis of our days. Much of this store of observations and empirical knowledge has been lost after settlement. Also the fellaheens of our days are poor observers of nature. And the final wording by priests was made just by that class of people, which was furthest from nature. Many points of earlier tradition were not understood any more, as later we will show in details, when discussing the manna problem. Thus the wording of the Bible was just made at a time and by a class which was least competent to understand and observe nature. And it should not be forgotten, that the Bible is not a book where natural history finds its adequate place. We must learn to read between the lines, in order to sift out the remainders of nomad animal lore, which the Bible still contains. And in this direction FRAZER and his method of comparative folklore have given a first lead.

The problem of totemism in ancient Israel has been often tackled. R. PATAY (1947) strongly maintains that the social structure of Israel does not even show any traces of a totemistic organisation. Furthermore, there are no legends or beliefs of the animal ancestry of certain people or individuals. More important is the comparison of Hebrew tribes with animals in the benedictions of JACOB (Genesis 49 : 9 ff.) and of MOSES (Deuter. 33 : 17 ff.). These comparisons are:

TRIBE	JACOB'S BENEDICTION	MOSES' BENEDICTION
Judah	lion	—
Issachar	ass	—
Dan	serpent	lion's whelp
Naphthali	gazelle	—
Joseph	—	wild bull
Benjamin	wolf	—
Gad	—	lion

The lion appears as the symbol of three tribes, and once—for Dan—where the other benediction refers to the serpent. This looseness of use in the comparison deprives them of any value as totemistic residues. If those would be existent their application should be strict. Also the personal names and group names derived from animals are of no importance in this connection. Bachar, Gemali, Ebulon, Susi, Bne Hamor, Ahbar, Thola, Bne Haleb, Hagav, Deborah, etc. show no relation to totemism. The reference to domestic animals is self-explanatory. Why mice, grasshoppers and dogs are used in names remains obscure. But there is no primary connection between them and ancient totems, as preserved in other Oriental peoples.

Finally we find a few cases where animal idolatry is mentioned in the Old Testament, the aversion to which is expressed by the second command: the adoration of the golden calf, the healing by the serpent. Even the figures of the bulls, the cherubs, etc. on the ritual vessels of Solomon's temple should be mentioned here. Yet these were almost certain cultural influences from the ancestral home in Mesopotamia. We may safely conclude, that no indication has been found, so far, in the Old Testament which could be used as a proof for ancient totemism in Israel.

INDEXES

4. 3. INDEX OF THE LATIN NAMES OF ANIMALS AND SPECIES OF ANIMALS

4. 2. INDEX OF CITATIONS

4. 2. 1. HOLY SCRIPTURE

Zechariah 14, 20 — 180
APOCRYPHA:
Ecclesiasticus 9, 30 — 199
Esdras 1, 7-9 — 209
— 7, 7 — 209
II Maccabaeans 9, 6 — 73

NEW TESTAMENT
St. Matthew 3, 4 — 77
— 4, 18 — 200
— 13, 45, — 200
— 13, 47 ff. — 200
— 17, 27 — 200

St. John 21 — 200
The Revelation of St. John 9, 5 —
200

4. 2. 2. CLASSICAL AUTHORS *

Aelianus — 8, 75, 144-146
—, Var. Hist. 1 : 2 — 68
—, Peri zoon idiotetos 1 : 20 — 80
—, — 1 : 21 — 75
—, — 2 : 17 — 145
—, — 2 : 25 — 146
—, — 2 : 48 — 145
—, — 3 : 42 — 62
—, — 4 : 1, 13 — 58
—, — 4 : 26 — 145
—, — 4 : 46 — 146
—, — 5 : 53 — 144
—, — 5 : 56 — 144/145
—, — 6 : 7 — 57
—, — 6 : 17 — 145
—, — 6 : 20 — 145
—, — 6 : 22 — 145
—, — 7 : 9 — 126
—, — 10 : 43 — 145
—, — 10 : 46 — 126
—, — 11 : 10 — 126
—, — 11 : 25 — 145
—, — 11 : 28 — 74
—, — 12 : 5 — 47
—, — 13 : 11 — 10
—, — 16 : 39 — 145

Aesopus — 41, 46, 61, 65, 92
Alcman — 72
Agatharchides — 142
Alexander of Myndus — 58, 63
Anacreon, Ode *43* — 80
Androsthenes — 85
Antigonos of Karystos — 47
Apelles — 65
Apollonius 1 : 25 — 55

Aristophanes, The Birds, v. 1353 —
61
—, The Frogs, v. 114 f. — 73

Aristoteles — 8, 41, 49, 52, 55, 65,
79, 81, 117, 131/134, 134, 136,
137, 140, 211
—, Historia Animalium (H.A.)
passim — 80
—, — 2 : 2 — 132
—, — 2 : 3 — 133
—, — 2 : 4 — 132
—, — 2 : 7 — 133
—, — 4 : 5 — 48

—, — 5 : 1 : 5; 5 : 17 : 1-4 — 81
—, — 5 : 2 — 133
—, — 5 : 12 — 133
—, — 5 : 22 — 75
—, — 5 : 25 — 76
—, — 5 : 26 — 72
—, — 6 : 25 — 133
—, — 6 : 28 — 132
—, — 6 : 29 — 132
—, — 6 : 30 — 46, 132
—, — 7 : 4 — 132
—, — 8 : 10 — 133
—, — 8 : 11 — 133
—, — 8 : 12 — 132
—, — 8 : 14 — 132
—, — 8 : 27 — 131
—, — 9 : 6 — 133
—, — 9 : 7 — 131
—, — 9 : 19 — 131
—, — 9 : 24 — 132
—, — 9 : 26 — 75
—, — 9 : 37 — 133
—, — 9 : 47 — 133
—, De Partibus Animalium, *4 : 11*
—132
—, — *4 : 14* — 132
Aristoteles? "On marvellous Things
heard", *8, 10, 19, 23, 25, 26, 27,
72* — 133/134

Artemidorus, of Daldus 142, 143,
146/148
—, Oneirocritica *2 : 11* — 147
—, — *2 : 12* — 147
—, — *2 : 13* — 82, 147
—, — *2 : 14* — 147
—, — *2 : 16* — 147
—, — *2 : 20* — 147
—, — *2 : 22* — 81/82
—, — *2 : 56* — 148
—, — *3 : 5* — 148
—, — *3 : 6* — 82
—, — *3 : 7* — 82
—, — *3 : 8* — 82
—, — *3 : 11* — 148
—, — *3 : 12* — 148
—, — *3 : 28* — 148
—, — *3 : 49* — 82
—, — *3 : 64* — 148
—, — *3 : 65* — 148
—, — *4 : 56* — 146

—, — *5 : 64* — 82

Badrios, — 49
—, (Fable 33) — 56

Chares of Mytilene, Hist. Alexandri
7 — 85
Cicero, De divinatione 1 : 15 — 53
—, — 1 : 39 : 85 — 56/57
—, Epistolarum ad familiares *2 :11,
8 : 9* — 43
Claudianus — 47
Columella — 79
Ctesias — 52, 53, 55, 145, 146

Dio Cassius, Historia Romae 55 : 27
— 51
—, — 69 : 15 — 44
Diodorus Siculus 1 : 48 — 42
— 1 : 52 — 69
— 1 : 60 — 59
— *1 : 87* — 54, 61, 75
— 1 : 88 — 44
— 3 : 16 — 145
— 3 : 20 — 64
— 3 : 21 — 72
— 3 : 28 — 77/142
— *3 : 35 ff.* — 67
— 3 : 43 — 42
— 37 : 35 — 52
Dioscorides of Cilicia, Pharmacopoeia, 1 : 146, 2, 36; 2 : 38; 2 :56;
2 : 57, 64, 65, 66; 4 : 48 — 76
—, "On poisons and their antidotes" *1 : 1-3* — 76

Euenos of Askalon — 80

Flavius Vopiscus, De Probo 19 — 43

??, Geoponica, 14 : 2 — 41

Herodotus — 45, 46, 122, 125
—, Historiae 1 : 200 — 70
—, — 2 : 22 — 54
—, — *2 : 65 ff.* — 54
—, — 2 : 67 — 41
—, — 2 : 72 — 63/69
—, — *2 : 75 ff.* — 61
—, — 2 : 75, 76 — 61

* Translations in italics